Histotechnology

A Self Assessment Workbook

3rd Edition

Freida L Carson
PhD, HT(ASCP)
Department of Pathology (retired)
Baylor University Medical Center
Dallas, Texas

Publishing Team
Erik N Tanck (production)
Joshua Weikersheimer (publishing direction)

Notice

The views and opinions expressed by the authors are those of the authors only and do not necessarily reflect the views and opinions of the authors' employer or of the American Society for Clinical Pathology.

Trade names for equipment and supplies described are included as suggestions only. In no way does their inclusion constitute an endorsement of preference by the author or the ASCP. The author and ASCP urge all readers to read and follow all manufacturers' instructions and package insert warnings concerning the proper and safe use of products. The American Society for Clinical Pathology, having exercised appropriate and reasonable effort to research material current as of publication date, does not assume any liability for any loss or damage caused by errors and omissions in this publication. Readers must assume responsibility for complete and thorough research of any hazardous conditions they encounter, as this publication is not intended to be all inclusive, and recommendations and regulations change over time.

19 18 17 16 15 5 4 3 2 1

Printed in Singapore

Table of Contents

ISBN 978-089189-6401

Important Instructions

This book is intended to supplement the text *Histotechnology: A Self Instructional Text, 4th Edition.* It should be used to assess your knowledge after you have finished studying a chapter, including the color images, in the text. The questions are in several different formats to better assess your understanding of the theory. If you cannot answer most of the questions correctly, you should review the chapter in the text, and then repeat the examination. If you still cannot answer some of the questions correctly, then refer to that area of the chapter specifically. Problem solving questions will require a more comprehensive knowledge of the subject matter than those questions that simply recall information.

Although some of the questions may be similar to those on the Board of Registry certification examination, none of the questions in this book will appear as written on the examination. Questions in this book should not be memorized, and the author makes no claim that successful completion of the questions in this book will ensure success on the certification examination.

ISBN 978-089189-6401

Fixation *Questions*

1-43. The following are multiple choice questions. Please circle the letter in front of the correct answer. There is only 1 best answer.

1. The primary purpose of fixation is to:
   a. stop enzymatic action
   b. remove the water from the tissue
   c. provide support for the tissue
   d. autolyze the tissue

2. Which of the following fixatives contains picric acid, formalin, and acetic acid?
   a. Zenker
   b. Helly
   c. Bouin
   d. Zamboni

3. The volume of fixative should exceed the volume of the tissue by:
   a. 1× to 2×
   b. 5× to 10×
   c. 15× to 20×
   d. 25× to 50×

4. Tissue must be washed in running water after fixation in:
   a. Zenker solution
   b. absolute alcohol
   c. glyoxal
   d. formalin

5. Which of the following fixatives contains formalin, potassium dichromate, and mercuric chloride?
   a. Zenker
   b. Helly
   c. Carnoy
   d. Orth

6. Precipitate left in tissues that have been fixed in solutions containing mercuric chloride may be removed by immersion in:
   a. running water
   b. sodium thiosulfate
   c. weak ammonia water
   d. iodine

7. Commercial stock formaldehyde solutions contain:
   a. 4% formaldehyde
   b. 10% formaldehyde
   c. 37%-40% formaldehyde
   d. 98%-100% formaldehyde

ISBN 978-089189-6401

8. Formalin pigment would almost certainly be formed when the pH of the formalin is:
   a. 5.0
   b. 6.0
   c. 7.0
   d. 8.0

9. Formalin pigment may be removed from tissue by:
   a. running water
   b. alcoholic iodine
   c. alcoholic picric acid
   d. potassium permanganate

10. 10% formalin is the same as:
    a. 37%-40% formaldehyde
    b. 10% formaldehyde
    c. 4% formaldehyde
    d. 1% formaldehyde

11. For best results when using formalin as a routine fixative, it must be made:
    a. acidic
    b. basic
    c. neutral
    d. isoelectric

12. Absolute alcohol is indicated as a primary fixative if the tissue is to be processed for the demonstration of:
    a. fat
    b. immunofluorescence
    c. enzymes
    d. urate crystals

13. Putrefaction of tissue is caused by:
    a. enzymatic activity
    b. bacterial action
    c. aqueous fixatives
    d. overfixation

14. To prepare a 10% solution of formalin, which of the following amounts of water should be added to 100 mL of stock formaldehyde?
    a. 1,000 mL
    b. 900 mL
    c. 450 mL
    d. 10 mL

15. The ratio of stock solution to acid in Zenker fixative is:
    a. 95 parts stock to 5 parts hydrochloric acid
    b. 95 parts stock to 5 parts acetic acid
    c. 95 parts stock to 5 parts formaldehyde
    d. 99 parts stock to 1 part acetic acid

ISBN 978-089189-6401

16. Which of the following tissue changes will occur if acetic acid is used alone as a fixative?
    a. swelling
    b. shrinkage
    c. overhardening
    d. poor nucleoprotein preservation

17. A good fixative for central nervous system tissue to be stained with silver or gold techniques is:
    a. Zenker solution
    b. neutral buffered formalin
    c. Bouin solution
    d. formalin ammonium bromide

18. After fixing tissue in Bouin solution, the excess picric acid is frequently removed by washing in:
    a. running water
    b. absolute alcohol
    c. 50%-70% alcohol
    d. phosphate buffer

19. Carnoy fluid is prepared with acetic acid, alcohol, and:
    a. chloroform
    b. formalin
    c. acetone
    d. osmium tetroxide

20. The first and most important procedure in the preparation of a tissue for microscopic examination is the choice of:
    a. fixative
    b. dehydrating agent
    c. clearing agent
    d. staining technique

21. Fats are usually preserved best if the tissue is fixed in:
    a. osmium tetroxide
    b. Carnoy
    c. Bouin
    d. Helly

22. When alcohol is used as the primary fixative, one should expect:
    a. fat preservation
    b. excessive tissue shrinkage
    c. very soft tissue
    d. slow penetration

23. Generally, an increase in the temperature of the fixative solution:
    a. decreases the tissue autolysis
    b. decreases the fixative penetration
    c. increases the speed of fixation
    d. increases the volume of fixative needed

ISBN 978-089189-6401

24. Depending on the reagent used, which of the following may cause tissue to become overhardened?
    a. prolonged fixation
    b. abbreviated fixation
    c. inadequate dehydration
    d. incomplete clearing

25. Fixatives containing chromate salts usually require:
    a. additional fixation
    b. washing in water
    c. washing in alcohol
    d. no special treatment

26. Substitution of alcohol as the diluting solution for formaldehyde results in:
    a. slower fixation
    b. less hardening of tissue
    c. better retention of fats
    d. better preservation of glycogen

27. Zinc salts are added to some formalin fixatives to:
    a. prevent the loss of cytoplasmic structures
    b. provide superior nuclear detail
    c. decrease tissue shrinkage
    d. keep tissue from overhardening

28. Tissue fixed in glutaraldehyde is not satisfactory for:
    a. the periodic acid-Schiff (PAS) reaction
    b. electron microscopy
    c. argentaffin stains
    d. routine H&E stains

29. For immunofluorescence, the tissue should be:
    a. fixed in formalin
    b. fixed in alcohol
    c. fixed in B-5
    d. unfixed

30. Which of the following is a nonaqueous fixative?
    a. Carnoy
    b. Zenker
    c. Bouin
    d. Zamboni

31. Which of the following fixatives will leave the tissue protein uncoagulated?
    a. Zenker
    a. osmium tetroxide
    b. B-5
    c. zinc formalin

ISBN 978-089189-6401

32. To prevent polymerization of formaldehyde, which of the following is added to the commercial stock solutions?
    a. methyl alcohol
    b. formic acid
    c. paraformaldehyde
    d. sodium phosphate

33. Polymerized formaldehyde is known as:
    a. glutaraldehyde
    b. paraformaldehyde
    c. paraldehyde
    d. acetaldehyde

34. Formaldehyde reacts with protein side chains by combining with the:
    a. carboxyl group
    b. thiol group
    c. amino group
    d. phenolic group

35. Hollande solution is a modification of which of the following?
    a. Carnoy
    b. Zamboni
    c. Bouin
    d. Orth

36. Which of the following is a nonadditive fixative?
    a. mercuric chloride
    b. osmium tetroxide
    c. formaldehyde
    d. ethyl alcohol

37. Potassium dichromate increases availability of which of the following groups for binding dyes?
    a. –SH
    b. –COOH
    c. $-NH_2$
    d. –OH

38. The recommended minimum time for fixation in formalin is:
    a. 1 hour to 3 hours
    b. 4 hours to 5 hours
    c. 6 hours to 8 hours
    d. 9 hours to 10 hours

39. Methylene bridges are formed during the reaction of certain tissue groups with:
    a. osmium tetroxide
    b. formaldehyde
    c. picric acid
    d. chromium trioxide

ISBN 978-089189-6401

40. A disadvantage of osmium tetroxide fixation is that osmium:
    a. fixes fat poorly
    b. penetrates poorly
    c. coagulates tissue proteins
    d. impedes staining with basic dyes

41. The permissible exposure limit (PEL) for formaldehyde is currently:
    a. 0.5 ppm
    b. 0.75 ppm
    c. 1.0 ppm
    d. 2.0 ppm

42. Formaldehyde crosslinks proteins by reacting with which of the following groups?
    a. $-NH_2$
    b. $-COOH$
    c. S=S
    d. $-OH$

43. Which of the following must be used under a hood because it readily vaporizes and will fix the nasal mucosa?
    a. chromic acid
    b. formaldehyde
    c. zinc sulfate
    d. osmium tetroxide

44. Good fixation is indicated on an electron micrograph of a section of a plasma cell if the:
    a. nuclear envelope shows regularly spaced dilated areas
    b. mitochondria show no swelling or disruption
    c. channels of endoplasmic reticulum vary in width
    d. plasmalemma shows periodic infolding and breaks

45. One advantage of primary osmium fixation is that:
    a. specimens may remain in fixative indefinitely
    b. histochemistry can be performed on the fixed tissue
    c. lipids are rendered insoluble
    d. penetration of tissue is excellent

46. One advantage of primary aldehyde fixation is that:
    a. better penetration is obtained than with osmium
    b. lipids are rendered insoluble
    c. membrane-bound cavities tend to shrink
    d. membranes become electron dense

47. One advantage of primary buffered picric acid–formaldehyde fixation (PAF, Zamboni) is that:
    a. lipids are rendered insoluble
    b. lysosomes may be extracted during processing
    c. the solution does not contain hazardous chemicals
    d. specimens may remain in the fixative indefinitely

ISBN 978-089189-6401

48. When used as a primary fixative for electron microscopy, Millonig formaldehyde:
    a. makes histochemistry impossible
    b. renders lipids insoluble
    c. allows both light and electron microscopy
    d. requires that specimens be removed after 2-4 hours

49. When used as a primary fixative for electron microscopy, glutaraldehyde:
    a. makes histochemistry impossible
    b. renders lipids insoluble
    c. makes membranes electron dense
    d. requires that specimens be removed after 2-4 hours

50. Electron micrographs of buffered picric acid-formaldehyde (PAF, Zamboni) fixation show marked extraction of the lipids. This indicates that most likely:
    a. the specimen did not remain in the fixative long enough
    b. secondary osmium tetroxide fixation was not used
    c. dehydration of the tissue was inadequate
    d. the embedding medium was old

51. Satisfactory electron microscopy can be obtained on a specimen from the wet tissue file, if it has been fixed and stored in:
    a. Millonig formalin or formaldehyde-glutaraldehyde (4CF-1G)
    b. Bouin solution or buffered picric acid-formaldehyde
    c. osmium tetroxide or 2% glutaraldehyde
    d. neutralized formalin or buffered picric acid-formaldehyde

52. The pure polymer of formaldehyde is known as:
    a. acrolein
    b. glutaraldehyde
    c. paraldehyde
    d. paraformaldehyde

53. The solution of buffered 4% paraformaldehyde is cloudy. The most likely explanation is that the:
    a. pH is slightly >7.0
    b. paraformaldehyde is not totally depolymerized
    c. solution was not refrigerated after preparation
    d. tonicity of the solution is too low

54. Depolymerization of paraformaldehyde occurs with:
    a. chilling of the solution
    b. the addition of acid
    c. adjusting the tonicity
    d. heating of the solution

55. A specimen will not be considered optimally fixed if the nuclei show:
    a. crisp chromatin patterns
    b. bubbling
    c. well defined membranes
    d. a lack of perinuclear space

ISBN 978-089189-6401

56. Complete the following chart:

Pigment	*Preventable (yes or no)*	*Removable (yes or no)*	*If removable, how?*
Formalin			
Mercury			
Chromium			

57-88. The following statements are either true or false. Circle T if the statement is true, circle F if the statement is false.

57. Formalin fixation stabilizes lipids. **[T\F]**

58. Acetic acid is an excellent nuclear fixative. **[T\F]**

59. Fat is well preserved by Carnoy solution. **[T\F]**

60. Formalin penetrates rapidly but fixes slowly. **[T\F]**

61. 10% formalin is a 1:4 dilution of commercial formalin. **[T\F]**

62. Zenker fixative contains formaldehyde, mercuric chloride, and potassium dichromate. **[T\F]**

63. Fixation in Helly solution will preserve erythrocytes, while fixation in Zenker solution will not. **[T\F]**

64. Bouin solution contains picric acid, formaldehyde, and hydrochloric acid. **[T\F]**

65. Any fixative containing mercuric salts will leave a pigment in the tissue. **[T\F]**

66. Mercury pigment may be removed from tissue by immersion in sodium thiosulfate. **[T\F]**

67. Formalin ammonium bromide is a very good fixative for connective tissue. **[T\F]**

68. The fixing fluid considered best for the preservation of nuclear detail is buffered formalin. **[T\F]**

69. Formalin pigment can be removed from tissue by immersion in alcoholic picric acid. **[T\F]**

70. The volume of the fixative should exceed the volume of the tissue by 1-2 times. **[T\F]**

71. Tissue left in a fixative beyond the defined time may become excessively hard. **[T\F]**

72. Acetic acid is a useful addition to many compound fixatives because of its shrinking action. **[T\F]**

73. Since formalin is a coagulant fixative it is considered an excellent fixative for paraffin embedding. **[T\F]**

74. Acetone is sometimes used when a rapid acting fixative is needed. **[T\F]**

ISBN 978-089189-6401

75. A fixative stops autolysis and putrefaction. [T\F]

76. If tissues have been fixed in an aqueous fixative, uric acid crystals cannot be demonstrated. [T\F]

77. A good fixative should penetrate slowly. [T\F]

78. If one wishes to prevent the formation of a pigment, formalin solutions must be buffered to a pH >7.0. [T\F]

79. Concentrated commercial solutions of formaldehyde are 37%-40% by weight of the gas formaldehyde dissolved in water. [T\F]

80. Osmium tetroxide chemically fixes fat. [T\F]

81. Helly, Zenker, and Orth solutions all contain mercury. [T\F]

82. Chrome pigment can be prevented by washing the tissues with water following fixation. [T\F]

83. B-5 fixative contains formaldehyde and potassium dichromate. [T\F]

84. Glutaraldehyde is frequently used to fix specimens for electron microscopy. [T\F]

85. Orth solution is the best fixative for pheochromocytomas when immunohistochemistry is not to be performed. [T\F]

86. Heat and desiccation are methods of fixation. [T\F]

87. Glyoxal fixatives are rapid-acting compared to formaldehyde. [T\F]

88. Zinc is a satisfactory replacement for mercury in some fixative solutions. [T\F]

89. Match the following techniques/tissue components on the left with the preferred fixative or fixatives on the right. Some fixatives may not be used. Some techniques may be matched with more than 1 fixative.

Technique/Tissue Component	Fixative
____A. Connective tissue	a. absolute alcohol
____B. Electron microscopy	b. Bouin solution
____C. Enzyme histochemistry on muscle	c. 10% aqueous formalin
____D. Immunofluorescence	d. frozen section (no fixation)
____E. Pheochromocytomas	e. Orth solution
____F. Phosphotungstic acid hematoxylin	f. osmium tetroxide (PTAH) for cross-striations
____G. Urate crystal	g. Zamboni solution
	h. Zenker solution

ISBN 978-089189-6401

90. Match each of the following fixatives on the left with its component chemicals on the right. Some reagents may not be matched. Some chemicals may be matched with >1 fixative. Some fixatives will contain multiple component chemicals.

Fixative Solution	Component Chemicals
____A. B-5	a. 95% alcohol
____B. Bouin	b. absolute alcohol
____C. Carnoy	c. acetic acid
____D. 10% neutral buffered formalin	d. chloroform
____E. Gendre	e. copper acetate
____F. Helly	f. formaldehyde
____G. Hollande	g. mercuric chloride
____H. Orth	h. osmium tetroxide
____I. Zamboni	i. paraformaldehyde
____J. Zenker	j. picric acid
	k. potassium dichromate
	l. sodium chloride
	m. sodium phosphate, dibasic
	n. sodium phosphate, monobasic

91-94 Each of the following numbered words or phrases is associated with one, both, or neither of the headings listed as A or B above it. Within the parentheses on the right, place the appropriate letter for that word or phrase. Write:

A, if the numbered phrase is associated with A only
B, if the numbered phrase is associated with B only
C, if the numbered phrase is associated with both A and B
D, if the numbered phrase is associated with neither A nor B

91.

A. B-5 fixative	1. Contains potassium dichromate	[ ]
B. Orth fixative	2. Contains formaldehyde	[ ]
C. both	3. Contains acetic acid	[ ]
D. neither	4. Is recommended for lymph nodes	[ ]
	5. Sections must be treated with iodine	[ ]

92.

A. Mercury pigment	1. Is water soluble	[ ]
B. Acid hematin	2. Is deposited in tissue during fixation (formalin) pigment	[ ]
C. both	3. Can be removed with Lugol iodine	[ ]
D. neither	4. Can be prevented by using a neutral pH	[ ]
	5. Can be removed with alcoholic picric acid	[ ]

93.

A. Zenker fluid	1. Contains mercuric chloride and potassium dichromate	[ ]
B. Helly fluid	2. Preserves erythrocytes in bone marrow sections	[ ]
C. both	3. Contains acetic acid	[ ]
D. neither	4. Contains formadehyde	[ ]
	5. Must be washed out with running water	[ ]

ISBN 978-089189-6401

94.

A. 10% neutral-buffered formalin	1. May lyse erythrocytes	[ ]
B. Bouin solution	2. Excess fixative should be removed before processing	[ ]
C. both	3. Dehydration should be started with 65%-70% alcohol	[ ]
D. neither	4. Should be buffered for use	[ ]
	5. Contains mercuric chloride	[ ]

95-103. The following are problem-solving questions.

95. H&E stained sections fixed in formalin show a brown microcrystalline deposit lying on top of the tissue. This can most likely be prevented in the future by:
    a. filtering the hematoxylin solution before use
    b. decreasing the time in formalin solution
    c. raising the pH of the formalin >6.0
    d. washing the tissue after fixation

96. H&E stained sections show a brown microcrystalline deposit lying on top of the tissue. It is especially heavy in bloody areas of the tissue. This pigment can most likely be removed by treating the tissue with:
    a. running water
    b. iodine and sodium thiosulfate
    c. potassium permanganate
    d. alcoholic picric acid

97. H&E stained sections FAIL to reveal uric acid crystals on a case with a clinical diagnosis of gout. One possible explanation for the false negative result could be that the specimen was fixed in a solution other than:
    a. absolute alcohol
    b. B-5 solution
    c. buffered formalin
    d. Bouin solution

98. At the time of embedding, a white deposit is noted on tissue fixed in unbuffered zinc formalin and then transferred to phosphate buffered formalin. One possible explanation could be that the tissue was:
    a. left in the zinc formalin too long
    b. subjected to incompatible fixatives
    c. transferred to buffered formalin without washing
    d. not washed before placing in 70% alcohol

99. Blocked tissue, which has been fixed in Bouin solution, is pulled from the file after being stored for several years. New sections are cut and stained with H&E. No nuclear staining is noted on the new sections, although the original sections stained very well. The most likely explanation is that the:
    a. picric acid was not removed sufficiently before processing
    b. pH of the fixative was wrong at the time of fixation
    c. formaldehyde used in the fixative solution
    d. paraffin used in embedding has broken down

100. Electron microscopic studies on a section of tumor fixed in 10% neutral buffered formalin reveal very poor cell preservation. This could be prevented in the future by:
    a. postfixing the tissue in osmium tetroxide
    b. fixing some of the tumor in glutaraldehyde solution
    c. holding in saline until the need for electron microscopy can be determined
    d. washing the tissue in running water prior to placing in osmium

101. H&E stained sections of liver fixed in 10% neutral buffered formalin show a marked difference in staining between the periphery and center of the tissue. More nuclear bubbling is also noted in the center part of the section. This is most likely due to:
    a. underdehydration during processing
    b. incomplete fixation prior to beginning dehydration
    c. poor paraffin infiltration
    d. overheated embedding paraffin

102. H&E stained sections of liver fixed in the microwave oven show marked pyknotic, overstained nuclei. This can probably be prevented in the future by ensuring that the temperature is kept below:
    a. 25°C
    b. 37°C
    c. 55°C
    d. 75°C

103. The fixative used by the laboratory is being changed from formalin to glyoxal. It will most likely be necessary to:
    a. wash tissue before processing
    b. decrease routine staining times
    c. check for correct staining of *Helicobacter pylori*
    d. monitor laboratory personnel for exposure monthly

ISBN 978-089189-6401

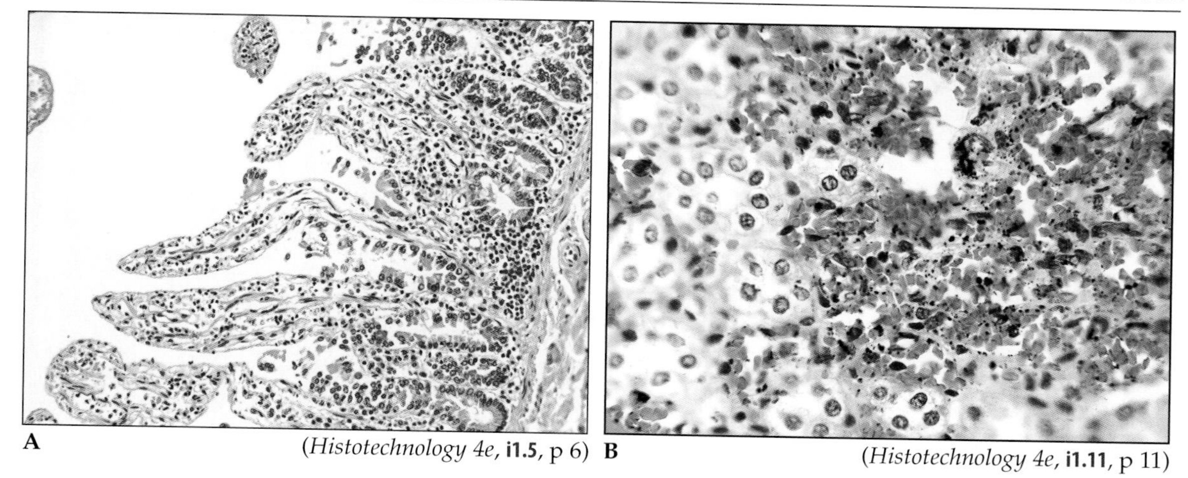

A (*Histotechnology 4e*, **i1.5**, p 6) B (*Histotechnology 4e*, **i1.11**, p 11)

104-118. The following questions refer to images A-E as specified.

104. The tissue shown in image A is:
    a. stomach
    b. esophagus
    c. small intestine
    d. colon

105. The tissue shown in image A is:
    a. well preserved
    b. autolyzed
    c. mechanically damaged
    d. overfixed

106. The problem shown in image A could have been prevented by:
    a. placing the tissue into fixative sooner
    b. handling the tissue more carefully during gross examination
    c. decreasing the fixation time
    d. buffering the fixative

107. The tissue component that should be present but is missing in the tissue shown in image A is the:
    a. lamina propria
    b. muscularis mucosa
    c. epithelium
    d. adventitia

108. The pigment seen in image B is most likely:
    a. iron
    b. formalin
    c. mercury
    d. bile

109. The pigment seen in image B could most likely be removed by treating with:
    a. alcoholic iodine
    b. alcoholic picric acid
    c. dilute hydrochloric acid
    d. running water

ISBN 978-089189-6401

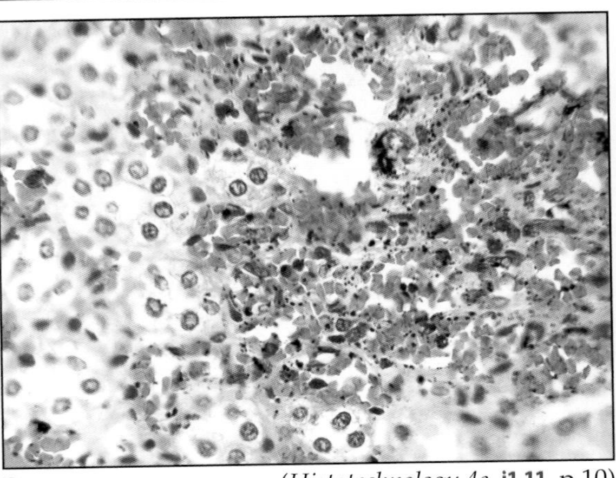

B (*Histotechnology 4e*, **i1.11**, p 10)

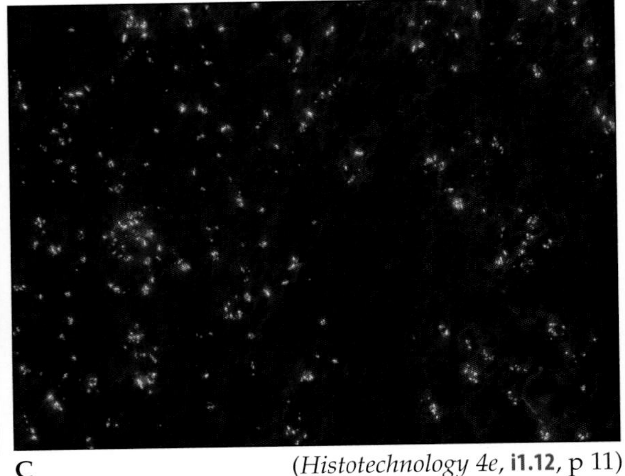

C (*Histotechnology 4e*, **i1.12**, p 11)

110. The pigment shown in image B most likely:
    a. is an exogenous hematogenous pigment
    b. is an endogenous nonhematogenous pigment
    c. occurred during fixation with mercury
    d. occurred during fixation with acidic formalin

111. The pigment shown in image B could have been prevented by:
    a. washing well after fixation
    b. keeping the pH of the fixative >6.0
    c. treating the tissue with iodine and sodium thiosulfate
    d. substituting paraformaldehyde for the formaldehyde

112. The tissue in image C has been screened for artifactual pigment by the use of:
    a. fluorescent microscopy
    b. dark field microscopy
    c. polarizing microscopy
    d. electron microscopy

113. The technique used in image C utilizes a/an:
    a. polarizer & analyzer
    b. halogen lamp
    c. electron gun
    d. oblique light

114. The phenomenon shown is image C is:
    a. fluorescence
    b. electron transmission
    c. birefringence
    d. refractive index

ISBN 978-089189-6401

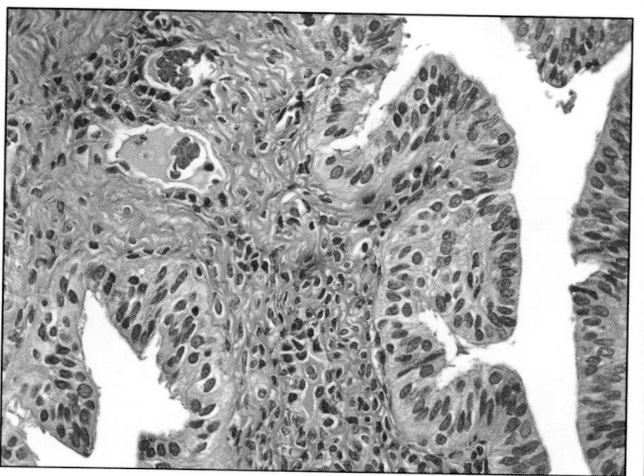

D (*Histotechnology 4e*, **i1.29**, p 28)

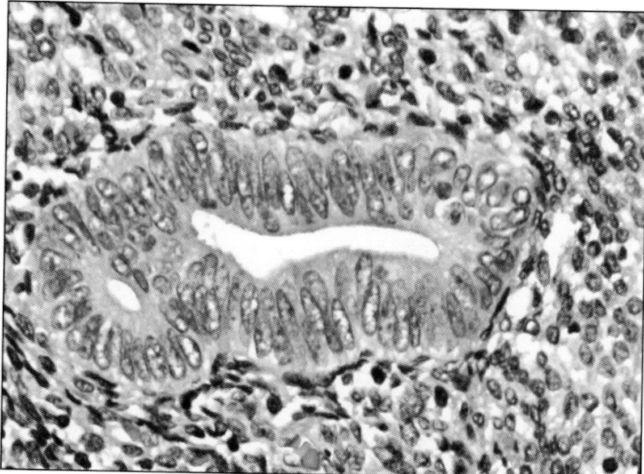

E (*Histotechnology 4e*, **i1.29**, p 28)

115. The nuclear problem seen in image D is most commonly due to:
    a. old hematoxylin
    b. incomplete fixation
    c. overdehydration
    d. incomplete paraffin infiltration

116. The nuclear problem seen in image D is:
    a. lack of chromatin definition
    b. euchromatin is unstained
    c. poor differentiation with acid alcohol
    d. cell shrinkage

117. The nuclear problem seen in the gland in image E is:
    a. smudgy nuclei
    b. pyknotic nuclei
    c. mitosis
    d. nuclear bubbling

118. The nuclear problem seen in image E is most commonly due to:
    a. prolonged fixation
    b. incomplete fixation
    c. overdehydration
    d. incomplete paraffin removal

ISBN 978-089189-6401

Fixation *Answers*

Question	Answer	Discussion	*Histotechnology* Page
1	a	Enzymes are protein and are rendered inactive by fixation; this is very important because enzymatic action causes autolysis.	2
2	c	Of the fixatives listed, only Bouin solution contains picric acid, formalin, and acetic acid.	20
3	c	In order to prevent depletion of fixative molecules and changing the character of the fixative by the solution of soluble salts in the tissue, the ratio of fixative to tissue should be large (15× to 20 times)	5
4	a	A pigment may be formed when tissue is taken from a chromate-containing solution (Zenker) directly into an alcoholic solution; therefore, tissue should be washed well with running water before processing.	17
5	b	Helly solution contains formaldehyde, potassium dichromate, and mercuric chloride.	21
6	d	Mercury pigment is removed by treating sections with Gram or Lugol iodine.	25
7	c	Commercial stock formaldehyde solution contains 37%-40% formaldehyde; this is diluted 1:10 for use.	10
8	a	Formalin pigment tends to form if the pH of the solution drops <6.0, and so would almost certainly form in a solution of pH 5.0.	11
9	c	Alcoholic picric acid is most commonly used to remove formalin pigment.	25
10	c	10% formalin is a 1:10 dilution of 37%-40% formaldehyde; therefore a 10% solution is the same as 3.7%-4% formaldehyde	10
11	c	The best results are obtained when formalin has a pH close to 7.0, or neutrality. This is close to the physiological pH, and the formation of formalin pigment should be prevented except when large amounts of blood are present.	11
12	d	Urate crystals are soluble in aqueous solution; therefore, absolute alcohol is indicated for fixation.	24
13	b	Bacterial action causes tissue putrefaction.	2
14	b	10% formalin is a 1:10 of stock formaldehyde, which is considered 100% formalin; therefore, 100 mL of stock + 900 mL of water = 1,000 mL of a 1:10 dilution.	10

ISBN 978-089189-6401

Question	Answer	Discussion	*Histotechnology* Page
15	b	5 mL of acetic acid is added to every 95 mL of Zenker/Helly stock to prepare 100 mL of Zenker fixative. Formaldehyde is used in Helly solution, not Zenker.	21
16	a	Acetic acid swells tissue and is used in some fixatives to counteract swelling.	10
17	d	Formalin ammonium bromide is a good fixative for central nervous system tissue, especially when the Cajal astrocyte procedure is to be performed.	13
18	c	50%-70% alcohol is commonly used to remove excess Bouin solution from tissues before processing.	20
19	a	Chloroform is one of the components of Carnoy fluid.	24
20	a	The choice of fixative is extremely important, because that often determines which special stains can be done on the tissue.	7
21	a	Osmium tetroxide is the only fixative solution that will chemically fix fats, making them insoluble in the processing reagents.	16
22	b	Alcohol excessively shrinks tissue, but when combined with formaldehyde, the shrinkage effect of the alcohol is minimized.	24
23	c	In general, an increase in the temperature of the fixative solution will increase the speed of fixation but also increase autolysis.	4
24	a	Prolonged fixation in some fixatives will cause excessive hardening.	7
25	b	Chromate containing fixatives must be washed well before placing in alcoholic solutions, or a precipitate may form.	17
26	d	Alcoholic formalin preserves glycogen very well.	24
27	b	Zinc has replaced mercury in many fixatives because it gives similar results, especially with nuclear fixation.	17, 22
28	a	Glutaraldehyde is a dialdehyde, and one aldehyde group is usually not involved in cross-linking reactions; this leaves one aldehyde group free to react with Schiff reagent, giving a false positive result.	14
29	d	Tissue for immunofluorescence should not be fixed, but frozen unfixed for sectioning.	7
30	a	Carnoy solution contains only absolute alcohol, chloroform, and acetic acid; no water is in the solution.	24
31	b	Osmium tetroxide is a noncoagulating fixative.	4,16

Question	Answer	Discussion	*Histotechnology* Page
32	a	Methyl alcohol is added to the 37%-40% formaldehyde solutions to prevent polymerization.	10
33	b	Paraformaldehyde is polymerized formaldehyde.	10
34	c	A major site of reaction of formaldehyde is with the amino group on the side chains for amino acids.	10
35	c	Hollande solution is a modification of Bouin solution. It contains copper acetate in addition to acetic acid, picric acid, and formaldehyde.	21
36	d	Ethyl alcohol is a nonadditive, precipitating fixative; all of the others listed are additive.	4
37	c	Potassium dichromate reacts with both carboxyl (–COOH) and hydroxyl (–OH) groups, and it increases the reactive amino (–NH_2) groups that are present, resulting in an increased affinity for eosin.	17
38	c	Formalin should have at least 6 hours to 8 hours to act before the rest of processing is begun. Guidelines for testing for human epidermal growth factor receptor 2 (HER2) recommend that the breast biopsies be fixed in 10 NBF for a minimum of 6 hours.	7
39	b	Formaldehyde reacts with amino groups on the side chains of amino acids to form methylene bridges that link protein chains together.	10
40	b	Osmium tetroxide penetrates only a few cell layers, and so sections must be very thin for fixation.	16
41	b	The permissible exposure limit for formaldehyde is currently 0.75 ppm.	14
42	a	Formaldehyde reacts with the amino group (NH_2) to cross-link proteins.	10
43	d	Osmium tetroxide is very hazardous because it vaporizes very readily and must be used under a chemical fume hood; it readily fixes the nasal mucosa and the conjunctiva of the eye.	16
44	a	Mitochondria are very sensitive indicators of the quality of fixation; they will show no swelling or disruption if the fixation is good.	25
45	c	Osmium tetroxide renders lipids insoluble, giving excellent membrane preservation.	25
46	a	Formaldehyde allows much better penetration of the tissue than osmium tetroxide; specimens must be minced very small for good osmium penetration.	25
47	d	Specimens can remain in buffered PAF fixative solution at room temperature indefinitely.	

ISBN 978-089189-6401

Question	Answer	Discussion	*Histotechnology* Page
48	c	Millonig formaldehyde is a dual purpose fixative; that is, it allows electron microscopy to be done on any stored specimen remaining, and preselection of specimens for electron microscopy prior to fixation is no longer necessary.	13
49	d	Specimens cannot remain in glutaraldehyde indefinitely; tissue should be fixed in glutaraldehyde no longer than overnight, and preferably only 2-4 hours.	14
50	b	Secondary fixation with osmium tetroxide is necessary to fix lipids. After primary aldehyde fixation, up to 93% of lipids can be extracted; with osmium postfixation, only 7% can be extracted. Lipids are also not well preserved with primary PAF fixation unless secondary osmium tetroxide fixation is used.	25
51	a	Both Millonig formalin and formaldehyde-glutaraldehyde (4CF-1G) are dual purpose fixatives, allowing both light and electron microscopy.	13, 21, 25
52	d	Paraformaldehyde is the pure polymer of formaldehyde.	10
53	b	When paraformaldehyde solutions are slightly cloudy, it usually indicated that the paraformaldehyde was not totally depolymerized.	10
54	d	Depolymerization of paraformaldehyde occurs by heating the solution and then adding NaOH until the solution clears.	13
55	b	Nuclear bubbling indicates that the specimen is not optimally fixed.	9, 26, 28

56	**Pigment**	**Preventable (Yes or No)**	**Removable (Yes or No)**	**If Removable, How?**
	Formalin	Yes	Yes	Saturated alcoholic picric acid, alkaline alcohol
	Mercury	No	Yes	Iodine followed by sodium thiosulfate
	Chromium	Yes	Questionable	Partially removed by acid alcohol (Bancroft & Stevens)

Question	Answer	Discussion	*Histotechnology* Page
57	F	Lipids are preserved by formaldehyde, but they are not made insoluble; subsequent processing will remove the lipids.	10
58	T	Acetic acid is added to many fixatives because of its ability to fix nucleoproteins.	9,10

ISBN 978-089189-6401

Question	Answer	Discussion	*Histotechnology* Page
59	F	Fat is dissolved by Carnoy solution, which contains absolute alcohol, acetic acid, and chloroform.	24
60	T	Formalin penetrates and adds very quickly, but it fixes very slowly because it takes a long time to cross-link the tissue proteins.	11
61	F	10% formalin is a 1:10 dilution of commercial formalin.	10
62	F	Zenker fixative does not contain formaldehyde; it contains acetic acid, and Helly fixative contains formalin.	21
63	T	Helly solution will reserve erythrocytes, but Zenker will not because it contains acetic acid.	21
64	F	Bouin solution does not contain hydrochloric acid; it contains acetic acid.	20
65	T	Mercuric salts will cause a fixation pigment in tissue; this cannot be prevented.	15
66	F	Mercury pigment is removed by iodine; the iodine is then removed by sodium thiosulfate.	25
67	F	Formalin ammonium bromide is only recommended for central nervous system tissue.	12, 13
68	F	Formaldehyde is not a good nuclear fixative; acetic alcohol and Carnoy solution are preferred for nuclear fixation.	9
69	T	Formalin pigment is removed by alcoholic picric acid solution.	25
70	F	The volume of fixative should exceed that of the tissue by 15× to 20 times.	5
71	T	Tissue left in some fixatives beyond the defined time may become overhardened.	7
72	F	Acetic acid swells tissue and is added to fixatives to counteract a shrinking effect of another component.	10
73	F	Formalin is a noncoagulating fixative and was not considered by Baker to be excellent for paraffin embedding.	10
74	T	Acetone is sometimes used for very rapid fixation.	23
75	T	Fixation stops autolysis and putrefaction by stabilizing enzymes and destroying microorganisms.	2
76	T	Uric acid crystals are water soluble and cannot be demonstrated following fixation with an aqueous fixative.	23

ISBN 978-089189-6401

Question	Answer	Discussion	*Histotechnology* Page
77	F	Fixatives should penetrate rapidly in order to halt any postmortem changes in the tissue. Autolysis is a very common problem when fixation is delayed in enzyme rich tissues.	2
78	F	Buffering at approximately neutrality (pH 7.0) should prevent the formation of formalin pigment; buffering above pH 7.0 is not indicated.	11
79	T	Commercial formaldehyde solution contains 37%-40% by weight of gas dissolved in water.	10
80	T	Osmium tetroxide will fix and preserve ~93% of lipids present in a tissue section.	16
81	F	Orth solution does not contain mercury; Helly and Zenker do.	21,22
82	T	Chrome pigment can be prevented by washing the tissues with water before processing.	17
83	F	B-5 fixative contains formaldehyde and mercuric chloride.	19
84	T	Glutaraldehyde is frequently used as the primary fixative for tissues for electron microscopy.	14
85	T	Orth solution is the recommended fixative for pheochromocytomas unless immunohistochemistry is to be performed.	7
86	T	Heat and desiccation are physical methods of fixation.	2,3
87	T	Glyoxal fixatives act more rapidly than formalin fixatives.	15
88	T	Zinc has successfully replaced mercury in some fixatives, such as B-5.	17
89A	b	Bouin solution is preferred for connective tissue, especially if trichrome stains are to be done.	7
89B	f, g	Both osmium tetroxide and Zamboni are used for electron microscopy.	16,22
89C	d	Most enzyme histochemistry procedures require frozen sections.	7
89D	d	Specimens for immunofluorescence should be frozen without fixation.	7
89E	e	Orth solution is preferred to preserve the chromaffin granules.	7
89F	h	Zenker solution is preferred for the demonstration of muscle cross-striations by the PTAH technique.	7
89G	a	Because glycogen is water soluble, absolute alcohol is the preferred fixative.	7
90A	f, g	B-5 contains formaldehyde and mercuric chloride.	19

ISBN 978-089189-6401

Question	Answer	Discussion	*Histotechnology* Page
90B	c, f, j	Bouin solution contains acetic acid, formaldehyde, and picric acid.	20
90C	b, c, d	Carnoy solution contains absolute alcohol, acetic acid, and chloroform.	24
90D	f, m, n	10% neutral buffered formalin contains formaldehyde, and monobasic and dibasic sodium phosphates.	13
90E	a, c, f, j	Gendre solution contains 95% alcohol, acetic acid, formaldehyde, and picric acid.	20
90F	f, g, k	Helly solution contains formaldehyde, mercuric chloride, and potassium dichromate.	21
90G	c, e, f, j	Hollande solution contains acetic acid, copper acetate, formaldehyde, and picric acid,	21
90H	f, k	Orth solution contains formaldehyde and potassium dichromate.	22
90I	i, j, m, n	Zamboni solution contains paraformaldehyde, picric acid, and monobasic and dibasic sodium phosphates.	22
90J	c, g, k	Zenker solution contains acetic acid, mercuric chloride, and potassium dichromate.	21
91 -1	B	Only Orth contains potassium dichromate.	21,22
91-2	C	Both B-5 and Orth solutions contain formaldehyde.	221,22
91-3	D	Neither B-5 nor Orth solution contains acetic acid.	21,22
91-4	A	B-5, or a zinc substitute, is recommended for lymph nodes.	20
91-5	A	Sections must be treated with iodine to remove the mercury pigment formed during fixation with B-5.	20
92-1	D	Neither pigment is water soluble; sections must be treated chemically for removal.	25
92-2	C	Both pigments are deposited during fixation.	11,15
92-3	A	Only mercury pigment can be removed with iodine.	25
92-4	B	A neutral pH will prevent the formation of formalin pigment.	11
92-5	B	Formalin pigment can be removed with alcoholic picric acid.	25
93-1	C	Both Zenker and Helly solutions contain mercuric chloride and potassium dichromate.	21
93-2	B	Because it contains formaldehyde instead of acetic acid, it will preserve erythrocytes.	21
93-3	A	Only Zenker solution contains acetic acid.	21
93-4	B	Only Helly solution contains formaldehyde.	21

ISBN 978-089189-6401

Question	Answer	Discussion	*Histotechnology* Page
93-5	C	Both solutions must be followed by running water before processing in order to prevent the formation of chromate pigment.	21
94-1	B	Because of the acetic acid present, Bouin solution may lyse erythrocytes, but buffered formalin will not.	9,20
94-2	B	Tissue fixed in Bouin solution should be washed with 50% alcohol to remove the excess picric acid. If picric acid remains in the tissue, staining results will change over time.	17,20
94-3	A	The phosphates used to buffer formalin solutions will precipitate in alcohol >70%, so dehydration should begin in solutions no >70%; 65% alcohol is preferred for beginning dehydration.	13
94-4	A	Formalin becomes acidic on standing and this allows the formation of formalin pigment; therefore, it should be buffered to approximately neutrality.	11
94-5	D	Neither of these solutions contains mercuric chloride.	12,20
95	c	The brown-microcrystalline pigment is most likely formalin pigment, and it should not form if the solution pH is >6.0.	11
96	d	Formalin pigment may even form in very bloody areas with solutions buffered to a pH of 7.0; it can be removed with alcoholic picric acid.	11
97	a	Urate crystals are water soluble, so a nonaqueous fixative, such as absolute alcohol, must be used.	7
98	c	Zinc will be precipitated by phosphates present in buffered formalin, so the tissue must be washed before transferring.	17,18
99	a	If picric acid is not removed sufficiently (preferably neutralized), staining will be affected in blocks after prolonged storage.	17
100	b	10% neutral buffered formalin does not preserve ultrastructure well, so either Millonig formalin or gluteraldehyde should be used for some of the tissue. Postfixation in osmium tetroxide should follow both formalin and glutaraldehyde for fixation of the fat, especially that in the cell membranes.	13,14,25
101	b	Tissue that has not been completely fixed prior to beginning dehydration will show the effects of alcoholic fixation in the central portion, including a difference in staining and more nuclear bubbling.	6
102	c	The temperature is critical and according to Hopwood should not exceed 55°C. The absolute maximum temperature is 68°C.	3

ISBN 978-089189-6401

Question	Answer	Discussion	*Histotechnology* Page
103	c	Glyoxal is not a satisfactory fixative if silver stains for *Helicobacter pylori* are needed (as on gastric biopsies), as staining is unsatisfactory.	15
104	c	The presence of villi identifies this tissue as small intestine.	5,6
105	b	Fixation has been delayed on this specimen, and autolysis has occurred.	5,6
106	a	Placing the tissue in fixative sooner would have prevented the problem.	5,6
107	c	The outermost layer of the mucosa, or the epithelium, is missing in this section of small intestine.	5,6
108	b	Formalin pigment is especially prone to formation in blood rich areas.	11
109	b	An alcoholic solution of picric acid would remove formalin pigment.	11
110	d	The formalin pigment most likely occurred during fixation with acidic formalin	11
111	b	Formalin pigment usually does not form if the pH of the solution is kept >6.0.	11
112	c	The section has been screened for formalin pigment by the use of polarizing microscopy.	11
113	a	Polarizing microscopy uses a polarizer and an analyzer; a halogen lamp is used with fluorescence microscopy, an electron gun is used in electron microscopy, and oblique light is used in dark field microscopy.	55-57
114	c	Birefringence is the phenomenon shown in this image.	55
115	b	The problem is most likely due to incomplete fixation before beginning processing.	28
116	a	A lack of chromatin definition, or smudgy nuclei, is seen in this image; euchromatin does not stain with the H&E.	28
117	d	Nuclear bubbling is seen in this image. The nuclei have a soapsuds appearance.	28
118	b	Incomplete fixation is the most likely cause of nuclear bubbling; however, it can be caused by drying slides that have not been drained well either in the microwave oven or at too high a temperature.	28

ISBN 978-089189-6401

Processing *Questions*

1-18. The following are multiple choice questions. Please circle the letter in front of the correct answer. There is only 1 best answer.

1. Which of the following is a dehydrating agent?
   a. formalin
   b. xylene
   c. benzene
   d. alcohol

2. A clearing agent for use in processing tissues for paraffin embedding must be miscible with the:
   a. fixative and paraffin
   b. dehydrant and paraffin
   c. fixative and dehydrant
   d. paraffin and water

3. Dioxane is a reagent that can be used:
   a. for both fixing and dehydrating tissues
   b. for both dehydrating and clearing tissues
   c. in very small volume ratios
   d. for long periods without changing

4. All of the following reagents can be used to dehydrate tissue EXCEPT:
   a. benzene
   b. absolute alcohol
   c. dioxane
   d. acetone

5. Most commonly, the paraffin used for embedding tissues is kept at approximately:
   a. 37°C
   b. 52°C
   c. 60°C
   d. 65°C

6. A disadvantage of the use of dioxane in processing tissues is that it is:
   a. toxic
   b. likely to harden tissues
   c. not miscible with water
   d. explosive

7. The chief objection to the use of xylene as a clearing agent for processing tissues is that xylene is:
   a. likely to harden tissue
   b. hydroscopic
   c. only slightly miscible with paraffin
   d. the most volatile of the hydrocarbons

ISBN 978-089189-6401

8. A good paraffin for routine use is one with a melting point of:
    a. 50°C to 52°C
    b. 55°C to 58°C
    c. 60°C to 62°C
    d. 63°C to 65°C

9. All of the following chemicals are clearing agents EXCEPT:
    a. chloroform
    b. dioxane
    c. ethanol
    d. xylene

10. Overheating of the paraffin used for embedding may cause:
    a. air bubbles in the block
    b. cracking of the block
    c. tissue to adhere to the cassette
    d. poor infiltration

11. One advantage of the paraffin technique is that:
    a. hard objects cut easily
    b. there is practically no tissue distortion
    c. serial sections are easy to obtain
    d. microtomy artifacts are uncommon

12. When cutting paraffin embedded tissues, if the tissue seems hard and brittle, one source of trouble is likely to be:
    a. inadequate fixation
    b. incomplete dehydration
    c. overheated paraffin
    d. poor infiltration

13. The process of removing water from tissue is called:
    a. dehydration
    b. reduction
    c. oxidation
    d. clearing

14. Reagents that both clear and dehydrate are called:
    a. dealcoholization reagents
    b. universal solvents
    c. essential oils
    d. clearing agents

15. Paraffin that is considered soft:
    a. is required for use with high room temperature
    b. is best for embedding and sectioning hard tissues
    c. has a melting point of ~56°C to 58°C
    d. is most useful when thick sections are desired

ISBN 978-089189-6401

16. When used for clearing, cedarwood oil must be followed by:
    a. alcohol
    b. xylene
    c. a universal solvent
    d. paraffin

17. Paraffin is cooled as rapidly as possible after embedding tissue in order to:
    a. prevent the formation of large crystals
    b. remove air bubbles from the paraffin
    c. lower the melting point of the paraffin
    d. aid infiltration into the tissue

18. The dehydration and clearing steps can be omitted when using:
    a. celloidin
    b. epoxy resin
    c. glycol methacrylate
    d. water soluble wax

19. Match the reagent on the left with its use on the right. >1 use may apply to some reagents.

Reagent

______A. Benzene
______B. Cedarwood oil
______C. Limonene derivatives
______D. Dioxane
______E. Carbowax
______F. Chloroform
______G. Ethyl alcohol
______H. Celloidin
______I. Xylene
______J. Isopropanol
______K. Araldite
______L. Tetrahydrofuran
______M. Toluene
______N. Aliphatic hydrocarbons

Use

a. dehydrant
b. clearing
c. infiltration/embedding

20-38. The following statements are either true or false. Circle T if the statement is true, circle F if the statement is false.

20. Specimens for electron microscopy are embedded in glycol methacrylate. **[T\F]**

21. Sections processed by the celloidin method show less shrinkage than when processed by the paraffin technique. **[T\F]**

22. Frozen sections are specified for processing tissue for the demonstration of most enzymes. **[T\F]**

23. Overheating of the paraffin used for infiltration will cause shrinkage and overhardening of the tissue. **[T\F]**

ISBN 978-089189-6401

24. Skin sections are embedded so that the epithelial surface is face-down in the block. [T\F]

25. Ion exchange resin and electrolytic methods of decalcification fall under the broad heading of "acid methods."

26. When undecalcified bone is to be sectioned, it must be embedded in Carbowax. [T\F]

27. Heating the solution is a good method of increasing the rate of decalcification. [T\F]

28. Tissue will contain ice crystal artifacts when frozen slowly. [T\F]

29. Tissues are usually infiltrated with paraffin directly from an essential oil. [T\F]

30. A chelating agent exchanges another ion for the calcium ion. [T\F]

31. Carbowax is a blend of liquid polyethylene glycol and wax. [T\F]

32. One result of incomplete clearing is poor infiltration with Carbowax. [T\F]

33. Bone sections should be embedded parallel to the long axis of the block. [T\F]

34. If phosphate buffered formalin fixation is followed by dehydration beginning with 80% alcohol, phosphates may be precipitated. [T\F]

35. The best method of checking Zenker fixed tissue for the completeness of decalcification is radiologic examination. [T\F]

36. Xylene and toluene are aromatic hydrocarbons. [T\F]

37. One cause of uneven staining with H&E may be water contamination of the clearing agent on the processor. [T\F]

38. Toluene is the preferred clearing agent for microwave processing. [T\F]

39. Methylene blue can be used in the processing alcohols to dye tissues for identification when embedding. [T\F]

40. List 2 methods of freezing tissue.

    a. ______________________________

    b. ______________________________

41. List 3 methods to determine the endpoint of decalcification.

    a. ______________________________

    b. ______________________________

    c. ______________________________

ISBN 978-089189-6401

42-46. Each of the following numbered words or phrases is associated with one, both, or neither of the headings listed as A or B above it. Within the parentheses on the right, place the appropriate letter for that word or phrase. Write:

A, if the numbered phrase is associated with A only
B, if the numbered phrase is associated with B only
C, if the numbered phrase is associated with both A and B
D, if the numbered phrase is associated with neither A nor B

42.

A. Formic acid
B. Nitric acid
C. both
D. neither

1. Is used to decalcify specimens [ ]
2. Is used to check endpoint of decalcification [ ]
3. Frequently impairs staining reactions [ ]
4. May cause tissue damage after 48 hours [ ]
5. Is used with ion exchange resins [ ]

43.

A. Xylene
B. Tetrahydrofuran
C. both
D. neither

1. Is a universal solvent [ ]
2. Will dehydrate tissue [ ]
3. Will clear tissue for infiltration [ ]
4. Will not mix with water [ ]
5. Is not toxic [ ]

44.

A. Chloroform
B. Cedarwood oil
C. both
D. neither

1. Is a clearing agent [ ]
2. Must be followed by xylene or toluene [ ]
3. Is not flammable or combustible [ ]
4. Is a universal solvent [ ]
5. Does not make tissue transparent [ ]

45.

A. Epoxy resins
B. Glycol methacrylate
C. both
D. neither

1. Does not tolerate water [ ]
2. Requires the use of a transitional fluid [ ]
3. Frequently used for undecalcified bone [ ]
4. Used for 80 nm to 90 nm sections [ ]
5. Skin contact should be avoided [ ]

46.

A. Paraffin
B. Water soluble waxes
C. both
D. neither

1. Will infiltrate tissue directly from aqueous fixatives [ ]
2. Fat is dissolved out during processing [ ]
3. Embedding medium of choice for very hard tissue [ ]
4. Blocks are chilled for sectioning [ ]
5. Sections are floated out on warm water bath [ ]

ISBN 978-089189-6401

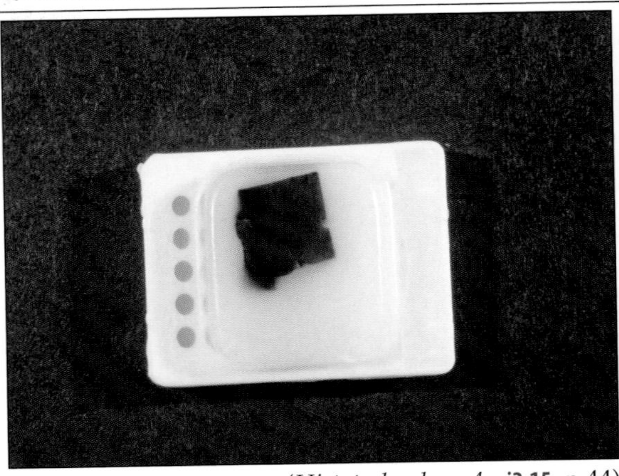

A (*Histotechnology 4e*, **i2.15**, p 44)

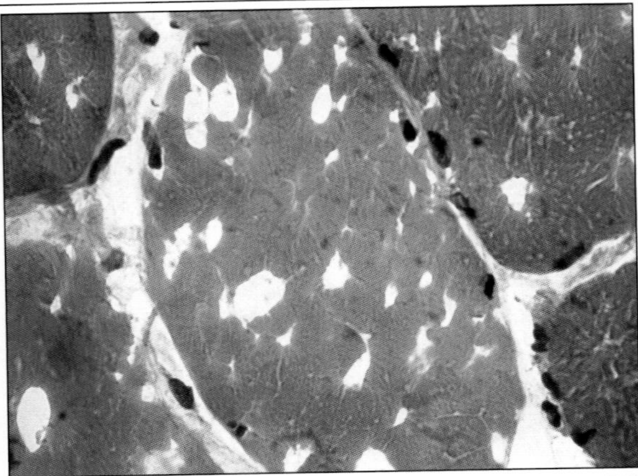

B (*Histotechnology 4e*, **i2.28**, p 50)

47-50. The following questions refer to images A-E as specified.

47. The tissue in the block shown in image A:
    a. has not been flattened appropriately
    b. should have been centered in the block
    c. has been sectioned too deep
    d. is properly embedded

48. What microtomy problem most likely will be caused when sectioning the block shown in image A?
    a. microscopic chatter
    b. holes in the tissue
    c. difficulty forming a ribbon
    d. compressed sections

49. The problem shown in image B is most likely caused by:
    a. delayed fixation
    b. improper positioning of the anti-roll plate
    c. freezing at a temperature of –150°C
    d. slow freezing

50. The problem shown in image C is:
    a. poorly processed tissue
    b. incorrect orientation of the tissue
    c. due to enzyme action
    d. tissue carryover during embedding

51. The problem shown in image C could have been prevented by:
    a. increasing the time in the dehydrating solutions
    b. opening the specimen, pinning it out, and adding fixative upon receipt
    c. carefully cleaning embedded forceps between specimens
    d. ensuring that the tissue is embedded at the same level

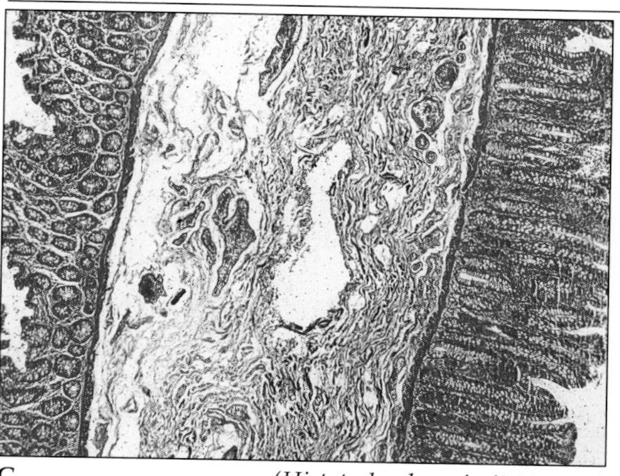

C (*Histotechnology 4e*, **i2.20**, p 46)

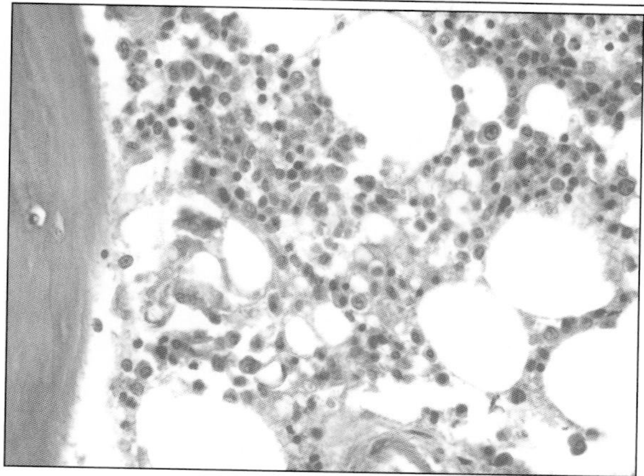

D (*Histotechnology 4e*, **i2.26**, p 50)

52. Which of the following layers is missing from the section shown in image C?
    a. mucosa
    b. lamina propria
    c. submucosa
    d. muscularis externa

53. The tissue shown in image D is:
    a. spleen
    b. cortical bone
    c. bone marrow
    d. kidney

54. The problem shown in image D could have been prevented by:
    a. using nitric acid for decalcification
    b. using the electrolytic method of decalcification
    c. placing directly into 70% alcohol after decalcification
    d. carefully monitoring the endpoint of decalcification

55. The problem shown in image D is most likely due to:
    a. incomplete fixation
    b. water carried over into xylene
    c. overdecalcification
    d. the use of EDTA for decalcification

ISBN 978-089189-6401

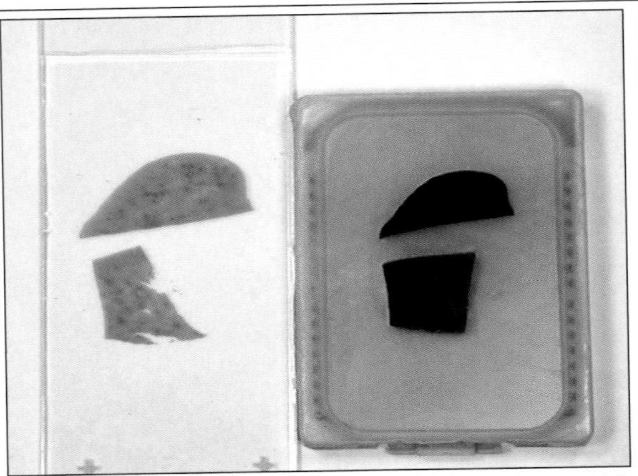

E (*Histotechnology 4e*, **i2.21**, p 46)

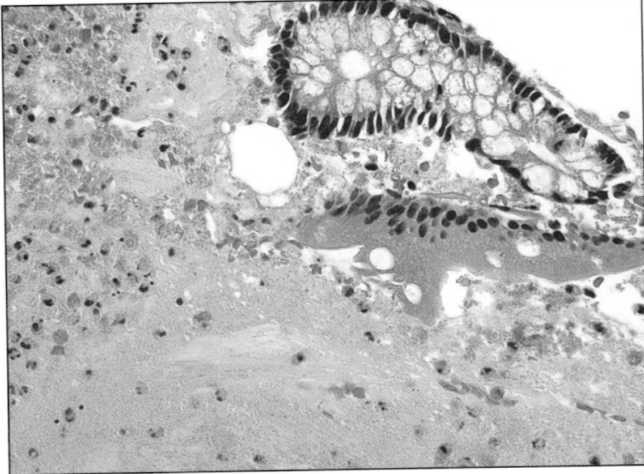

F (*Histotechnology 4e*, **i2.16** p 44)

56. The problem shown in image E could have been prevented by:
    a. ensuring that both sections were embedded flat and at the same level
    b. chilling the mold rapidly following embedding
    c. ensuring that the paraffin contains beeswax
    d. working slowly when adding several pieces of tissue to the same block

57. The problem shown in image E is most likely due to:
    a. incomplete fixation
    b. water contamination of the clearing agent
    c. improper embedding
    d. overheated embedding paraffin

58. The problem shown in image F is most likely due to :
    a. poor processing
    b. incorrect orientation
    c forceps metastasis
    d. improper paraffin temperature

59. The problem shown in image F could most likely have been prevented by:
    a. lowering the paraffin temperature
    b. more care in removing cassette lids
    c. more care in placing the specimen in the mold
    d. better cleaning of forceps between specimens

60. The problem shown in image F most like occurred during:
    a. microtomy
    b. processing
    c. fixation
    d embedding

ISBN 978-089189-6401

61-65. The following are problem solving questions.

61. During microtomy, it is noted that most of the tissue is very hard and shrunken. One of the first things to check to prevent this from happening in the future is the:
    a. presence of water in the clearing agent
    b. pH of the fixative
    c. temperature of the infiltrating paraffin
    d. freshness of the reagents on the processor

62. H&E stained sections show very uneven staining of the tissue, with poor nuclear detail. One possible cause is:
    a. overheating of the embedding paraffin
    b. water in the clearing agent
    c. prolonged fixation in formaldehyde
    d. fixation in zinc formalin

63. Phosphate buffered formaldehyde is used in the first 2 stations of the closed processor. A white precipitate is forming in the processor tubing, and the tissue is more difficult to cut than usual. One of the first things to check to correct the problem is the:
    a. presence of water in the clearing agent
    b. pH of the formalin solution
    c. time allowed in the fixative
    d. percent alcohol used as the first dehydrant

64. At microtomy, formalin fixed, paraffin embedded kidney sections are soft and mushy. This is most likely due to:
    a. inadequate paraffin infiltration of the fat present
    b. beginning dehydration with 95% alcohol
    c. overfixation of the tissue
    d. inadequate dehydration and clearing

65. The tissue has loosened from the chuck while frozen sectioning. This can most likely be prevented in the future by:
    a. ensuring a cold chuck before applying the embedding medium
    b. using a chuck containing embedding medium that was stored in the cryostat overnight
    c. applying more embedding medium to attach the tissue
    d. applying the embedding medium to a warm chuck

66. Tissue is processed with the following reagents:

10% neutral buffered formalin	2 changes
65% alcohol	1 change
95% alcohol	2 changes
100% alcohol	2 changes
aliphatic hydrocarbon	2 changes
paraffin	3 changes

ISBN 978-089189-6401

The tissue does not seem to be well cleared and infiltrated. This problem might be solved by adding:

a. formalin and deleting the 65% alcohol
b. 80% alcohol and deleting one 95% alcohol
c. an aliphatic hydrocarbon and deleting one 95% alcohol
d. an aliphatic hydrocarbon and deleting one fixative

67. Many of the zinc formalin fixed biopsy specimens are hard and brittle, and show microscopic chatter. This will result if the specimens are:
    a. left in fixative for 6 hours
    b. not washed after fixation
    c. dehydrated with >70% alcohol
    d. not treated for pigment removal

68-72. The following questions relate to the processing schedule with the processing started at 5:00 PM. Tissue had been grossed and placed in 10% NBF by 3:00 PM.

Formalin, 10%	2 hours (no heat, vacuum)
Alcoholic formalin	1 hour (no heat, no vacuum)
Alcoholic formalin	1 hour (no heat, no vacuum)
Alcohol, 95%	1 hour (vacuum only)
Alcohol, 95%	45 minutes (no heat, no vacuum)
Absolute alcohol	45 minutes (vacuum only)
Absolute alcohol	1 hour (no heat, no vacuum)
Xylene	1 hour (no heat, no vacuum)
Xylene	1 hour (vacuum only)
Paraffin	30 minutes (no vacuum)
Paraffin	1 hour (no vacuum)
Paraffin	1.5 hours (vacuum)

68. All of the tissues listed below could be processed very well on the above schedule EXCEPT:
    a. excisional breast biopsies
    b. gastric biopsies
    c. sections of spleen
    d. sections of myometrium

69. On the above schedule, tissue should be ready for embedding at approximately:
    a. 4:30 AM
    b. 5:00 AM
    c. 5:30 AM
    d. 6:00 AM

70. If the power went off at 11:45 PM, in which solution would be tissues be?
    a. 95% alcohol
    b. absolute alcohol
    c. xylene
    d. paraffin

ISBN 978-089189-6401

71. If the power went off at 11:45 PM and remained off for 2 hours, the tissue would be expected to be:
   a. overhardened
   b. mushy
   c. correctly processed
   d. incompletely dehydrated

72. If the power went off at 11:45 PM and remained off for 2 hours, microtomy on some tissues might show:
   a. central mushy spots
   b. thick and thin areas
   c. lengthwise scratches in the tissue
   d. chatter at the edges of the section

73-75. The following questions relate to the processing schedule. Vacuum is used at all stations, but heat is used only with the paraffin. Specimens should have been fixed in NBF for at least 45 minutes before beginning the processing.

Formalin, 10% neutral buffered	15 minutes
Alcohol, 65%	15 minutes
Alcohol, 95%	15 minutes
Alcohol, 95%	15 minutes
Absolute alcohol	15 minutes
Absolute alcohol	15 minutes
Xylene	15 minutes
Xylene	15 minutes
Paraffin	15 minutes
Paraffin	15 minutes
Paraffin	15 minutes

73. All of the following biopsy tissues would process well on the above schedule EXCEPT:
   a. gastric
   b. kidney
   c. excisional breast
   d. endometrial

74. If the power went off 2 hours 20 minutes after beginning processing, the tissue would be in the:
   a. first xylene
   b. second xylene
   c. first paraffin
   d. second paraffin

75. If the power remained off for 1 hour, the tissue:
   a. should need to be reprocessed
   b. should be embedded
   c. would be overhardened
   d. would be difficult to section

ISBN 978-089189-6401

Processing *Answers*

Question	Answer	Discussion	*Histotechnology* Page
1	d	Most dehydration solutions are alcohols.	32
2	b	Since alcohol is not miscible with paraffin, a clearing agent is inserted between the 2 reagents; therefore, a clearing agent is miscible with both the dehydrating agent (alcohol) and paraffin.	34
3	b	Dioxane is a universal solvent, or a reagent used in histology to perform both the dehydrating and clearing steps.	34
4	a	Benzene is not miscible with aqueous solutions; therefore, it cannot be used for dehydration.	35
5	c	Paraffin with a melting point of 55°C to 58°C is commonly used for routine work, and since the supply of melted paraffin is usually kept 2°C to 4°C above the melting point of paraffin, then the supply of melted paraffin is usually kept at ~60°C.	37
6	a	Dioxane is a cumulative toxin, with a PEL (permissible exposure limit) of 100 ppm recommended by OSHA , and 1 ppm REL (recommended exposure limit) with a 30-minute ceiling recommended by NIOSH.	34
7	a	Xylene tends to overharden tissue, with fibrous, muscular, central nervous system, and cartilaginous tissues especially affected.	34
8	b	Paraffin for routine work is most frequently that with a melting point of 55°C to 58°C.	37
9	c	Ethanol is a dehydrating agent, and it will not clear tissues.	33
10	b	The tissue is not in the melted embedding paraffin long enough for the tissue to be affected, but the overheating may affect the paraffin itself and may cause subsequent cracking of the block.	37
11	c	Serial sections are easily obtained with the paraffin technique.	37
12	c	Exposure to overheated paraffin on the tissue processor will result in hard and brittle, as well as shrunken, tissue.	37
13	a	Dehydration means the removal of water.	32

ISBN 978-089189-6401

Question	Answer	Discussion	*Histotechnology* Page
14	b	Universal solvents perform both the dehydration and clearing steps in tissue processing for paraffin embedding.	34
15	d	Paraffin that is considered soft (has a low melting point) is best for thick sections and for making ribbons; it does not allow thin sections and does not provide good support for hard tissues.	37
16	b	If oil remains in the tissue, microtomy is frequently difficult; therefore, cedar wood and other essential oils are removed with xylene before infiltrating with paraffin.	35
17	a	Rapid cooling of paraffin will prevent large paraffin crystals that will adversely affect sectioning quality.	44
18	d	If a water soluble wax is used for embedding, the tissue may be placed in the wax directly from aqueous fixatives.	39
19A	b	Benzene is a clearing agent.	35
19B	b	Cedarwood oil is a clearing agent.	35
19C	b	The limonene derivatives are clearing agents.	35
19D	a, b	Dioxane is a universal solvent; it dehydrates and clears.	34
19E	c	Carbowax is a water soluble embedding medium.	39
19F	b	Chloroform is a clearing agent.	35
19G	a	Ethyl alcohol is a dehydrating agent.	33
19H	c	Celloidin is an embedding medium.	40
19I	b	Xylene is a clearing agent.	34
19J	a	Isopropanol is a dehydrating agent.	33
19K	c	Araldite is an epoxy resin used for embedding EM specimens.	40
19L	a, b	Tetrahydrofuran is a universal solvent used for both dehydrating and clearing.	34
19M	b	Toluene is a clearing agent.	35
19N	b	Aliphatic hydrocarbons are used for clearing tissue.	36
20	F	Specimens for electron microscopy are embedded in epoxy resins.	41
21	T	Because no heat is involved, sections processed by the celloidin method show less shrinkage than with the paraffin technique.	40

ISBN 978-089189-6401

Answers for Processing

Question	Answer	Discussion	*Histotechnology* Page
22	T	Because fixation and/or heat will inactivate most enzymes, frozen sections are specified for processing tissue for their demonstration.	50
23	T	Because tissue remains in the overheated infiltration paraffin for some time, the tissue will become hardened and shrunken.	37
24	F	Skin sections should be embedded with the epithelial surface parallel to 1 side of the block.	2
25	T	Both the ion exchange resin and electrolytic methods use an acid for decalcification and therefore fall under the broad heading of "acid methods of decalcification."	47
26	F	Carbowax does not provide enough support for undecalcified bone; it must be embedded in glycol methacrylate.	40
27	F	Heat generated during decalcification may cause tissue destruction and a loss of cellular detail, as well as stainability.	47
28	T	Ice crystals will form in tissue that is slowly frozen.	50
29	F	If oil remains in the tissue, microtomy is frequently difficult; therefore, cedar wood and other essential oils are removed with xylene before infiltrating with paraffin.	35
30	F	Chelating agents bind ionized calcium ions, but no other ions are exchanged for the calcium ion.	48
31	T	Carbowax is a blend of polyethylene glycol and wax.	39
32	F	Carbowax will infiltrate tissue directly from aqueous fixatives.	39
33	F	Microtomy will be easier if bone sections are embedded diagonally in the block.	43
34	T	A precipitate may form if phosphate buffered formalin is followed immediately by alcohol with a concentration >70%.	33
35	F	Zenker is a metallic fixative, and metals will render the specimen opaque so that the endpoint cannot be determined by X-ray.	48
36	T	Xylene and toluene are aromatic hydrocarbons.	34
37	T	Uneven staining may be caused by water contamination of the clearing agent on the processor.	41
38	F	Most microwave processing uses only ethyl alcohol, isopropyl alcohol, and paraffin.	39

ISBN 978-089189-6401

Question	Answer	Discussion	*Histotechnology* Page
39	T	Methylene blue can be used in the processing alcohols to dye tissues especially as an aid for identifying small biopsy tissues.	32
40 a, b		Acceptable answers: cryostat, isopentane and liquid nitrogen, liquid nitrogen with talc dusted tissue, dry ice and acetone, liquid freon.	50
41 a, b, c		Mechanical, chemical, X-ray	48
42-1	C	Both acids may be used, although the process must be carefully monitored if using nitric acid.	47
42-2	D	Neither acid is used to check the endpoint of decalcification.	48
42-3	B	Staining reactions can be seriously impaired if decalcification with nitric acid is prolonged.	47
42-4	B	If decalcification is prolonged beyond 48 hours, nitric acid can cause serious problems with tissue stainability; formic acid is slower-acting and affords more latitude.	47
42-5	A	Formic acid is commonly used with ion exchange resins.	47
43-1	B	Tetrahydrofuran is a universal solvent; it will both dehydrate and clear tissue.	34
43-2	B	Tetrahydrofuran will dehydrate tissue.	34
43-3	C	Both xylene and tetrahydrofuran will clear tissue for infiltration.	34
43-4	A	Tetrahydrofuran will mix with water; xylene will not.	34
43-5	D	Both reagents are toxic.	34
44-1	C	Both are clearing agents.	35
44-2	B	If oil remains in the tissue, microtomy is frequently difficult; therefore, cedar wood and other essential oils are removed with xylene before infiltrating with paraffin.	35
44-3	A	Chloroform is neither flammable nor combustible, so disposal is a serious problem. Cedar wood oil is combustible, but not flammable.	35
44-4	D	Neither reagent is a universal solvent; neither dehydrates tissue.	35
44-5	A	Chloroform does not make tissue transparent, so transparency cannot be used to determine the endpoint of clearing.	35
45-1	A	Water is not tolerated by epoxy resins.	40

ISBN 978-089189-6401

Answers for Processing

Question	Answer	Discussion	*Histotechnology* Page
45-2	A	Epoxy resins are used to embed specimens for EM, and require the use of a transition fluid, synonymous with a clearing agent, prior to infiltration with the resin.	40
45-3	B	Glycol methacrylate is frequently used for embedding undecalcified bone specimens.	40
45-4	A	80-90 nm sections can only be cut on epoxy embedded material.	41
455	C	Skin contact should be avoided to prevent dermatitis with both of these reagents, and they should both be used under a hood.	41
46-1	B	Water soluble waxes will infiltrate tissue directly from aqueous fixatives.	40
46-2	A	Fat is dissolved out during processing for paraffin embedding. Fat is not dissolved and may be demonstrated in Carbowax embedded material.	39
46-3	D	Neither of these is the embedding medium of choice for very hard tissue; glycol methacrylate is the medium of choice for that.	37, 40
46-4	C	Both types of blocks are chilled before sectioning; because Carbowax is water soluble-cooling with ice should be avoided, and the blocks must be cooled in a refrigerator.	40
46-5	A	Carbowax (water soluble wax) sections must be floated on special solutions in order to avoid disruption and tissue disintegration that would occur on a regular water bath.	40
47	b	The tissue should have been centered in the block when embedding.	44
48	c	Ribboning will be more difficult on this block because of the small paraffin margin on 1 side of the block; the tissue should have been centered in the block when embedding.	44
49	d	The holes in this section are ice crystals formed by slow freezing.	50
50	b	This section of small intestine has rolled during grossing and therefore is not correctly oriented during embedding.	46
51	b	Gastrointestinal specimens should be opened and pinned out for fixation immediately upon receipt.	46
52	d	The muscularis externa cannot be seen in this section of small intestine; all layers should be seen in a properly fixed and embedded specimen.	46

ISBN 978-089189-6401

Question	Answer	Discussion	*Histotechnology* Page
53	c	The tissue is bone marrow; cortical bone is very dense and relatively acellular.	49
54	d	Carefully checking the endpoint of decalcification would have prevented the overdecalcification seen in this section.	48
55	c	The problem seen is most likely overdecalcification resulting in a lack of nuclear staining.	49
56	c	The tissue seen in the upper right is from another specimen, and the close attachment most likely is due to forceps metastasis at either the grossing or embedding table.	44
57.	d	The problem seen in this section could most likely have been prevented by better cleaning of forceps between specimens	43
58	d	The problem seen in this section most likely occurred at the embedding table. This artifact can also happen at the grossing table.	43
59	a	Carefully embedding both pieces of tissue at the same level and flattened by gentle pressure would have allowed complete sections of both pieces of tissue in the block.	46
60	c	One piece of the tissue was not embedded flat, so that a complete section was not obtained.	46
61	c	If the infiltrating paraffin is too hot, hard and brittle tissue will result.	37
62	b	Poor nuclear detail will result if the tissue is not properly cleared because of water carryover; this will result in poor infiltration with paraffin. The tissue is not in the embedding paraffin long enough to be affected by overheating.	34
63	d	If the first dehydrating alcohol is >70%, phosphate salts may precipitate in the tissue and in the processor tubing.	33
64	d	Soft, mushy tissues are usually the result of inadequate dehydration and clearing, and therefore poor paraffin infiltration.	32
65	d	The embedding medium and tissue will adhere better if applied to a warm chuck.	61
66	c	Because aliphatic hydrocarbons are less aggressive than xylene, 3 changes may be needed for good clearing. It is better to delete an alcohol than a fixative solution in order to ensure good fixation.	36
67	c	A precipitate may form with zinc formalin fixed tissues and in the processor tubing if dehydration is begun with >70% alcohol.	16,41

ISBN 978-089189-6401

Answers for Processing

Question	Answer	Discussion	*Histotechnology* Page
68	b	Most biopsies do not process well on an overnight processing cycle. Overdehydration most likely will result, and chatter will be seen on the edges of the microscopic sections. Because of the fat content, excisional breast biopsies are an exception and will process better on the overnight cycle.	37
69	c	The tissue should be ready to embed at 5:30 AM	38
70	b	The tissue will be in the second absolute alcohol.	38
71	a	The tissue will most likely be overhardened from the prolonged dehydration.	41
72	d	The tissue would be in absolute alcohol and would tend to be overhardened by prolonged dehydration. This might cause chatter at the edges of the sections.	41
73	c	Because of possible fat content, excisional breast biopsies will most likely not process well on the rapid processing schedule.	37
74	d	The tissue would be in the second paraffin.	38
75	b	The tissue would be within 10 minutes of the end of processing, so the tissue can be embedded shortly after the power goes off.	38

ISBN 978-089189-6401

Instrumentation *Questions*

1-31. The following are multiple choice questions. Please circle the letter in front of the correct answer. There is only 1 best answer.

1. The ability of the microscope to separate small details is defined as:
   a. magnification
   b. definition
   c. resolution
   d. numerical aperture

2. Sections 90 nm thick are commonly cut with a/an:
   a. sliding microtome
   b. ultramicrotome
   c. rotary microtome
   d. vibratome

3. Tissues embedded in glycol methacrylate are commonly cut with a/an:
   a. sliding microtome
   b. ultramicrotome
   c. rotary microtome
   d. vibratome

4. When cutting sections from paraffin blocks, the most common cause of unsatisfactory sections is:
   a. poor fixation of the tissue
   b. a flotation bath that is too hot
   c. paraffin with a low melting point
   d. a poor blade edge

5. The regular laboratory incubator maintains a temperature of about:
   a. 4°C
   b. 28°C
   c. 37°C
   d. 60°C

6. When the magnification can be changed without the need to refocus, the microscope objectives are said to be:
   a. parfocal
   b. binocular
   c. achromatic
   d. apochromatic

7. If a ribbon splits when cutting paraffin sections, the trouble is most likely due to:
   a. too much tilt in the blade
   b. nicks in the blade edge
   c. static electricity
   d. a loose block

ISBN 978-089189-6401

8. Care must be taken when using automatic coverslippers to ensure that:
   a. only no. 1 coverslips are applied
   b. only full baskets of slides are loaded on the coverslipper
   c. the mounting medium applied is correct for long term storage
   d. the mounting medium reservoir is cleaned daily

9. The temperature of the oven used to maintain a supply of melted paraffin for embedding tissue is most commonly about:
   a. 43°C
   b. 43°F
   c. 60°C
   d. 60°F

10. Doubly refractile particles are examined using:
    a. polarized light
    b. ultraviolet light
    c. electron microscopy
    d. dark field illumination

11. Crooked paraffin ribbons may be caused by:
    a. static electricity
    b. overchilled blocks
    c. too much blade tilt
    d. nonparallel block horizontal edges

12. When using a microscope with a ×10 ocular and a ×40 objective, the total magnification is approximately:
    a. 100
    b. 400
    c. 1,000
    d. 4,000

13. The clearance angle of the microtome blade is routinely :
    a. 3°-8°
    b. 15°-20°
    c. 30°-40°
    d. variable

14. The ordinary refrigerator, when operating normally, has a temperature that approaches:
    a. 0°C
    b. 0°F
    c. 4°C
    d. 40°F

15. When a lens for a light microscope has been corrected for 2 colors, it is said to be:
    a. orthochromatic
    b. achromatic
    c. apochromatic
    d. parfocal

ISBN 978-089189-6401

16. When using paraffin with a melting point of 55°C to 57°C, the most common temperature for floating sections on a flotation bath is approximately:
    a. 15°C to 20°C
    b. 35°C to 40°C
    c. 45°C to 50°C
    d. 55°C to 60°C

17. Compressed or wrinkled sections may be caused by:
    a. overchilled paraffin blocks
    b. defects in the blade edge
    c. the wrong blade tilt
    d. static electricity

18. The scanning objective on the light microscope is found:
    a. above the oculars
    b. at the lower end of the body tube
    c. below the substage condenser
    d. below the iris diaphragm

19. Various size holes are noted in sections of paraffin embedded liver on the flotation bath. With further ribboning, these holes decrease in size and disappear. The most likely cause of the holes is:
    a. overfixation of the tissue
    b. air trapped in the tissue
    c. facing the block too aggressively
    d. infiltration with overheated paraffin

20. Birefringent substances are best examined with which of the following microscopes?
    a. fluorescence
    b. electron
    c. light
    d. polarizing

21. During microtomy, the sections lift from the blade as the block is raised. The most likely cause is:
    a. a dull blade
    b. too much blade tilt
    c. an overchilled block
    d. defects in the blade edge

22. Microscopic examination of an H&E stained section reveals marked chatter, especially at the edges of the tissue. This was most likely caused by:
    a. a dull blade
    b. too little blade tilt
    c. an overheated flotation bath
    d. overdehydration of the tissue

23. During cryotomy, sections of varying thickness are obtained. This can most likely be corrected by:
    a. lowering the cryostat temperature
    b. warming the blade edge
    c. increasing the blade tilt
    d. decreasing the speed of sectioning

ISBN 978-089189-6401

24. When checking the pH of a staining solution, the pH meter should be calibrated using a standard solution with a pH value:
    a. closest to that of the staining solution
    b. approximating that of water
    c. in any range
    d. close to 7.0

25. The microwave oven creates heat in staining solutions by:
    a. convection
    b. conduction
    c. nonionizing radiation
    d. electrolytic action

26. Tissue components can be measured with the light microscope in a process known as:
    a. microtomy
    b. microscopy
    c. micrometry
    d. microdissection

27. A microscope that has 2 eyepieces is:
    a. parfocal
    b. binocular
    c. achromatic
    d. orthochromatic

28. When a lens for a light microscope has been corrected for 3 colors, it is said to be:
    a. orthochromatic
    b. achromatic
    c. apochromatic
    d. parfocal

29. The high dry objective on most microscopes has a magnification of approximately:
    a. ×4
    b. ×10
    c. ×45
    d. ×100

30. Tissues are subjected to a series of different reagents in a closed processor by:
    a. tissue transfer
    b. fluid transfer
    c. heat transfer
    d. linear transport

31. When processed on a short cycle, tissue must be:
    a. cut thin during grossing
    b. washed after fixation
    c. fixed in neutral buffered formalin
    d. started in 95% alcohol on the processor

ISBN 978-089189-6401

32. List 3 types of microscopy most associated with histotechnology.

 a. ______________________________

 b. ______________________________

 c. ______________________________

33. List the 2 most common types of electron microscopy.

 a. ______________________________

 b. ______________________________

34-55. The following statements are either true or false. Circle T if the statement is true, circle F if the statement is false.

34. Living cells are usually examined with the dark-field microscope. **[T\F]**

35. A 3-dimensional image is obtained with the transmission electron microscope. **[T\F]**

36. Another name for the ocular of a microscope is the eyepiece. **[T\F]**

37. The analyzer of the polarizing microscope is placed between the specimen and the eye. **[T\F]**

38. Steel blades are commonly used to section glycol methacrylate. **[T\F]**

39. The angle formed by the block face and the cutting facet of the blade is known as the bevel angle. **[T\F]**

40. When examined microscopically, 8 µm sections will show all nuclei in the same plane of focus. **[T\F]**

41. Slow freezing of tissue leads to the formation of ice crystals. **[T\F]**

42. An overheated cryostat motor is frequently caused by ice buildup in the cryostat chamber. **[T\F]**

43. If the histotechnologist is skilled, then the most critical factor in the laboratory becomes the care and maintenance of laboratory instrumentation. **[T\F]**

44. Routine care of the microtome requires a thorough cleaning and oiling every 2 weeks. **[T\F]**

45. Dust collecting on the cooling coils of the cryostat may cause the motor to run more slowly. **[T\F]**

46. The temperature of the room is very important when cutting frozen sections. **[T\F]**

47. Paraffin sections will not adhere well to clean untreated and uncharged glass slides. **[T\F]**

ISBN 978-089189-6401

48. Poly-L-lysine is a common additive to the flotation bath. [T\F]

49. Water in the flotation bath is a possible source of contamination on sections to be stained for microorganisms. [T\F]

50. New instruments are validated by the manufacturer and may be put into use immediately. [T\F]

51. Household microwave instruments may not be used in the laboratory. [T\F]

52. Bar codes may be linear or 3D. [T\F]

53. Most tissue contamination from floaters occurs in the deparaffinization steps. [T\F]

54. Side by side comparisons are the best form of instrument validation. [T\F]

55. Some staining kits may have the problem of disproportionate solution volumes. [T\F]

56. Match the instrument in the left column with the closest correct temperature listed on the right. >1 letter may apply to some instruments. Some letters may be used more than once or not at all.

Instrument	Temperature
____A. Laboratory incubator	a. 60°C
____B. Infiltrating paraffin container	b. 45°C
____C. Flotation bath	c. 7°C
____D. Cryostat	d. 22°C
____E. Refrigerator	e. 4°C
____F. Freezer	f. –20°C
	g. –50°C
	h. –70°C

57-62. Each of the following numbered words or phrases is associated with one, both, or neither of the headings listed as A or B above it. Within the parentheses on the right, place the appropriate letter for that word or phrase. Write:

A, if the numbered phrase is associated with A only
B, if the numbered phrase is associated with B only
C, if the numbered phrase is associated with both A and B
D, if the numbered phrase is associated with neither A nor B

57.

A. Fluorescence microscopy
B. Polarizing microscopy
C. both
D. neither

1. Typically used to examine Congo red stained sections [ ]
2. Used to examine auramine-rhodamine stained sections [ ]
3. Requires the use of a mercury or halogen lamp [ ]
4. Aids in the identification of crystals [ ]
5. Used to examine unstained cells [ ]

ISBN 978-089189-6401

58.

A. Too little blade tilt	1. Sections may be compressed, wrinkled, or jammed	[ ]
B. Too much blade tilt	2. Sections may have lengthwise splits	[ ]
C. both	3. Sections may show microscopic chatter	[ ]
D. neither	4. Ribbons may be crooked	[ ]
	5. Ribbons may not form	[ ]

59.

A. Mushy sections	1. May result from improper processing	[ ]
B. Chatter in sections	2. May result from a dull blade	[ ]
C. both	3. May result from a nick in the blade edge	[ ]
D. neither	4. May result from cutting too rapidly	[ ]
	5. May be corrected by soaking faced blocks	[ ]

60.

A. Cryostat	1. Usually maintained at 37°C	[ ]
B. Flotation bath	2. Usually maintained at –20°C	[ ]
C. both	3. Required for sectioning for immunofluorescence	[ ]
D. neither	4. May cause parched earth artifact in sections	[ ]
	5. Must be kept free of debris	[ ]

61.

A. Electron microscope	1. Uses an electron gun	[ ]
B. Light microscope	2. Focused by varying the strength of magnetic fields	[ ]
C. both	3. Maximum useful magnification of ×1,000	[ ]
D. neither	4. Requires a halogen lamp	[ ]
	5. Resolution of ~0.2 µm	[ ]

62.

A. pH 7.0 buffer solution	1. Is considered an acid solution	[ ]
B. pH 4.0 buffer solution	2. Is considered a basic solution	[ ]
C. both	3. Should be used to calibrate pH meter for adjusting the pH of the Warthin-Starry staining solution	[ ]
D. neither	4. Should be used to calibrate pH meter for measuring the pH of neutral buffered formalin	[ ]
	5. Is equivalent to the pH of pure water	[ ]

ISBN 978-089189-6401

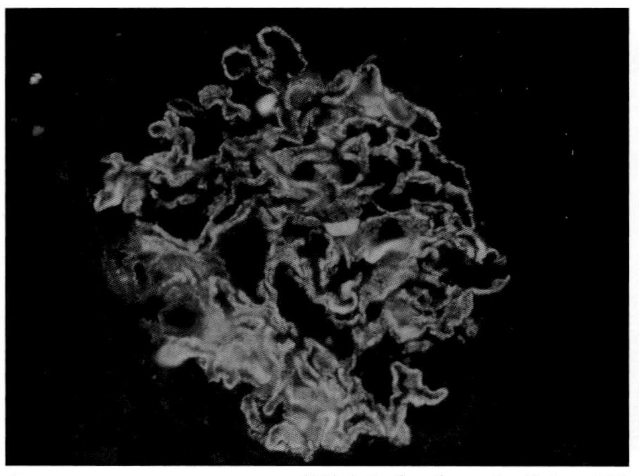

A (*Histotechnology 4e*, **i3.3**, p 55)

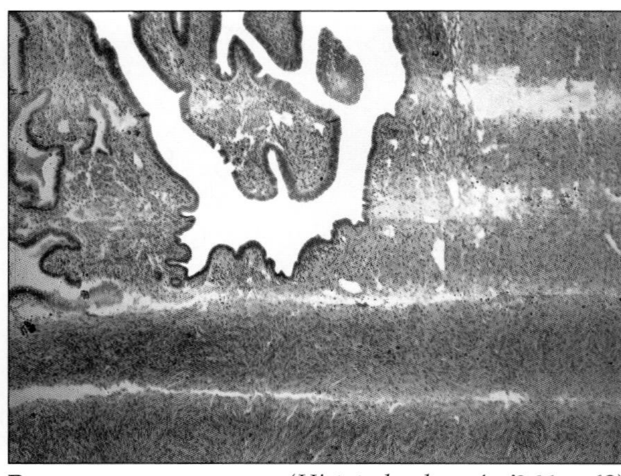

B (*Histotechnology 4e*, **i3.16**, p 63)

63-101. The following questions relate to images A-M as specified.

63. The type of microscope used to examine the section shown in image A was a/an:
    a. fluorescence microscope
    b. phase contrast microscope
    c. light microscope
    d. electron microscope

64. Tissue for the procedure shown in image A must be:
    a. fixed in formalin
    b. fixed in acetone
    c. fixed in B-5
    d. frozen unfixed

65. The technique shown in image A:
    a. uses metallic impregnation
    b. uses a fluorescent tagged antibody
    c. demonstrates birefringent material
    d. demonstrates scanning electron microscopy

66. The microscope used for the technique shown in image A most likely uses a/an:
    a. electron gun
    b. polarizer
    c. halogen lamp
    d. fluorescent screen

67. The section shown in image A is a section of:
    a. skin
    b. liver
    c. pancreas
    d. kidney

68. The problem shown in image B could most likely be corrected by:
    a. increasing the blade tilt
    b. increasing the clearance angle
    c. tightening the block and blade clamps
    d. moving the blade

Histotechnology Workbook 3e
ISBN 978-089189-6401

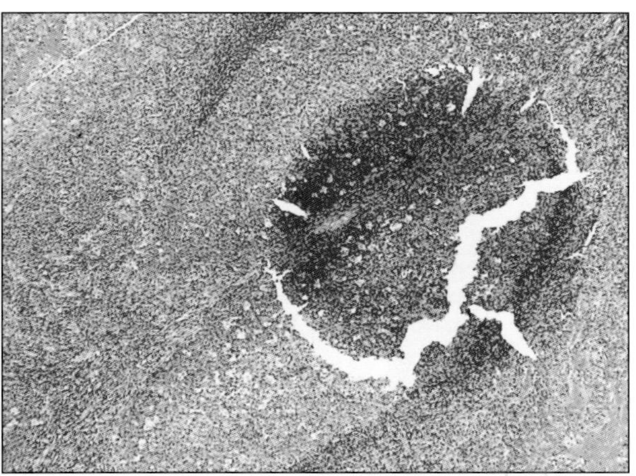

C (*Histotechnology 4e*, **i3.43**, p 74)

69. One cause of the problem shown in image B is:
    a. clamping the block too tightly
    b. too small a clearance angle
    c. a defect in the blade edge
    d. too much blade tilt

70. The problem shown in image B most often occurs when sectioning:
    a. brain
    b. uterus
    c. kidney
    d. lymph node

71. The problem shown in image C is the result of:
    a. poorly dissolved eosin
    b. overdrying the section
    c. mechanical damage to the section
    d. air trapped under the section

72. The problem shown in image C could most likely be prevented in the future by:
    a. allowing the flotation bath water to stand overnight
    b. avoiding mechanical damage to the section
    c. making certain that the eosin is completely dissolved
    d. drying the section in a convection oven

73. The problem shown in image C occurs during:
    a. fixation
    b. processing
    c. microtomy
    d. flotation

ISBN 978-089189-6401

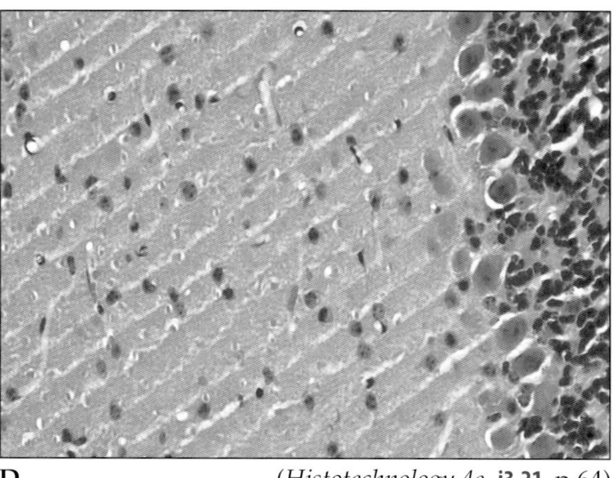

D (*Histotechnology 4e*, **i3.21**, p 64)

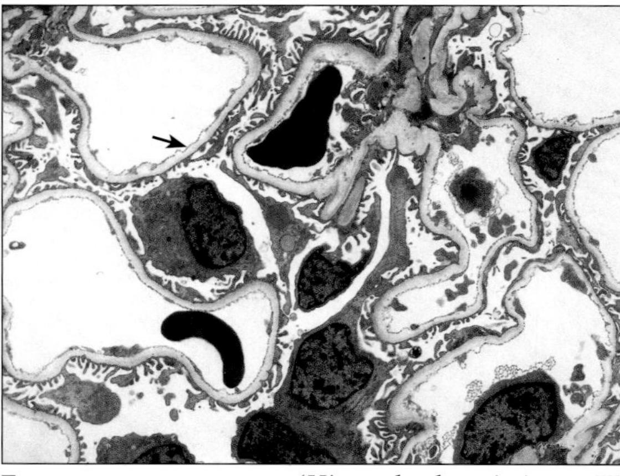

E (*Histotechnology 4e*, **i3.4**, p 57)

74. The problem shown in image D is most frequently the result of:
    a. poor fixation
    b. overdehydration
    c. incomplete clearing
    d. inadequate infiltration

75. The problem shown in image D could have been helped by:
    a. soaking the faced block
    b. increasing the clearance angle
    c. cutting slightly faster
    d. decreasing the flotation bath temperature

76. The problem shown in image D could be the result of:
    a. too large a clearance angle
    b. static electricity
    c. a defect in the blade edge
    d. too aggressive facing of the block

77. The tissue shown in image D is from the :
    a. central nervous system
    b. gastrointestinal tract
    c. uterus
    d. kidney

78. The type of microscopy shown in image E is:
    a. polarizing
    b. dark field
    c. phase contrast
    d. electron

79. The dark areas in image E are due to:
    a. transmitted electrons
    b. deflected electrons
    c. secondary electrons
    d. immunofluorescence

ISBN 978-089189-6401

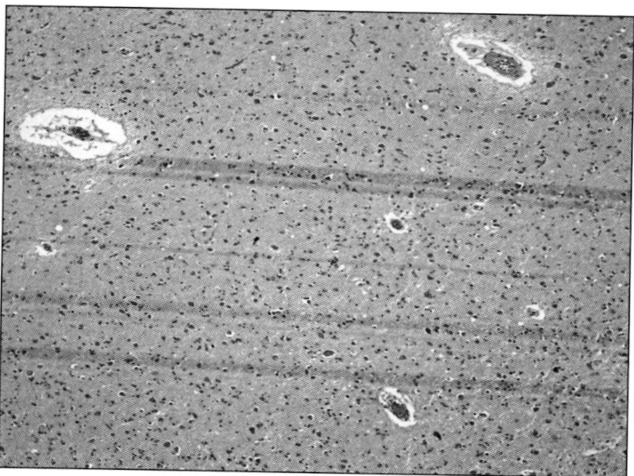

F (*Histotechnology 4e*, **i3.7**, p 60)

80. Shown in image E is a portion of a:
    a. pancreatic islet
    b. liver sinusoid
    c. kidney glomerulus
    d. prostatic gland

81. The arrow in the top left of image E is pointing to the:
    a. foot processes
    b. basement membrane
    c. mesangium
    d. convoluted tubule

82. The lines in the section shown in image F are most likely due to a/an:
    a. dull blade
    b. incorrect blade tilt
    c. poorly clamped block
    d. defects in the blade edge

83. The tissue shown in image F is most likely:
    a. pancreas
    b. brain
    c. liver
    d. kidney

84. The problem seen in image F could most likely be corrected by:
    a. moving to an unused part of the blade
    b. changing the blade tilt
    c. ensuring that the block is securely clamped
    d. sectioning less aggressively

ISBN 978-089189-6401

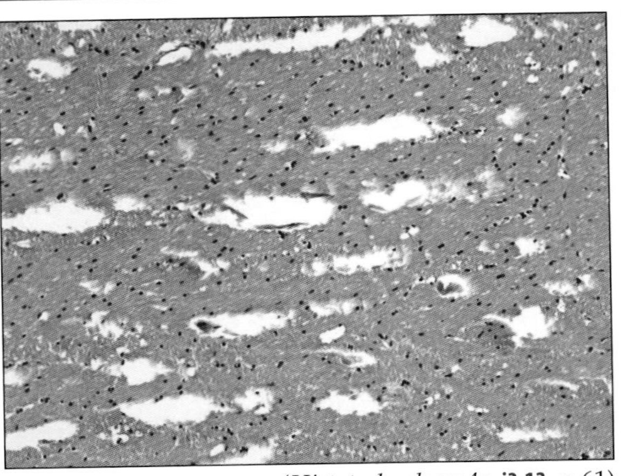

G (*Histotechnology 4e*, **i3.12**, p 61)

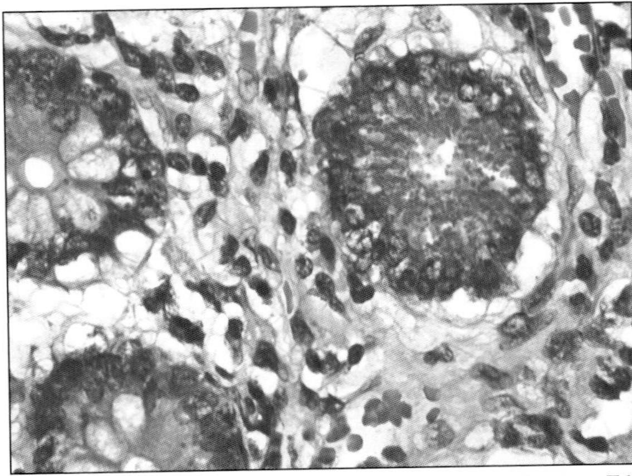

H (*Histotechnology 4e*, **i3.53**, p 76)

85. The problem seen in image G most likely could have been prevented by:
    a. ensuring that the blade was sharp
    b. changing the blade tilt
    c. sectioning less aggressively
    d. moving to an unused section of the blade

86. Once the problem seen in image G is apparent, the only way that a complete section can be obtained is to:
    a. reembed the tissue
    b. gently ribbon past the holes if tissue permits
    c. change the microtome blade
    d. soak the tissue in water

87. The problem shown in image H is most likely due to:
    a. prolonged fixation
    b. incomplete dehydration
    c. poor microtomy
    d. an improperly dried slide

88. The problem shown in image H could have been prevented by:
    a. ensuring correct fixation
    b. sectioning the tissue very slowly
    c. allowing the slide to drain well before drying at 60°C
    d. immediately drying the slides in the microwave oven

89. The artifact seen in image H is:
    a. excessive section thickness
    b. hypochromic nuclei
    c. cell shrinkage
    d. chatter

ISBN 978-089189-6401

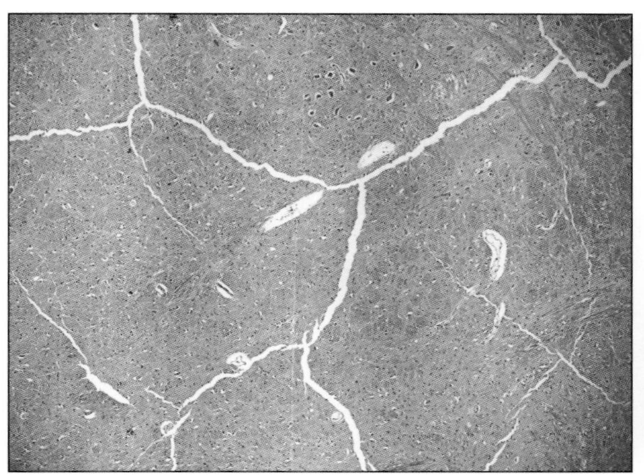

I (*Histotechnology 4e*, **i3.36**, p 71)

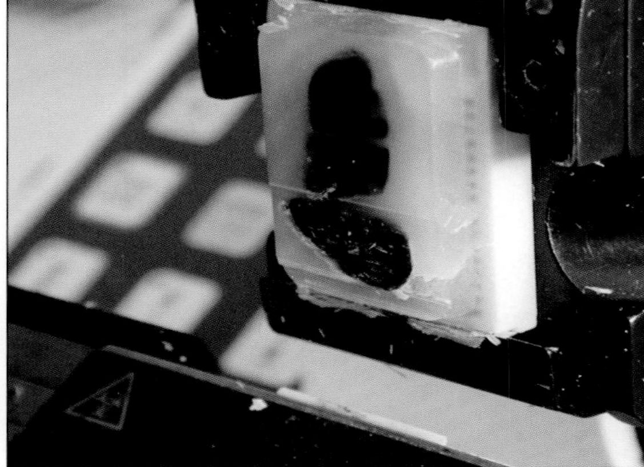

J (*Histotechnology 4e*, **i3.17**, p 63)

90. Which of the following is NOT a possible cause of the artifact seen in image I?
    a. improper processing of the tissue
    b. the use of a dull microtome blade
    c. the flotation bath too hot
    d. chilling the block with a fluorocarbon spray

91. The problem seen in image J is most likely due to a/an:
    a. improperly clamped block
    b. dull knife
    c. overhardened tissue
    d. poorly embedded tissue

92. The problem seen in image J will most likely have to be corrected by:
    a. changing the blade angle
    b. reembedding the tissue in another block
    c. soaking the block face
    d. reprocessing the tissue

ISBN 978-089189-6401

K (*Histotechnology 4e*, **i3.18**, p 63)

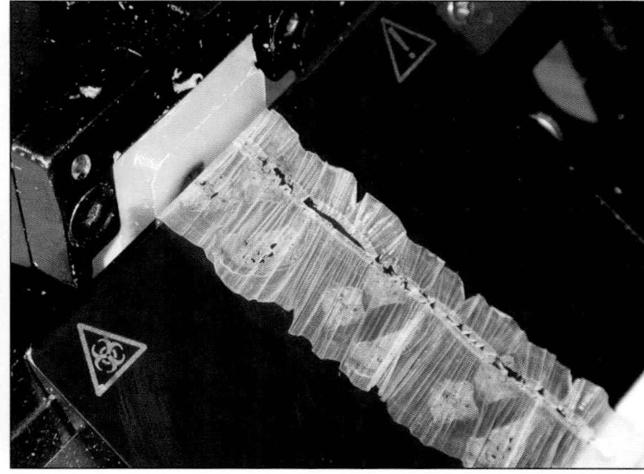
L (*Histotechnology 4e*, **i3.23**, p 65)

93. The problem shown in image K will most likely produce a slide with the problem shown in image:
    a. B
    b. F
    c. G
    d. I

94. The problem seen in image K can be corrected by:
    a. changing the blade angle
    b. retracting the block holder shaft
    c. tightening the block in the clamp
    d. changing the block orientation

95. The problem seen in image L most likely can be corrected by:
    a. cleaning the paraffin from the blade edge
    b. moving the blade to an unused area
    c. clamping the block more securely
    d. ribboning more slowly

96. The problem seen in image L could result from all of the following EXCEPT:
    a. improper use of forceps
    b. metallic staples
    c. poor blade edge
    d. extended block holder shaft

ISBN 978-089189-6401

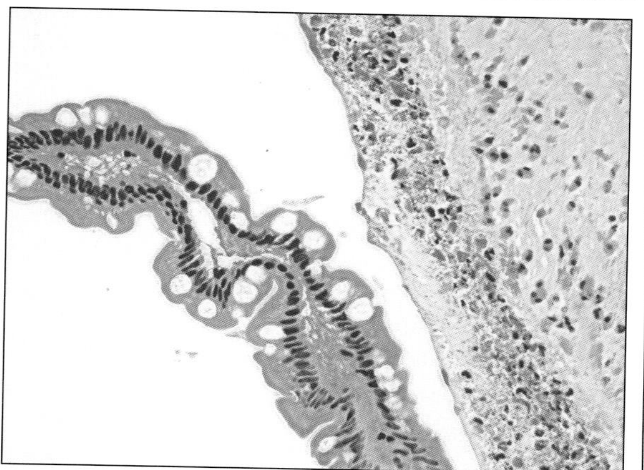

M (*Histotechnology 4e*, **i3.34**, p 69)

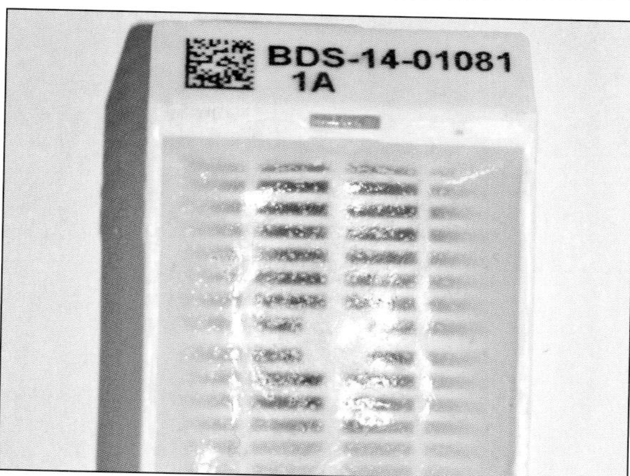

N (*Histotechnology 4e*, **i3.23**, p 65)

97. The problem seen in image M most likely is the result of:
    a. forceps metastasis
    b. cross-contamination during deparaffinization
    c. incorrect reagent order for staining
    d. automated coverslipping

98. The major source of the problem seen in image M is tissue carryover at:
    a. grossing
    b. embedding
    c. microtomy
    d. staining

99. While the problem seen in image M most likely cannot be totally eliminated, it might be reduce by:
    a. increasing the time of paraffin infiltration
    b. changing all staining solutions daily
    c. changing deparaffinization solutions often
    d. staining later in the day

100. The small square to the left of the surgical number in the cassette identification area as seen in image N is known as a:
    a. linear bar code
    b. 2D bar code
    c. 3D bar code
    d. decoration

101. The small square to the left of the surgical number in the cassette identification area as seen in image N is most helpful for:
    a. a repeat of the surgical number
    b. adding additional information
    c. ensuring that the patients name is on the cassette
    d. interfacing with computer and instrument information systems

Instrumentation *Answers*

Question	Answer	Discussion	*Histotechnology* Page
1	c	Resolution is the ability to distinguish between adjacent details or to reveal fine detail. Resolving power is measured as the least distance between 2 objects at which the objects still can be discerned as 2 separate structures rather than as a single blurred object.	54
2	b	The ultramicrotome is used to cut 90 nm (thin) sections for electron microscopy.	58
3	c	Glycol methacrylate embedded tissue is commonly sectioned with a rotary microtome, but glass knives are used for cutting good 1 µm2 µm sections	40,58
4	d	Although poorly fixed and processed tissue may section with some difficulty, the most common cause of unsatisfactory sections is a poor blade edge.	59
5	c	An incubator is usually maintained at approximately body temperature, or 37°C.	77
6	a	When objectives are parfocal, all objectives will have the focal point in the same plane, and magnification (objectives) can be changed without the need to refocus.	54
7	b	Nicks in the edge of the blade are the most common cause of split paraffin ribbons.	60
8	c	If the amount of mounting medium applied is incorrect, if there is too much xylene in the mounting medium, or if the ratio of xylene to mounting medium is incorrect, retraction of the mounting medium will occur and high power focusing does not project crisp cellular detail. The reservoir only needs to be cleaned weekly.	671
9	c	Ovens used to maintain a supply of melted paraffin for embedding tissue are commonly kept just above the melting point of the paraffin in use, or ~60°C.	76
10	a	Polarized light is used for examining doubly refractile particles or crystals such as talc, silica, or urate.	55
11	d	The upper and lower edges of the block should be parallel, or crooked ribbons may result.	60
12	b	Magnification is determined by multiplying the magnifications of the ocular and the objective, so 10 × 40 = 400.	54

ISBN 978-089189-6401

Question	Answer	Discussion	*Histotechnology* Page
13	a	The clearance angle is routinely 3°-8°, but the microtome design and type of blade can determine the angle.	59
14	c	Refrigerators are commonly kept at ~4°C and should never be allowed to reach a temperature >10°C.	78
15	b	Achromatic microscope lens are corrected for 2 colors, red and blue.	54
16	c	Flotation baths are commonly maintained 5°C to 10°C below the melting point of paraffin.	71
17	c	The wrong blade tilt, usually too little, is a common cause of compressed, wrinkled, or jammed sections. Rarely, too much tilt can also cause these problems.	64
18	b	All microscope objectives are located at the lower end of the body tube.	54
19	c	Holes that disappear from tissue sections as further ribboning is done are the result of facing the block too aggressively; this is because small flecks of tissue are removed from the block during rough facing, leaving a hole.	61
20	d	The polarizing microscope is used to examine substances that are birefringent, are doubly refractile, or exhibit anisotropism.	55
21	a	A dull blade or too little (not too much) blade tilt will cause lifting of the section for the blade as the block is raised.	62
22	d	Overdehydration of the tissue during processing will cause tissue to harden. During microtomy, this can cause chatter, or microscopic vibration, especially at the edge of some tissues.	64
23	c	Thick and thin, or variable, sections may be caused by too little blade tilt; increasing the tilt should resolve the problem. Worn or loose microtome parts can also cause the problem.	64
24	a	For the greatest accuracy, the pH meter should be calibrated with a standard solution having a pH value near that of the staining solution.	78
25	c	Microwave radiation is a nonionizing radiation that creates heat.	70
26	c	A process known as micrometry can be used to measure tissue components.	54
27	b	The eyepieces are called oculars; therefore, a microscope that has 2 eyepieces is binocular, and a microscope with only 1 eyepiece is monocular.	54

Question	Answer	Discussion	*Histotechnology* Page
28	c	Apochromatic lens are those that have been corrected for 3 colors as well as other lens aberrations.	54
29	c	High dry lens commonly have a ×40 to ×45 magnification, intermediate lens a ×10 to ×20 magnification, and scanning lens a ×2.5 to ×4 magnification. Oil immersion lens have ×90 to ×100 magnification.	54
30	b	Closed processors employ fluid transfer, in which the tissue is stationary and the fluids are pumped in and out of the pressurized chamber containing the tissue.	67
31	a	For adequate processing on a short cycle, tissue must be cut thin at the grossing station.	68
32a,b,c	a, b, c	Light, polarizing, and fluorescent microscopy are most often associated with histotechnology.	54-57
33a,b	a, b	Transmission (TEM) and scanning (SEM) are the most common types of electron microscopes; however, there are also reflection (REM), scanning transmission (STEM), and low voltage (LVEM) electron microscopes.	57
34	F	Living cells are examined by phase-contrast microscopy, not darkfield.	56
35	F	Scanning electron microscopy (SEM) yields a dramatic 3-dimensional image of the surface of the specimen. A 2-dimensional image is seen with transmission electron microscopy (TEM).	57
36	T	The eyepiece of the microscope is known as the ocular.	54
37	T	With polarizing microscopy, the polarizer is between the light source and the specimen, while the analyzer is between the specimen and the eye.	55
38	F	Glass knives are usually used for sectioning glycol methacrylate embedded tissue.	58
39	F	The angle formed by the block face and the cutting facet of the blade is known as the clearance angle.	59
40	F	Sections must be <6 μm in thickness to ensure that all nuclei will be in the same plane of focus.	59
41	T	Ice crystals form in tissues with slow freezing.	50, 66
42	F	Dust on the refrigerant coils may cause the motor to overheat; ice buildup in the chamber does not affect the motor.	67

ISBN 978-089189-6401

Question	Answer	Discussion	*Histotechnology* Page
43	T	Proper care and maintenance of laboratory instrumentation is critical and is second only to the skill of the histopathology personnel.	80
44	F	Cleaning of the microtome should be performed daily, and lubrication done as recommended by the manufacturer.	58
45	F	Dust on the refrigerant coils may cause the motor to overheat, but should not affect the speed of the motor.	67
46	F	The temperature is not an important factor when cutting frozen sections.	66
47	T	Paraffin sections will not adhere well to clean untreated glass slides; an adhesive is usually added to the flotation bath, or adhesive-coated or positively-charged slides are commonly used to ensure adherence.	72-73
48	F	Poly-L-lysine is used to coat slides; it is not added to the flotation bath.	73
49	T	Both water and adhesives have been reported as sources for contamination of the flotation bath.	73
50	F	New instruments must be validated by the laboratory before they are put into use.	80
51	T	A household microwave instrument may not be used in the laboratory. The CAP checklist should be referred to before implementing microwave technology.	37
52	F	Bar codes are linear (1D) and 2D.	77
53	T	Although it was believed in the past that most floaters occurred in the flotation bath, it is now known that most floaters occur during the deparaffinization step of the staining process	69
54	T	Side by side comparisons are the best form of instrument validation.	80
55	T	Some staining kits may have the problem of disproportionate solution volumes, causing one to break into a new kit to replace only one reagent	80
56A	c	An incubator is usually maintained at approximately body temperature, or 37°C.	77
56B	a	The embedding paraffin is usually kept 2°C to 4°C above the melting point of the paraffin, or ~60°C.	37
56C	b	Flotation baths are commonly maintained 5°C to 10°C below the melting point of paraffin, or ~45°C to 48°C.	71

ISBN 978-089189-6401

Question	Answer	Discussion	*Histotechnology* Page
56D	f	Commonly cryostats are operated at approximately –20°C for most tissues, but may need to be colder or warmer for various tissues to section well.	66
56E	e	Refrigerators are commonly kept at ~4°C and should never be allowed to reach a temperature >10°C.	78
56F	f, h	The typical laboratory freezer is kept at approximately –20°C; however, a –70°C freezer is desirable for long term storage.	78
57-1	B	Congo red stained sections show apple green birefringence in the amyloid deposits when viewed with polarization.	55
57-2	A	Auramine-rhodamine is a fluorescent dye used to stain acid-fast organisms.	57
57-3	A	Mercury, xenon, or halogen bulbs are the usual light sources for fluorescence microscopy.	56
57-4	B	Polarizing microscopy is frequent used to aid in the identification of crystals such as talc and urate.	55
57-5	D	The phase-contrast microscope is used for the examination of unstained living cells.	56
58-1	A	Compressed and wrinkled sections are cause by too little blade tilt.	64
58-2	D	The blade tilt will not cause lengthwise splits in the ribbon; this will be caused by a defect in the blade, calcium, or a metal object present in the tissue.	60
58-3	B	Too much blade tilt is one of the causes of microscopic chatter; others are overdehydration and cutting too rapidly.	64
58-4	D	Crooked ribbons are caused when the horizontal block edges are not parallel, or when the lower edge of the block is not parallel to the blade edge.	60
54-5	C	The most common cause of failure to ribbon is a dull blade, but the blade tilt is also important in obtaining a good ribbon.	62
59-1	C	Chatter may be due to overdehydration and mushy sections due to incomplete dehydration and clearing.	60,65
59-2	B	Chatter may result from a dull blade, cutting too fast, and overdehydration.	64
59-3	D	Neither chatter nor mushy sections are cause by a nick in the blade edge; a lengthwise split in the ribbon would be the result.	60,64
59-4	B	Chatter may result from cutting too fast.	65

ISBN 978-089189-6401

Question	Answer	Discussion	*Histotechnology* Page
59-5	B	Soaking faced blocks will help restore moisture and help correct microscopic chatter resulting from overdehydration.	64
60-1	D	Neither is kept at 37°C; that is the temperature of the laboratory incubator.	66, 71,78
60-2	A	The cryostat is usually maintained at –20°C.	66
60-3	A	Unfixed, frozen sections must be used for immunofluorescence.	7
60-4	B	Parched earth may result if the flotation bath is too hot, or when improperly processed tissue is floated on the bath.	71
60-5	C	The cryostat must be kept free of the infection hazard posed by debris by frequently picking up the tissue shavings with a piece of alcohol-dampened gauze and discarding in a biohazard bag; debris on the flotation bath presents the hazard of carryover to another specimen.	66-67
61-1	A	An electron gun is the electron source for the electron microscope.	57
61-2	A	The electron beam is focused by varying the strength of electromagnetic fields.	57
61-3	B	The maximum useful magnification of the light microscope is ×1,000.	56
61-4	D	Neither requires a halogen lamp; the fluorescence microscope requires either a mercury, xenon, or halogen lamp.	54-57
61-5	B	The light microscope can resolve images no less than 0.2 µm apart.	54
62-1	B	pH 4.0 is a acid solution, anything below pH 7.0 is acidic.	78
62-2	D	Neither buffer solution is basic.	78
62-3	B	The Warthin-Starry stain is done at pH 4.0, so the pH meter should be calibrated with a pH 4.0 buffer.	78-
62-4	A	The pH of neutral buffered formalin is approximately pH 7.0, so the pH meter should be calibrated with a pH 7.0 buffer.	78
62-5	A	Pure water has a pH of 7.0.	78
63	a	Fluorescence microscopy was used on the kidney biopsy.	56
64	d	Immunofluorescence microscopy on kidney biopsies requires unfixed frozen sections.	56

ISBN 978-089189-6401

Question	Answer	Discussion	*Histotechnology* Page
65	b	Most likely the tissue has been tagged with fluorescein isothiocyanate (FITC), a fluorescent dye.	56
66	c	The light source for fluorescence microscopy is either a mercury, xenon, or halogen bulb.	56
67	d	A kidney glomerulus is shown in this image.	56
68	c	Washboarding, venetian blinds, or undulations in the section are caused by a major vibration; this usually results from either the blade or the block not being securely clamped in the microtome.	63
69	d	This artifact can also be cause by too much blade tilt or too large a clearance angle.	62
70	b	Very hard tissue, such as uterus, is most prone to this artifact.	63
71	d	Air has been trapped under the section during flotation.	74
72	a	Allowing the water for the flotation bath to stand overnight will allow any entrapped air to escape and may help in preventing this artifact.	74
73	d	Air trapped underneath the paraffin section occurs during flotation.	74
74	b	Most likely, this tissue has been overdehydrated.	64
75	a	The microchatter seen in this image could most likely have been helped by soaking the faced block in ice water.	64
76	a	Too large a clearance angle, or too much blade tilt, can also cause microchatter.	64
77	a	The tissue shown is from the central nervous system.	64
78	d	Electron microscopy was used for image E.	57
79	b	In the final image, deflected electrons will produce electron-dense, or dark, areas in the image; transmitted electrons produce light areas.	57
80	c	A portion of a kidney glomerulus is seen in image E.	57
81	b	The arrow is indicating the basement membrane.	57
82	d	Multiple defects in the blade edge have caused the blade lines seen in this section. Paraffin collected on the blade can also cause this defect.	60
83	b	The tissue in image F is most likely brain.	60

ISBN 978-089189-6401

Question	Answer	Discussion	*Histotechnology* Page
84	a	Moving to an unused part of the blade will most likely correct the problem.	60
85	c	The tissue shown in image G has been sectioned too aggressively so that small flecks of tissue have been removed from the block.	61
86	b	If there is enough tissue in the block, gently ribboning past the holes is the only way to get a complete section; however, potentially valuable tissue may be lost. Preventative action is best.	62
87	d	If water remains in the tissue and the slide is placed in a hot dryer, the artifact of nuclear bubbling, cell shrinkage, and tissue separation will most likely result.	76
88	c	Allowing the slide to drain for several minutes before ensuring drying at no >60°C should prevent this problem; if time allows, prolonged air drying is optimal.	76
89	c	The cells are shrunken and artifactual space is introduced because of drying the slides in a hot dryer without previously draining or wicking the excess water from the slide.	76
90	b	The problem seen in image I is not the result of a dull knife; all of the others may cause this problem. Spraying blocks with fluorocarbon sprays can even crack the block.	71
91	a	The knife has chopped into the block seen in image J; this can be caused by an improperly clamped block or blade.	63
92	b	Most likely the tissue seen in image J will have to be reembedded.	63
93	a	The block holder shaft has been extended too far in image K; this will most likely cause washboarding or chatter in the sections as seen in image B.	63
94	b	Retracting the block holder shaft will correct the problem seen in image K	63
95	b	Moving the blade to an unused area should correct the problem of a split in the ribbon seen in image L.	65
96	d	An extended block holder shaft will cause chatter but not lengthwise splits in the ribbon; all of the other listed causes can cause the problem seen in image L.	63-65

ISBN 978-089189-6401

Question	Answer	Discussion	*Histotechnology* Page
97	b	The cross-contamination seen in image M most likely occurred during the deparaffinization step of the staining process.	69
98	d	Although cross-contamination can occur at any of the steps listed, the major source is the deparaffinization step of the staining process.	69
99.	c	The best solution for reducing the cross-contamination that occurs during staining is to change the deparaffinization reagents frequently.	69
100	b	The small square is a 2D bar code.	77
101	d	Bar codes are very helpful for interfacing with instrument and laboratory computer systems.	77

ISBN 978-089189-6401

Safety Questions

1-24. The following are multiple choice questions. Please circle the letter in front of the correct answer. There is only 1 best answer.

1. Silver nitrate falls into which of the following hazard classifications?
   a. mechanical
   b. biological
   c. chemical
   d. fire

2. Which of the following chemicals is both toxic and flammable?
   a. chloroform
   b. xylene
   c. mercury
   d. hydrochloric acid

3. Formaldehyde is considered a:
   a. possible carcinogen
   b. strong oxidizer
   c. flammable liquid
   d. weak acid

4. Which of the following is an explosive compound that should not be stored in the laboratory?
   a. mercuric chloride
   b. anhydrous picric acid
   c. glacial acetic acid
   d. chloroform

5. A type A fire extinguisher should be used on fires involving:
   a. paper or wood
   b. electrical equipment
   c. hydrocarbons
   d. reactive metals

6. Which of the following is concerned with human immunodeficiency virus (HIV) and hepatitis B virus (HBV)?
   a. Laboratory Standard
   b. Hazard Communication Standard
   c. Formaldehyde Standard
   d. Bloodborne Pathogen Standard

7. Which of the following may be disposed of in the sanitary sewer system according to Environmental Protection Agency (EPA) and Centers for Disease Control (CDC) guidelines?
   a. silver nitrate
   b. absolute alcohol
   c. pulverized tissue
   d. blood

ISBN 978-089189-6401

8. In a hazard communication program, records of employee training must be kept for:
   a. 1 year
   b. 5 years
   c. duration of employment
   d. duration of employment plus 30 years

9. The Formaldehyde Standard mandates a time weighted average (TWA) exposure limit of:
   a. 0.5 ppm
   b. 0.75 ppm
   c. 1.25 ppm
   d. 2.0 ppm

10. Following monitoring, the time weighted average (TWA) of formaldehyde is found to be 0.60 ppm. This means that:
    a. no further monitoring needs to be done
    b. monitoring must be repeated in 30 days
    c. a medical surveillance program must be established
    d. any action depends on the short term exposure limit (STEL)

11. Which of the following types of extinguishers should be used on a fire involving electric equipment?
    a. A
    b. B
    c. C
    d. D

12. Which of the following types of extinguishers should be used on a fire involving xylene?
    a. A
    b. B
    c. C
    d. D

13. Development of a chemical hygiene plan is mandated under which of the following?
    a. Laboratory Standard
    b. Hazard Communication Standard
    c. Formaldehyde Standard
    d. Bloodborne Pathogen Standard

14. Monitoring of formaldehyde exposure shows the STEL to be 2.0 ppm. This means that:
    a. no further monitoring needs to be done
    b. monitoring must be repeated in 30 days
    c. a medical surveillance program must be established
    d. any action depends on the time weighted average (TWA) and action level

15. The amount of a chemical substance that when ingested is expected to cause the death of half of an experimental animal population is known as the:
    a. LD_{50}
    b. PEL
    c. STEL
    d. TWA

ISBN 978-089189-6401

16. Concentrated hydrochloric acid may NOT be disposed of in the sanitary sewer because it is classified as:
    a. carcinogenic
    b. oxidizing
    c. corrosive
    d. flammable

17. Isopentane is a very hazardous chemical because it has:
    a. a corrosive nature
    b. to be handled as an oxidizer
    c. been classified as a carcinogen
    d. a flash point <0°C

18. Hydrochloric acid (~6N) has been splashed on a small area of the left arm of a laboratory worker. The most appropriate action is to:
    a. quickly neutralize the acid
    b. wash the arm briefly and report to the emergency room
    c. wash the arm for 10 minutes with cold water and soap, then seek medical attention
    d. immediately go to the emergency room

19. CAP and NFPA define the maximum working volume (gallons) of flammable liquids (Class I, II, and III) allowed per 100 ft^2 outside a storage cabinet as:
    a. 1
    b. 3
    c. 5
    d. 10

20. When used in a National Fire Protection Association (NFPA) diamond, which of the following numbers indicates a minor hazard?
    a. 1
    b. 2
    c. 3
    d. 4

21. The left blue diamond in the NFPA chemical hazard label provides information on which of the following?
    a. flammability
    b. reactivity
    c. special warnings
    d. health hazards

22. The top red diamond in the NFPA chemical hazard label provides information on which of the following?
    a. flammability
    b. reactivity
    c. special warnings
    d. health hazards

ISBN 978-089189-6401

23. The right yellow diamond in the NFPA chemical hazard label provides information on which of the following?
    a. flammability
    b. reactivity
    c. special warnings
    d. health hazards

24. Which of the following describe prions?
    a. viruses
    b. fungi
    c. protozoa
    d. abnormal proteins

25. The revised Hazard Communication Standard requirements for labels of chemicals will now require all of the following EXCEPT:
    a. pictogram
    b. signal word
    c. disposal requirements
    d. hazard statement

ISBN 978-089189-6401

26-49. The following statements are either true or false. Circle T if the statement is true, circle F if the statement is false.

26. According to universal precautions, specimen containers must be labeled with a biohazard warning label if they contain potentially infectious material. **[T\F]**

27. Specimens may be returned to the patient without any risk to the patient. **[T\F]**

28. Cryogenic sprays pose little risk when used to freeze tissue in a cryostat. **[T\F]**

29. All infectious waste should be placed in biohazard containers. **[T\F]**

30. Ergonomics associates cumulative trauma disorders with the working environment. **[T\F]**

31. A safety data sheet (SDS) on each chemical used in the laboratory must be available to all employees. **[T\F]**

32. The PEL for an 8-hour shift for formaldehyde is 0.5 ppm. **[T\F]**

33. Class D fires are of marked concern in histopathology. **[T\F]**

34. Some automatic Halon extinguishers cannot be used in areas in which employees would be expected to remain after discharge of the extinguishing agent. **[T\F]**

35. The volume of liquid stored in a flammable storage cabinet is unregulated. **[T\F]**

36. Hydrated picric acid poses less hazard than anhydrous picric acid. **[T\F]**

37. Acids should be diluted by pouring the concentrated acid into water. **[T\F]**

38. Reactions as severe as anaphylaxis have been noted due to the increased use of vinyl gloves. **[T\F]**

39. Prions are sensitive to formaldehyde fixation. **[T\F]**

40. Because of a dramatic increase in tuberculosis in health care settings, a documented tuberculosis exposure control plan should be in place. **[T\F]**

41. Signal words are used on labels to indicate relative level of severity of a hazard. **[T\F]**

ISBN 978-089189-6401

42. Match the hazard listed in the right column with the area or reagent listed in the left column. >1 hazard may be given for each.

____A. Frozen section
____B. Ethyl alcohol
____C. Mercuric chloride
____D. Gross dissection
____E. Isopentane
____F. 10% formalin
____G. Radiology
____H. Chromic acid
____I. Toluene
____J. Acetone
____K. Chloroform
____L. Glutaraldehyde
____M. Pararosaniline
____N. Methanol
____O. Autopsy area
____P. Osmium tetroxide
____Q. Cryostat
____R. Blood serum

a. flammable
b. radioactive
c. biological
d. poison
e. carcinogenic

ISBN 978-089189-6401

Safety *Answers*

Question	Answer	Discussion	*Histotechnology* Page
1	c	Silver nitrate is a chemical hazard.	14
2	b	Xylene is the only chemical listed that is both toxic and flammable; chloroform and mercury are toxic but nonflammable, and hydrochloric acid is corrosive.	**15 ,34,35, 90**
3	a	Formaldehyde is considered a carcinogen, a reducing substance, nonflammable, and although it may become slightly acidic on standing, is not considered a weak acid.	**13**
4	b	Anhydrous picric acid is very explosive and should always contain at least 10% moisture. The other chemicals listed are neither flammable nor explosive.	9, ,15, 17,-35
5	a	Type A fire extinguishers include water based, foam or loaded stream, and multipurpose dry extinguishers; these are used on fires involving ordinary combustible materials such as wood, plastics, paper, and textiles.	91
6	d	Human immunodeficiency virus (HIV) and hepatitis B virus (HBV) are bloodborne pathogens and therefore fall under OSHA's Bloodborne Pathogen Standard. This standard is intended for the protection of all workers who might come into contact with potentially infectious material, especially specimens from patients who are HIV+ or who have been infected with the hepatitis B virus.	86
7	d	According to the Environmental Protection Agency (EPA), blood may be disposed of in the sanitary sewer system (eg, sink).	87
8	d	Under the Laboratory Standard, employers must establish a training program for employees who work with hazardous substances; employees should be trained or oriented before their initial job assignments and then at least annually thereafter. This training should be carefully documented and maintained in the employee's file for the duration of employment plus 30 years.	14,89, 90
9	b	The permissible exposure limit (PEL) of formaldehyde is 0.75 ppm. This is measured as the time weighted average (TWA), or the average concentration after measuring or monitoring for an 8-hour period.	14,90

Question	Answer	Discussion	*Histotechnology* Page
10	c	If the TWA exceeds the action level, a medical surveillance program must be put in place. If subsequent formaldehyde TWA of 0.5 ppm or lower, averaged over a 8-hour period, can be achieved in 2 separate samples taken at least 7 days apart and the short term exposure limit (STEL) is also within limits, then no further monitoring is necessary unless there are changes in the procedure or processes.	14,90
11	c	Electrical fires are Class C fires and must be extinguished with a nonconductive media. Class C fires can be put out using extinguishers that contain Halon, carbon dioxide, or dry chemicals.	91
12	b	Xylene falls into the category of Class B fires, or those involving flammable liquids and gases; they require that oxygen be blocked from the fuel in order to be extinguished. Class B fire extinguishers include carbon dioxide, dry chemical, foam and loaded-stream, and Halon.	91
13	a	The Laboratory Standard (Occupational Exposure to Hazardous Chemicals in the Laboratories) requires a chemical hygiene plan for implementing practices to minimize exposure to hazardous chemicals.	89
14	d	The maximum allowable STEL for formaldehyde is 2.0, so no action would be taken based on this. Any action would depend on the TWA for an 8-hour shift or on the action level.	90
15	a	The LD_{50} is the calculated dose of a chemical substance expected to cause the death of 50% of an experimental animal population, as determined by exposure to the substance by any route other than inhalation.	90
16	c	The acids are considered corrosive substances because they fulfill the criteria for a corrosive substance, which is defined as a chemical that causes visible destruction of, or irreversible alterations in, living tissue by chemical action at the site of contact.	90
17	d	Isopentane is very hazardous because it has a flashpoint below –51°C.	91
18	c	If only a small area of the skin is contaminated, that area should be flushed with cold water and washed with a mild detergent or soap and water. Medical attention should then be sought if necessary. Never neutralize any acid or base spilled on the body.	92

ISBN 978-089189-6401

Question	Answer	Discussion	*Histotechnology* Page
19	a	CAP and NFPA define the maximum working volume of flammable and combustible solvents with flashpoints <200°C allowed outside of a storage cabinet as 1 gallon per 100 ft^2. 2 gallons per 100 ft^2 may be stored in safety cans or safety cabinets.	92
20	a	NFPA ratings range from 0-4, with 0 indicating no hazard and 4 indicating an extreme hazard; thus 1 indicates only a slight hazard.	94
21	d	The blue diamond is on the left of the NFPA chemical hazard label, and it indicates any health hazards.	**94**
22	a	The red diamond at the top of the NFPA chemical hazard label provides information on reagent flammability.	94
23	b	The right yellow diamond of the NFPA chemical hazard label indicates reagent reactivity.	94
24	d	Prions are abnormal proteins; Creutzfeldt-Jakob is an example of a prion disease that affects primarily nervous tissue.	87
25	c	The revised Hazard Communication Standard does not require that disposal requirements be on chemical labels.	93
26	T	According to universal precautions, specimen containers must be labeled with a biohazard warning if they contain potentially infectious material (unfixed material).	86
27	F	There is risk with returning specimens to the patient; a written policy for whether to return specimens to patients should be established, taking into consideration the chemical and biological risks associated with both fixed and unfixed specimens.	87
28	F	Cryogenic sprays or procedures that create aerosols are very dangerous because they markedly increase the possibility of exposure to pathogenic organisms; cryogenic sprays should not be used in the frozen section area.	87
29	T	To insure proper handling and treatment, all infectious waste should be segregated into clearly identified biohazard containers.	87
30	T	Ergonomics is the science of adapting the working environment to the anatomic, physiologic, and psychological characteristics of personnel in order to prevent crippling repetitive stress injuries.	88
31	T	During the work shift, the SDSs must be accessible to all employees; this is mandated by the Laboratory Standard.	89

ISBN 978-089189-6401

Question	Answer	Discussion	*Histotechnology* Page
32	F	The PEL or TWA for formaldehyde for an 8-hour shift is 0.75 ppm.	89
33	F	Class D fires involve combustible and reactive elements, such a metallic sodium, potassium, magnesium, and lithium. These are not used in histopathology.	91
34	T	In areas in which employees would normally remain after the automatic discharge of the extinguishing agent, OSHA prohibits the use of Halon 1211 and carbon dioxide.	91
35	F	Both CAP and NFPA define the maximum working volume of flammable and combustible solvents with flashpoints <200°C allowed outside a storage cabinet as 1 gallon per 100 ft^2, and that stored in safety cans and cabinets as 2 gallons per 100 ft^2.	92
36	T	Anhydrous picric acid is a very dangerous explosive compound and should contain at least 10% moisture to be safe.	16
37	T	When diluting acids, always pour the acid into the water, never the reverse.	95
38	F	Latex sensitivity, not vinyl sensitivity, can cause symptoms ranging from contact dermatitis to systemic reactions as severe as anaphylaxis.	86
39	F	Prions are resistant to formaldehyde fixation; they are susceptible to 1 N sodium hydroxide for 1 hour, concentrated formic acid for 1 hour, and 5% sodium hypochlorite for 2 hours.	87
40.	T	Because of the dramatic increase in drug resistant tuberculosis, CAP requires that a documented exposure control plan be in place.	86
41.	T	Signal words such as "danger" are used on labels to indicate the relative severity of a hazard.	
42A	c	The frozen section area is a biological hazard.	86
B	a, d	Ethyl alcohol is flammable and moderately toxic.	33
C	d	Mercuric salts are very toxic or poisonous compounds.	15
D	c	Because of dealing with unfixed tissue, the gross dissection area is a biological hazard.	86-87
E	a	Isopentane is extremely flammable.	91
F	d, e	10% formalin is toxic by inhalation and inhalation, and is a possible carcinogen.	13-14
G	b	Radiology is by its name a radiological hazard.	94

ISBN 978-089189-6401

Question	Answer	Discussion	*Histotechnology* Page
h	d, e	Chromium compound are highly toxic and also a carcinogen.	17
i	a, d	Toluene is flammable and toxic.	35
j	a	Acetone is very flammable.	34
k	e	Chloroform is a carcinogen.	35
l	d	Glutaraldehyde is toxic by ingestion. It should be treated much the same as formaldehyde.	14
m	e	Pararosaniline is a probable carcinogen	90
n	a, d	Methanol is flammable and poisonous.	33
o	c	Because of unfixed tissue, the autopsy area is a biological hazard.	87
p	d	Osmium tetroxide is extremely hazardous because it vaporizes readily and fixes the nasal mucosa and conjunctiva of the eye; it is toxic by inhalation.	16
q	c	Because of dealing with unfixed tissue, the cryostat is a biological hazard.	67
r	c	Because blood is unfixed, it carries a risk of HIV, HBV, etc.	87

ISBN 978-089189-6401

Laboratory Mathematics & Solution Preparation *Questions*

1-20. The following are multiple choice questions. Please circle the letter in front of the correct answer. There is only 1 best answer.

1. 1 cm is equivalent to:
   a. 10 micrometers
   b. 100 micrometers
   c. 1,000 micrometers
   d. 10,000 micrometers

2. 1 µm is equivalent to:
   a. 1 hundredth part of a centimeter
   b. 1 thousandth part of a centimeter
   c. 1 10-thousandth part of a meter
   d. 1 millionth part of a meter

3. 1 kilogram is equal to about:
   a. 7.2 pounds
   b. 4.54 pounds
   c. 2.2 pounds
   d. 2.7 pounds

4. 1 cubic centimeter equals:
   a. 0.0001 liter
   b. 0.001 liter
   c. 0.01 liter
   d. 0.1 liter

5. Buffered solutions are important because these solutions:
   a. resist pH changes when either a weak acid or a weak base is added
   b. significantly enhance the ability of most dyes to stain tissue
   c. have significantly enhanced basic properties
   d. are always neutral in reaction

6. When 1 formula weight (gram molecular weight) of a chemical is dissolved in 1 L of solution, the solution is called:
   a. normal
   b. standard
   c. molar
   d. buffered

ISBN 978-089189-6401

7. Which of the following should be used to make a 2-molar solution of NaCl? (Na = 23 and Cl = 35.5)
   a. 58.5 g of NaCl added to 1,000 mL of water
   b. 117.0 g of NaCl added to 1,000 mL of water
   c. 58.5 g of NaCl diluted up to a total volume of 1,000 mL
   d. 117.0 g of NaCl diluted up to a total volume of 1,000 mL

8. Which of the following pHs is considered acidic?
   a. 6.5
   b. 7.0
   c. 7.5
   d. 8.0

9. To prepare a one normal solution of Na_2SO_4, which of the following is correct? (Na = 23, S = 32, O = 16)
   a. Add 142 g of Na_2SO_4-1,000 mL of water.
   b. Add 71 g of Na_2SO_4-100 mL of water.
   c. Bring 142 g of Na_2SO_4 to a total volume of 1,000 mL with water.
   d. Bring 71 g of Na_2SO_4 to a total volume of 1,000 mL with water.

10. 3.75 mL of ammonium hydroxide diluted to 500 mL is equal to a:
   a. 0.075% solution
   b. 0.75% solution
   c. 0.13% solution
   d. 1.3% solution

11. 1 microliter is equivalent to:
   a. 0.1 milliliter
   b. 0.01 milliliter
   c. 0.001 milliliter
   d. 0.0001 milliliter

12. 2 mL of a 1:50 dilution of antibody are needed. If beginning with an undiluted antibody, which of the following dilutions is correct?
   a. 0.4 mL diluted to 2.0 mL
   b. 4 µL diluted to 2.0 mL
   c. 40 µL diluted to 2.0 mL
   d. 400 µL diluted to 2.0 mL

13. What temperature on the Fahrenheit scale corresponds to 20°C (rounded to the nearest whole number)?
   a. 29 $(C + 32) \times 5/9$
   b. 43 $(C \times 5/9) + 32$
   c. 68 $(C \times 9/5) + 32$
   d. 78 $(C + 32) \times 9/5$

14. What temperature in Celsius corresponds to 20°F?
   a. –21°
   b. –6.6°
   c. 30°
   d. 68°

ISBN 978-089189-6401

15. 3 in is equivalent to approximately:
    a. 0.13 cm
    b. 7.6 cm
    c. 76 cm
    d. 7.6 cm

16. How many milliliters of a 5% solution will 2.5 g make?
    a. 25
    b. 50
    c. 125
    d. 250

17. 2.5 g of light green dissolved in 500 mL of water is equivalent to which of the following percent solutions?
    a. 0.2
    b. 0.25
    c. 0.50
    d. 1.25

18. How many milliliters of 0.1N NaOH will 2.0 g make?
    (Na = 23, O = 16, H = 1)
    a. 50
    b. 200
    c. 500
    d. 1,000

19. How many grams of KOH is required to prepare 200 mL of a 0.2 N solution?
    (K = 39.10, O = 16, H = 1)
    a. 2.24
    b. 5.61
    c. 11.22
    d. 22.44

20. How many grams of $CaCl_2$ is required to prepare 500 mL of a 0.2 N solution?
    (Ca = 40.08, Cl = 35.45)
    a. 1.11
    b. 2.22
    c. 5.54
    d. 11.10

ISBN 978-089189-6401

21-30. The following are solution preparation problems.

21. Prepare 500 mL of 1% HCl in 70% alcohol (use absolute alcohol).

22. Prepare 500 mL of 2% ferric chloride (begin with a 10% solution).

23. Prepare 500 mL of 0.25% light green.

24. Prepare 500 mL of 0.5% phloxine. The present dye has a dye content of 85%, and the new dye has a dye content of 75%.

25. Prepare 150 mL of 3% alcian blue. The present dye has a dye content of 82%, and the new dye has a dye content of 90%.

26. Only 1 g of fast green is left in the bottle. How much of a 0.25% solution will this amount make?

27. Prepare 50 mL of 5% silver nitrate (begin with a 20% solution).

28. Prepare 100 mL of 0.2 M $CaCl_2$ (see problem 20 for atomic weights).

29. Prepare 5 mL of a 1:1,000 dilution of antibody.

30. Prepare 1 mL of a 1:100 dilution of antibody.

ISBN 978-089189-6401

Laboratory Mathematics & Solution Preparation *Answers*

Question	Answer	Discussion	*Histotechnology* Page
1	d	100 cm = 1,000,000 µm, therefore 1 cm = 10,000 µm.	101
2	d	1 µm (1 µm) = one millionth part of a meter.	101
3	c	1 lb = 454 g; 1 kg = 1,000 g; therefore, 1,000 g ÷ 454 = 2.2 lb.	101
4	b	1 cc = 1 mL = one-thousands part of a liter, or 0.001 liter.	101
5	a	Solutions are buffered so that they resist pH changes after dilution, or after the addition of small amounts of acids or bases.	102
6	c	1 formula weight of a chemical dissolved in 1 L of solution is equal to a 1 M (molar) solution.	100
7	d	The formula weight of NaCl is 58.5; 58.5 g/L = 1 M, or 117.0 g/L = 2 M.	100
8	a	A pH of 7.0 is considered neutral; a pH <7.0 is acidic; and a pH >7.0 is basic.	78
9	d	The formula weight of Na_2SO_4 is 142; the equivalent weight is 71, so 71 g of Na_2SO_4 diluted to 1,000 mL = a 1 N solution.	100
10	b	3.75 mL/500 mL = 0.75 mL/100 mL, or 0.75%.	98
11	c	1,000,000 µL = 1,000 mL; therefore, 1 µL = 0.001 mL.	101
12	c	1000 ÷ 50 = 20 µL/1 mL, or 40 µL/2 mL.	273
13	c	(20 × 9/5) + 32 or (20 × 1.8) + 32 = 36 + 32 = 68°.	101
14	b	(20-32) × 0.555 = –12 × 0.555 = –6.6°.	101
15	b	1 in = 2.54 cm; 2.54 × 3 = 7.6.	101
16	b	2.5:x = 5:100; 5 × = 250; x =50 mL.	98
17	c	x:100 = 2.5:500; 500 × = 250; x = 0.50%.	98
18	c	40 g/L = 1 N; 4 g/L = 0.1 N; therefore 2 g will make 500 mL of 0.1 N.	100
19	a	56.10 g/L = 1 N; 11.22 g/L = 0.2 N; therefore 2.24 g will be required to make 200 mL of a 0.2 N solution.	100
20	c	110.98 g/L = 2 N; 11.098 g/L = 0.2 N; therefore 11.098 ÷ 2 = 5.5 g required for 500 mL of a 0.2 N solution.	100
21	5 mL HCl, 495 mL of 70% alcohol (346.5 mL of absolute alcohol and 148.5 mL of water).		98
22	100 mL 10% ferric chloride, 400 mL water.		98

ISBN 978-089189-6401

Question	Answer Discussion	*Histotechnology* Page
23	1.25 g light green in 500 mL solvent.	98
24	2.5 g of present dye = 2.83 g new dye.	99
25	4.5 g of present dye = 4.1 g new dye.	99
26	400 mL.	99
27	12.5 mL 20% silver nitrate, 37.5 mL water.	99
28	2.22 g $CaCl_2$ diluted to 100 mL.	99
29	0.005 mL, or 5 µL, diluted to 5 mL.	273
30	0.01 mL, or 10 µL, diluted to 1 mL.	273

ISBN 978-089189-6401

Nuclear & Cytoplasmic Staining *Questions*

1-50. The following are multiple choice questions. Please circle the letter in front of the correct answer. There is only 1 best answer.

1. Harris hematoxylin is used on tissue sections to stain:
    a. fat
    b. glycogen
    c. nuclei
    d. cytoplasm

2. Ripening of hematoxylin is a process of:
    a. hydrolysis
    b. oxidation
    c. mordanting
    d. reduction

3. The active staining chemical in ripened hematoxylin solutions is:
    a. hematein
    b. hematin
    c. hematoxylin
    d. hemosiderin

4. The most important step in regressive hematoxylin staining is:
    a. postmordanting in picric acid
    b. use of hematoxylin containing glycerin
    c. differentiation in acid-alcohol
    d. washing in water after the hematoxylin

5. Hematein is formed in Mayer hematoxylin solution by the addition of:
    a. mercuric oxide
    b. potassium permanganate
    c. exposure to air
    d. sodium iodate

6. Mordants are used to:
    a. change the refractive index of the tissue
    b. link tissue constituents more closely to the dye
    c. help differentiate stains
    d. oxidize staining solutions

ISBN 978-089189-6401

7. During H&E staining, if ammonia is incompletely removed by washing, the result may be:
   a. fading of hematoxylin
   b. poor staining with eosin
   c. understained nuclei
   d. hazy appearance of finished section

8. The combination of a dye and a mordant is called a/an:
   a. base
   b. accelerator
   c. lake
   d. buffer

9. Mercuric oxide was used in the original formula for Harris hematoxylin to:
   a. form hematein
   b. prevent oxidation
   c. serve as the mordant
   d. stabilize the solution

10. DNA can be demonstrated with:
    a. eosin
    b. pyronin
    c. the Feulgen reaction
    d. fast green

11. All of the following are aluminum hematoxylins EXCEPT:
    a. Gill
    b. Harris
    c. Mayer
    d. Weigert

12. Which of the following hematoxylins is not readily decolorized with acidic solutions?
    a. Harris
    b. Delafield
    c. Wiegert
    d. Ehrlich

13. Natural resins are rarely used for mounting sections today because they:
    a. are inherently acidic
    b. dry too fast
    c. must be dissolved in toluene
    d. evaporate from under the coverslip

14. Which of the following stains requires mounting with aqueous mounting media?
    a. Fite
    b. oil red O
    c. Grocott
    d. H&E

ISBN 978-089189-6401

15. Which type of metal salt serves as the mordant in Weigert hematoxylin?
    a. iron
    b. aluminum
    c. mercury
    d. tungsten

16. Acetic acid is added to Harris hematoxylin to:
    a. keep heterochromatin from staining
    b. make nuclear staining more specific
    c. ripen the hematoxylin
    d. form a dye lake

17. A dye that may be substituted for hematoxylin in routine staining is:
    a. phloxine
    b. methylene blue
    c. carmine
    d. celestine blue

18. Which of the following is a good example of a polychrome stain?
    a. alcian blue
    b. Congo red
    c. Giemsa
    d. Kinyoun

19. Which of the following is stained rose by the methyl green-pyronin (MGP) technique?
    a. heterochromatin
    b. deoxyribonucleic acid
    c. ribonucleic acid
    d. Golgi apparatus

20. The chemical group in dyes that confers the property of color is called a/an:
    a. chromogen
    b. chromophore
    c. auxochrome
    d. mordant

21. An auxochrome is a/an:
    a. ionizing group present in dyes
    b. dye group conferring color
    c. negatively charged protein
    d. mordant-dye combination

22. Which of the following is formed when hematoxylin is subjected to the action of sodium iodate?
    a. a dye lake
    b. hematein
    c. hematin
    d. a polychrome

ISBN 978-089189-6401

23. Heterochromatin is stained by:
    a. hematoxylin
    b. eosin
    c. pyronin
    d. light green

24. Which of the following techniques is an example of dye absorption?
    a. H&E
    b. methyl green-pyronin
    c. Feulgen
    d. oil red O

25. If placed in a solution with a pH below the IEP, cytoplasmic proteins will be:
    a. basophilic
    b. acidophilic
    c. polychromatic
    d. anionic

26. Differentiating in the H&E stain is an example of using:
    a. excess mordant
    b. a weak acid
    c. oxidizers
    d. buffers

27. A tissue component that takes up a cationic dye is said to be:
    a. basophilic
    b. acidophilic
    c. chromophoric
    d. absorbent

28. Into which of the following dye categories does eosin fall?
    a. polychromatic
    b. cationic
    c. anionic
    d. amphoteric

29. For the best cytoplasmic staining, the pH of the eosin should be between:
    a. 3.0 and 4.0
    b. 4.6 and 5.0
    c. 5.6 and 6.5
    d. 7.0 and 8.0

30. Ethylene glycol functions in Gill hematoxylin solutions to:
    a. oxidize the hematoxylin
    b. mordant the solution
    c. increase the acidity
    d. prevent a surface sheen

ISBN 978-089189-6401

31. Which of the following hematoxylin solutions will stain the mucin in goblet cells?
    a. Gill
    b. Mayer
    c. Harris
    d. Weigert

32. The Feulgen reaction demonstrates:
    a. DNA only
    b. RNA only
    c. both DNA and RNA
    d. phosphoric acid groups

33. The Feulgen reaction is unsatisfactory on tissue fixed in:
    a. neutral buffered formalin
    b. Zenker solution
    c. B-5 fixative
    d. Bouin solution

34. Romanowsky type stains are combinations of:
    a. acid and basic dyes
    b. 2 neutral dyes
    c. 2 basic dyes
    d. 2 acid dyes

35. Nuclear staining is made more selective by adding which of the following to hematoxylin solutions?
    a. ethyl alcohol
    b. chloral hydrate
    c. ethylene glycol
    d. acetic acid

36. Hematoxylin is converted to a dye lake in the Mayer formula by adding which of the following to the solution?
    a. sodium iodate
    b. citric acid
    c. ammonium aluminum sulfate
    d. chloral hydrate

37. A large quantity of Delafield hematoxylin stock solution must be maintained because of:
    a. slow hematein formation
    b. the nature of the mordant
    c. accelerated dye depletion
    d. rapid overoxidation

ISBN 978-089189-6401

38. To link hematoxylin to tissue DNA, which of the following must be added?
    a. acid
    b. oxidizer
    c. stabilizer
    d. mordant

39. Hematoxylin becomes a dye only when it:
    a. is used progressively
    b. is oxidized
    c. influences the isoelectric point of proteins
    d. is polychromed

40. Romanowsky type stains are usually preferred for the demonstration of:
    a. erythrocytes
    b. platelets
    c. leukocytes
    d. histiocytes

41. For the most transparency and clarity when viewing well stained microscopic sections, the refractive index of the mounting medium should be:
    a. above that of the tissue
    b. near that of the tissue
    c. below that of the tissue
    d. near that of air

42. Synthetic resins are preferred over natural resins because the synthetic resins:
    a. dry more slowly, preventing cracking of the resin
    b. indicate age of preparations by turning yellow
    c. preserve the intensity of the stains with time
    d. have a slight acidity when dissolved in xylene

43. Aqueous mounting media have an index of refraction that is:
    a. significantly below that of the tissue
    b. near that of the tissue
    c. significantly above that of the tissue
    d. near that of the hydrocarbons

44. A decrease in section transparency can be caused by using:
    a. xylene as the solvent for the mounting medium
    b. mounting medium with a refractive index of 1.51-1.55
    c. mounting medium that has become too thick
    d. number 1 coverslips for mounting sections

45. Fixation with neutral buffered formalin will cause tissue cytoplasm to:
    a. take up more hematoxylin
    b. take up more eosin
    c. be more difficult to blue
    d. resist acid decolorization

ISBN 978-089189-6401

46. If the pH of the staining solution is between 4.6 and 5.0, eosin combines with which of the following tissue chemical groups?
    a. $-COO^-$
    b. $-NH_3^+$
    c. $-PO_3^-$
    d. N=N

47. Which of the following can be added to an aqueous mounting medium to prevent bleeding of aniline dyes into the surrounding medium?
    a. cane sugar
    b. Canada balsam
    c. glycerine
    d. gelatin

48. The Giemsa stain is most satisfactory if the pH is between:
    a. 5.6 and 6.0
    b. 6.0 and 6.4
    c. 6.4 and 6.9
    d. 7.0 and 7.5

49. Which of the following hematoxylin solutions must be used within a few days after preparation?
    a. Harris
    b. Delafield
    c. Gill
    d. Weigert

50. A organelle that causes the cytoplasm to show increased basophilia is the:
    a. rough endoplasmic reticulum
    b. Golgi apparatus
    c. mitochondrion
    d. lysosome

ISBN 978-089189-6401

51-64. The following statements are either true or false. Circle T if the statement is true, circle F if the statement is false.

51. Basic dyes have a negative charge. **[T\F]**

52. Oxidizers are sometimes used for differentiation. **[T\F]**

53. Eosin is differentiated by the dehydrating alcohols. **[T\F]**

54. An increase or decrease in the pH of the staining solution can alter staining by changing tissue and/or dye charges. **[T\F]**

55. Staining can be influenced by the fixative used. **[T\F]**

56. Ferric chloride is both mordant and oxidizer. **[T\F]**

57. Gill hematoxylin is an iron hematoxylin. **[T\F]**

58. An increase in temperature usually increases the rate of staining. **[T\F]**

59. Frozen sections can be stained with toluidine blue O. **[T\F]**

60. Resinous mounting media have an index of refraction much lower than that of the tissue. **[T\F]**

61. Resinous mounting media are usually dissolved in toluene, xylene, or xylene substitute. **[T\F]**

62. "The more, the better" is a good practice for applying mounting medium. **[T\F]**

63. The nucleolus of plasma cells is stained green with the methyl green-pyronin technique. **[T\F]**

64. Bouin solution is a good fixative for tissue to be stained with the Feulgen reaction. **[T\F]**

ISBN 978-089189-6401

65-70. Each of the following numbered words or phrases is associated with one, both, or neither of the headings listed as A or B above it. Within the parentheses on the right, place the appropriate letter for that word or phrase. Write:

A, if the numbered phrase is associated with A only
B, if the numbered phrase is associated with B only
C, if the numbered phrase is associated with both A and B
D, if the numbered phrase is associated with neither A nor B

65.

A. Mayer hematoxylin
B. Harris hematoxylin
C. both
D. neither

1. Most frequently used as a progressive stain [ ]
2. Preferred for immunohistochemical stains [ ]
3. Contains ammonium or potassium aluminum sulfate [ ]
4. Hematein was traditionally formed by mercuric oxide [ ]
5. The pH was traditionally adjusted by the addition of citric acid [ ]

66.

A. Synthetic resin
B. Natural resin
C. both
D. neither

1. Yellows as the preparations age [ ]
2. Causes fading of stains with prolonged storage [ ]
3. Dries and becomes nonsticky very quickly [ ]
4. Usually dissolves in water [ ]
5. Causes gradual fading of Romanowsky stains [ ]

67.

A. Feulgen
B. Methyl green-pyronin
C. both
D. neither

1. Demonstrates DNA [ ]
2. Demonstrates RNA [ ]
3. Demonstrates rough endoplasmic reticulin [ ]
4. Time of hydrolysis is critical [ ]
5. Stains plasma cell cytoplasm red [ ]

68.

A. Sodium iodate
B. Ammonium aluminum sulfate
C. both
D. neither

1. Used in the preparation of Weigert hematoxylin [ ]
2. Changes hematoxylin to hematein [ ]
3. Acts as a mordant in hematoxylin solutions [ ]
4. Used in the preparation of Mayer hematoxylin [ ]
5. Used to adjust the pH of the hematoxylin [ ]

69.

A. Ammonium aluminum sulfate
B. Ferric chloride
C. both
D. neither

1. Serves as a mordant in hematoxylin solutions [ ]
2. Ripens hematoxylin solutions [ ]
3. Used in the preparation of Weigert hematoxylin [ ]
4. Used in the preparation of Harris hematoxylin [ ]
5. Hematoxylin solutions are usually stable [ ]

70.

A. Hematein
B. Hematin
C. both
D. neither

1. May be formed by the action of formaldehyde [ ]
2. May be formed by the action of air and light [ ]
3. More common in bloody tissues [ ]
4. Is an artifact [ ]
5. Is formed by combining with aluminum [ ]

ISBN 978-089189-6401

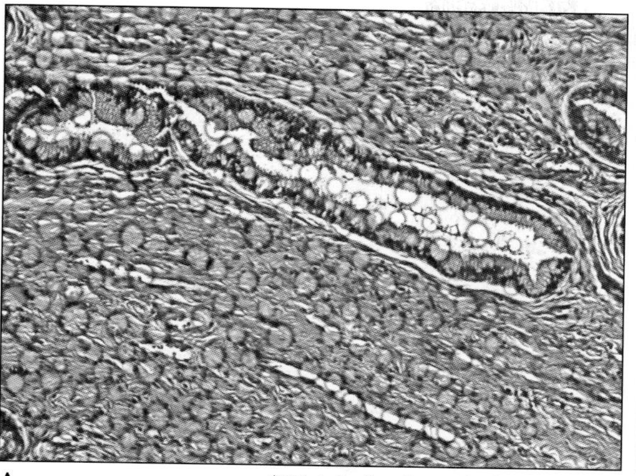
A (*Histotechnology 4e*, **i6.38**, p 133)

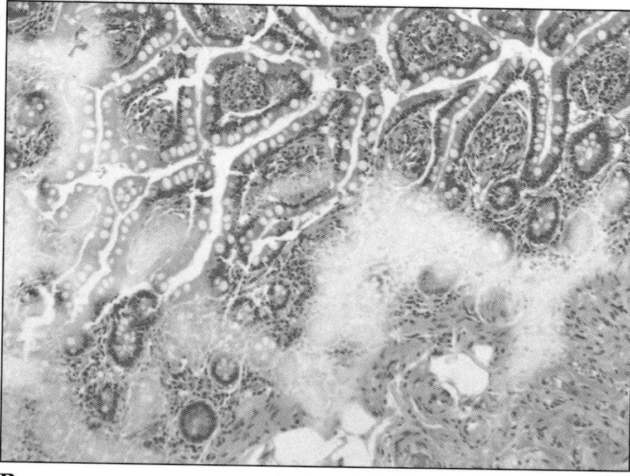
B (*Histotechnology 4e*, **i6.14**, p 121)

71-105. The following questions relate to images A-L as specified.

71. The problem shown in image A could have been prevented by:
    a. leaving the slides in deparaffinizing xylene for a longer time
    b. using freshly opened mounting medium
    c. dehydrating the sections more completely
    d. drying the slides longer before staining

72. The problem shown in image A could be corrected best by removing the cover glass from the sections and:
    a. remounting with fresh mounting medium
    b. redehydrating and reclearing with fresh solutions
    c. decolorizing and restaining with fresh hematoxylin
    d. adjusting the pH of the eosin and restaining the cytoplasm

73. The problem demonstrated in image A is:
    a. the use of overoxidized hematoxylin
    b. poor bluing of the hematoxylin
    c. inadequate differentiation of the eosin
    d. incomplete dehydration of the section

74. One possible cause of the problem shown in image B is:
    a. excessive dehydration with alcohol
    b. overdecolorization of the sections
    c. inadequately ripened hematoxylin
    d. incomplete removal of the paraffin

75. One possible cause of the problem shown in image B is:
    a. the use of old hematoxylin
    b. overdecolorization of the hematoxylin
    c. incomplete drying of the slides prior to staining
    d. fading of the stains due to the use of natural resin mountant

76. The problem shown in image B could be corrected best by removing the cover glass and:
    a. redrying the slide before restaining
    b. redehydrating and reclearing with fresh solutions
    c. decolorizing and restaining the slide
    d. adjusting the pH of the eosin and restaining the cytoplasm

ISBN 978-089189-6401

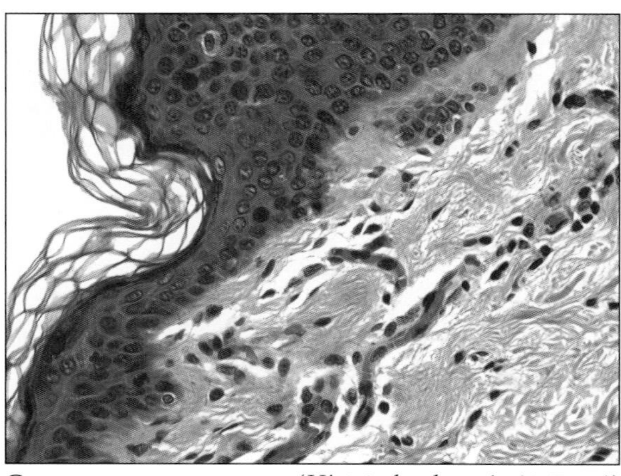

C (*Histotechnology 4e*, **i6.17**, p 1)

D (*Histotechnology 4e*, **i6.44**, p 135)

77. The problem shown in image C was most likely caused by:
    a. inadequate differentiation
    b. insufficient bluing
    c. incomplete clearing
    d. old hematoxylin

78. The problem shown in image C could probably be corrected in the future by decreasing the time in the:
    a. hematoxylin
    b. bluing solution
    c. eosin
    d. alcohols

79. The problem shown in image C probably would not occur if the aluminum hematoxylin used had been that of:
    a. Mayer
    b. Harris
    c. Delafield
    d. Weigert

80. The tissue shown in image C is:
    a. esophagus
    b. cervix
    c. skin
    d. tonsil

81. The epithelium shown in image C is:
    a. columnar
    b. cuboidal
    c. pseudostratified columnar
    d. keratinizing stratified squamous

82. One possible cause of the problem shown in image D is:
    a. mounting medium that is too thick
    b. the wrong thickness of cover glass
    c. inadequate dehydration and clearing
    d. evaporation of the mounting medium

ISBN 978-089189-6401

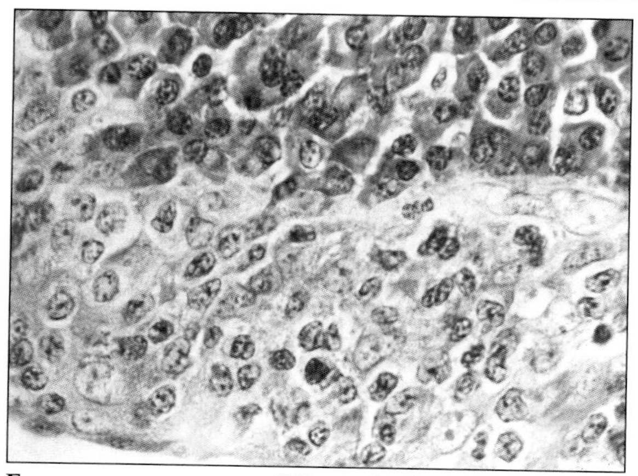

E (*Histotechnology 4e*, **i6.33**, p 129)

83. The problem shown in image D could be caused by:
    a. air trapped under the section during flotation
    b. mounting medium with too high a refractive index
    c. the use of a warped cover glass
    d. inadequate dehydration of the section

84. The problem shown in image D most likely could be corrected in the future by using mounting medium that is:
    a. further thinned with xylene
    b. allowed to thicken
    c. dissolved in xylene
    d. from a freshly opened bottle

85. The cells that show intense pink cytoplasmic staining in image E are most likely:
    a. plasma cells
    b. eosinophils
    c. melanocytes
    d. goblet cells

86. The stain shown in image E is:
    a. the Feulgen reaction
    b. methyl green-pyronin
    c. periodic acid-Schiff (PAS)
    d. Giemsa

87. The intense rose color shown by the cytoplasm of some cells in image E is most likely due to:
    a. mitochondria
    b. Golgi apparatus
    c. deoxyribonucleic acid
    d. rough endoplasmic reticulum

88. The tissue component stained blue-green in image E is:
    a. ribonucleic acid
    b. deoxyribonucleic acid
    c. smooth endoplasmic reticulum
    d. the Golgi apparatus

ISBN 978-089189-6401

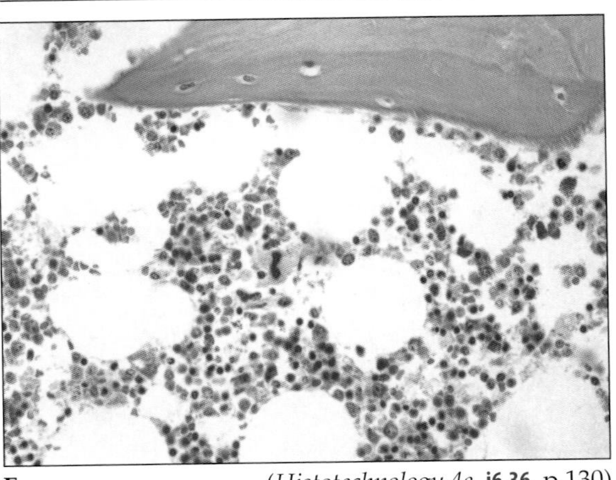

F (*Histotechnology 4e*, **i6.36**, p 130)

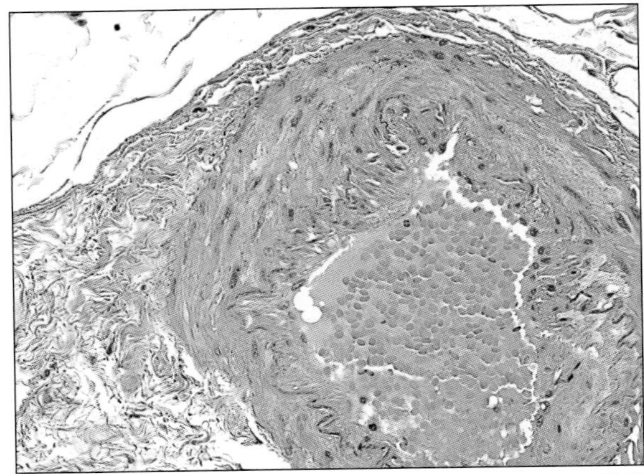

G (*Histotechnology 4e*, **i6.23**, p 124)

89. The reagent that gives the rose-red color in the section shown in image E is:
    a. Schiff reagent
    b. phloxine
    c. carmine
    d. pyronin

90. The cells showing the intense red cytoplasm in image F are:
    a. erythrocytes
    b. plasma cells
    c. basophils
    d. neutrophils

91. The stain shown in image F is:
    a. the Feulgen reaction
    b. methyl green-pyronin
    c. H&E
    d. Giemsa

92. The tissue shown in image F is:
    a. bone marrow
    b. lung
    c. lymph node
    d. fatty liver

93. The problem shown in image G is:
    a. overstaining with eosin
    b. pH of eosin was below the IEP
    c. eosin does not show 3 shades
    d. nuclei are unstained

ISBN 978-089189-6401

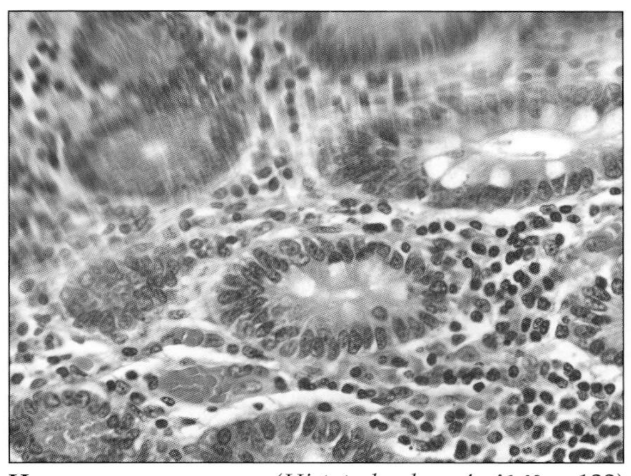

H (*Histotechnology 4e*, **i6.40**, p 133)

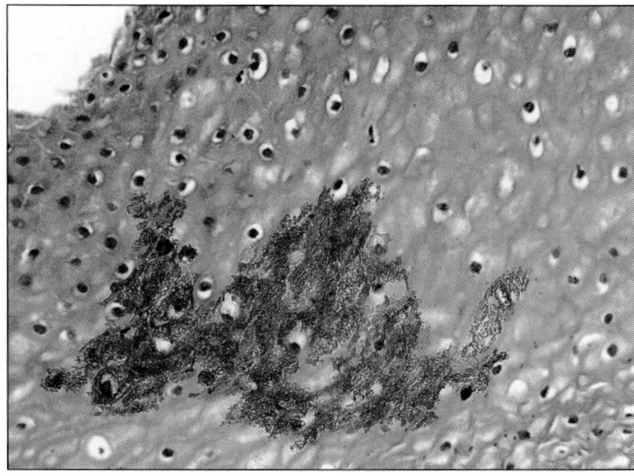

I (*Histotechnology 4e*, **i6.41**, p 134)

94. The problem shown in image G could be prevented by:
    a. increasing the staining time in eosin
    b. lowering the pH of the eosin
    c. differentiating the eosin better in the lower dehydrating alcohols
    d. ensuring that the bluing solution is totally removed by washing

95. The tissue structure shown in image G is a/an:
    a. blood vessel
    b. bile duct
    c. vas deferens
    d. fallopian tube

96. The problem shown in image H is:
    a. retraction of mounting medium
    b. incomplete dehydration and clearing
    c. mounting medium was too thick
    d. mounting medium on top of cover glass

97. The problem shown in image H could be corrected by removing the coverslip and:
    a. carefully applying a new one
    b. applying thinned mounting medium
    c. taking through fresh dehydration and clearing agents
    d. ensuring that the slide does not dry before mounting

98. The problem shown in image I is due to:
    a. an air bubble trapped beneath the cover slip
    b. tissue drying before coverslipping
    c. retracted mounting medium
    d. incomplete dehydration

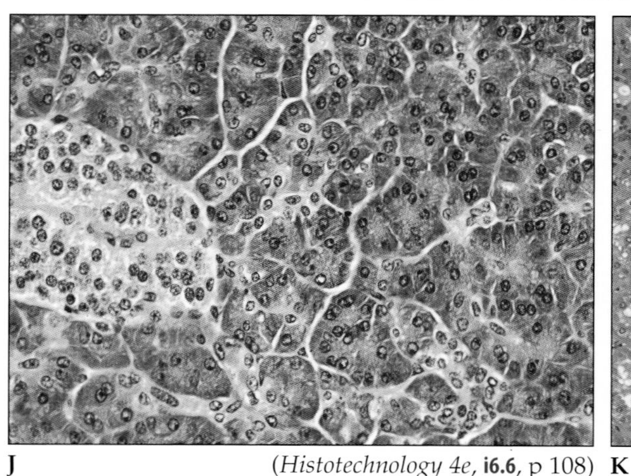

J (*Histotechnology 4e*, **i6.6**, p 108)

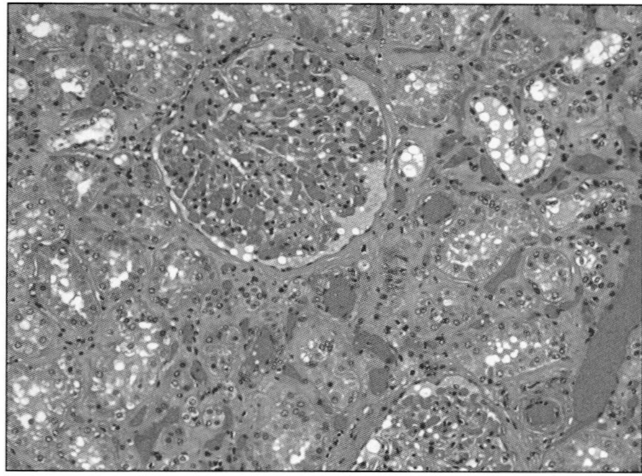

K (*Histotechnology 4e*, **i6.22**, p 124)

99. The tissue shown in image J is:
    a. liver
    b. kidney
    c. pancreas
    d. salivary gland

100. The blue staining of the cytoplasm in image J is due to:
    a. poor hematoxylin differentiation
    b. the Golgi apparatus
    c. mitochondria
    d. rough endoplasmic reticulin

101. The tissue shown in image K is:
    a. liver
    b. adrenal gland
    c. kidney
    d. spleen

102. Evaluation of the stain shown in image K reveals:
    a. 3 shades of eosin staining
    b. 2 shades of eosin staining
    c. 1 shade of eosin staining
    d. excellent nuclear and cytoplasmic staining

103. The component stained red in image L is:
    a. ribonucleic acid
    b. deoxyribonucleic acid
    c. nucleoli
    d. rough endoplasmic reticulum

104. The staining technique shown in image L is the:
    a. Feulgen
    b. carbol fuchsin
    c. methyl green-pyronin
    d. nuclear fast red counterstain

ISBN 978-089189-6401

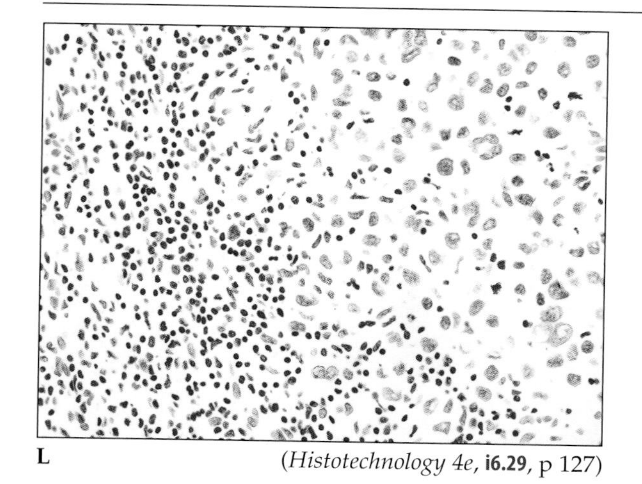

L (*Histotechnology 4e*, **i6.29**, p 127)

105. Tissue to be stained by the procedure demonstrated in image L should NOT be fixed in:
    a. neutral buffered formalin
    b. glutaraldehyde
    c. Bouin
    d. glyoxal

106-122. The following are problem solving questions.

106. Microscopic examination of an H&E stained section shows nuclei with well defined chromatin patterns, crisp nuclear membranes, and very pale pink staining of the cytoplasm and erythrocytes. These results indicate:
    a. overdifferentiation with acid alcohol
    b. the use of overripened hematoxylin
    c. a probable pH problem with the eosin
    d. the proper staining of an H&E

107. An H&E stained section shows reddish brown stained nuclei, pink cytoplasm, and bright rose-red erythrocytes. These results indicate:
    a. prolonged dehydration in lower alcohols
    b. the use of overripened hematoxylin
    c. a probable pH problem with the eosin
    d. overtreatment with ammonium hydroxide

108. H&E stained sections show very uneven staining, with some areas of the slide well stained and other areas unstained. These results indicate that most likely the:
    staining solutions were too dilute
    a. sections were cut too thin
    b. paraffin was not completely removed
    c. sections were overfixed

ISBN 978-089189-6401

109. While staining a rack of sections, it is noted that the water following the rehydrating alcohols turns very cloudy. This can most likely be corrected by:
  a. drying subsequent slides more thoroughly
  b. changing the deparaffinizing reagent
  c. changing the alcohols
  d. changing the water

110. H&E stained sections reveal brown pigmentlike stippling and rare glossy black nuclei. This most likely has been caused by a mounting medium that:
  a. is dissolved in xylene
  b. has become too thick
  c. has been thinned too much
  d. was applied after letting the slide dry

111. H&E stained sections of liver show very dark nuclei and some blue staining of the cytoplasm. This is most likely caused by:
  a. a marked amount of rough endoplasmic reticulum
  b. overstaining with Mayer hematoxylin solution
  c. inadequate differentiation of the hematoxylin
  d. too long a period of time in the bluing solution

112. H&E stained sections of small intestine reveal muscle, collagen, and red blood cells all stained the same shade of pink. This indicates:
  a. that the stain is correct
  b. poor differentiation of the eosin
  c. inadequate bluing before the eosin
  d. that the slides were left in xylene too long

113. A blue-black precipitate is seen on H&E stained sections. This could probably be prevented in the future by:
  a. filtering the hematoxylin
  b. decreasing the amount of acid in the hematoxylin
  c. increasing the dehydration time prior to clearing
  d. changing the bluing solution more frequently

114. Water bubbles are seen microscopically on H&E stained sections. This could probably be prevented in the future by:
  a. drying the slides completely before beginning the stain
  b. changing the hydrating alcohols more frequently
  c. making sure that the dehydration step is complete
  d. increasing the time in the last xylene prior to coverslipping

115. Microscopic examination of an H&E stained section of kidney is very difficult. Some areas of the tissue cannot be brought into focus, while other areas show excellent detail. This is most likely due to:
  a. incomplete dehydration prior to mounting
  b. mounting medium on top of the cover glass
  c. air bubbles trapped during flotation
  d. too much heat during processing

ISBN 978-089189-6401

116. H&E stained sections show hazy blue nuclei, but recuts from tissue processed a week previously and stained in the same basket show excellent nuclear staining. One possible cause of the problem is:
    a. the use of too much heat during processing
    b. incomplete dehydration prior to mounting
    c. the use of overripened hematoxylin
    d. mounting medium on top of the cover glass

117. A Feulgen stain is requested on a section of Bouin fixed lymph node. The best course of action is to:
    a. do the stain as requested
    b. increase the time of hydrolysis
    c. ask if there is tissue in another fixative
    d. leave the sections longer in Schiff reagent

118. Sections for special stains have been accidentally stained with hematoxylin. To remove the hematoxylin, place the sections in:
    a. acid alcohol
    b. dilute ammonia
    c. lithium carbonate
    d. isopropyl alcohol

119. The last dehydrating absolute alcohol in the H&E staining setup is very pink. This indicates that the alcohol:
    a. probably contains xylene
    b. is functioning properly
    c. is contaminated with water
    d. may be acidic

120. The protocol for a new automated stainer is needed, and one thing that must be decided is how often to change solutions. The best choice is to rotate the solutions:
    a. hourly
    b. daily
    c. bi-weekly
    d. based on slides stained

121. Giemsa staining is poor on a bone marrow section. This problem might be corrected in the future by:
    a. allowing working solution to age
    b. changing the pH of the staining solution
    c. increasing the dehydration and clearing times
    d. decreasing time for aldehyde-fixed tissues

122. Microscopic review of H&E stained sections reveal an artifact known as "cornflaking." This is caused by:
    a. hematoxylin precipitate
    b. excessive formalin pigment
    c. slide drying before mounting
    d. paraffin remaining on the slide

ISBN 978-089189-6401

Nuclear & Cytoplasmic Staining *Answers*

Question	Answer	Discussion	*Histotechnology* Page
1	c	Harris hematoxylin is a hemalum stain (hematoxylin mordanted with either ammonium aluminum sulfate or potassium aluminum sulfate), and hemalum stains are used almost exclusively to stain nuclei	113
2	b	Oxidation of hematoxylin is necessary and may be achieved naturally by exposing the solution to atmospheric oxygen, or by using oxidizing agents; this process is also called ripening.	112
3	a	Hematein is the oxidation (ripening) product of hematoxylin, hematoxylin is not a dye, hematin is formalin pigment, and hemosiderin is iron pigment	112
4	c	Regressive hematoxylin staining is the process of overstaining with hematoxylin (more properly the hematein-metal complex) and then removing the excess dye, or differentiating, with acid-alcohol.	111
5	d	Hematein is formed by oxidation of hematoxylin, all of the choices will oxidize hematoxylin, but the oxidizing agent used in Mayer hematoxylin is sodium iodate.	112, 114
6	b	Oxidized hematoxylin has little affinity for tissue but becomes a strong dye with a particular affinity for nuclei when combined with a metallic mordant, linking the tissue constituents more closely to the metal-hematein lake.	112
7	b	In order to achieve good cytoplasmic staining, the pH of the eosin is critical; if too much ammonia is carried over into the eosin, cytoplasmic staining will be lacking.	116
8	c	The combination of a dye and a mordant is called a lake; thus oxidized hematoxylin + metallic mordant = metal-hematein lake	112
9	a	Mercuric oxide was used in the original formula for Harris hematoxylin, but because of toxicity, sodium iodate is currently used.	113
10	c	The Feulgen reaction is used to demonstrate DNA; DNA will also stain with methyl green	126
11	d	Weigert is an iron hematoxylin; Mayer, Gill, and Harris hematoxylins all are mordanted with aluminum.	113-115

ISBN 978-089189-6401

Question	Answer	Discussion	*Histotechnology* Page
12	c	Iron hematoxylins (eg., Weigert) are not readily decolorized with acidic solutions while aluminum hematoxylins (Harris, Delafield, Ehrlich) are readily decolorized.	115
13	a	Natural resins, such as Canada balsam and gum dammar, are inherently acidic and caused fading of some stains after several years.	131
14	b	Aqueous mounting media are used when dehydrating and clearing will adversely affect the stain; organic solvents present in synthetic resinous media will dissolve the fat stained by Oil Red O. The other stains listed will be unaffected by organic solvents.	131,184
15	a	The mordant in Weigert hematoxylin is an iron salt, ferric chloride; thus frequently this hematoxylin is used when followed by acidic solutions because it resists decolorization with acidic staining solutions	115
16	b	More selective nuclear staining can be achieved by adding either an excess of acid or an excess of aluminum salt.	113
17	d	Celestine blue may be substituted for hematoxylin in the H&E procedure and gives identical results. A dye-mordant solution is the active stain with an iron salt as the mordant.	115
18	c	Of the stains listed, only the Giemsa is a polychrome stain. A polychromatic stain is a compound dye or dye mixture containing components of different colors.	129-130
19	c	Ribonucleic acid (RNA) is stained rose by the pyronin while deoxyribonucleic acid (DNA) is stained green by the methyl green in the MGP technique.	128
20	b	The chemical group in dyes that confer color are called chromophores; chromogens are benzene derivatives containing chromophoric groups; and auxochromes are charged tissue groups that enable the dye to link firmly to tissue.	110
21	a	Auxochromes are ionizing groups that enable the dye to link firmly to tissue; dye groups conferring color are chromophores.	110
22	b	When hematoxylin is subjected to the action of sodium iodate, oxidation occurs with the formation of hematein.	112

ISBN 978-089189-6401

Question	Answer	Discussion	*Histotechnology* Page
23	a	Heterochromatin is the substance in the nucleus that is stainable by hematoxylin. Euchromatin is also present in the nucleus, but is not stained by hematoxylin	107
24	d	The fat stain (ORO) is an example of purely physical staining, with the dye absorbed (soaked up) by, and dissolved in, the lipid.	109
25	b	At a pH below 6.0, cytoplasmic proteins will develop a predominance of positive charges and will attract acid (anionic, negatively charged) dyes; thus they are said to be acidophilic.	110
26	b	A weak acid is used for differentiating hematoxylin in the H&E; excess mordant is used for differentiating Verhoeff elastic stain, potassium ferrocyanide (oxixdizer) is used as the second differentiating solution in the Weil myelin stain.	111
27	a	Cationic dyes (positively charged) are also called basic dyes; therefore, components taking up cationic, or basic dyes, are basophilic (philos = loving).	110
28	c	The auxochrome in eosin is –COO–, which is negatively charged, making it an acid or anionic dye	116
29	b	Eosin staining is best at a pH between 4.6 and 5.0; below a pH of 4.0, the amount of charged eosin is greatly decreased because eosin is converted to a free acid at lower pHs. The pH must be below 6.0 to develop a net positive charge on the proteins.	116
30	d	Ethylene glycol is an excellent solvent for hematoxylin, preventing the formation of surface precipitates; sodium iodate is the oxidizer, aluminum salt is the mordant, and acetic acid increases the acidity.	114
31	a	Because Gill hematoxylin does not have an excess of aluminum ions to out-compete the hematoxylin for binding with sulfated mucins, which will be positively charged at the pH of the hematoxylin solution, goblet cell sulfated mucin will stain.	114
32	a	Only DNA is demonstrated by the Feulgen reaction. The molecular structure of RNA is different and hydrolysis with hydrochloric acid does not occur as it does with DNA; thus, RNA is not demonstrated.	126
33	d	Bouin solution hydrolyzes the nuclei excessively during fixation, therefore, tissue fixed in Bouin solution is unsatisfactory for use with the Feulgen reaction.	127

ISBN 978-089189-6401

Question	Answer	Discussion	*Histotechnology* Page
34	a	Romanowsky-type stains are a combination of the basic dye, methylene blue, and the acid dye, eosin.	129
35	d	Nuclear staining is made more selective by adding an excess of either an acid or aluminum. The H^+ ion of the acid and/or aluminum ions will compete with hematoxylin for binding with weakly acidic groups in the cytoplasm.	113
36	c	Either ammonium or potassium aluminum sulfate provides the aluminum ions to mordant Mayer hematoxylin and form a dye lake.	114
37	a	Delafield is oxidizes by air and light, with no chemical oxidizer added; therefore, a large quantity must be maintained because of slow ripening and hematein formation.	113
38	d	Mordants are necessary to link hematoxylin to tissue DNA because oxidized hematoxylin has little affinity for tissue without a mordant.	112
39	b	Hematoxylin is not a dye; by oxidation to hematein, it becomes a weak anionic dye.	112
40	c	Romanowsky-type stains are those most commonly used to demonstrate leukocytes because of the beautiful differentiation of the various cell lines.	130
41	b	As the refractive index of the mounting medium approaches that of the tissue, the tissue becomes more and more transparent.	131
42	c	Synthetic resins are preferred because they harden more quickly, do not cause fading of stains because they are neutral in reaction, and do not yellow with age.	131
43	a	Aqueous mounting media have an index of refraction that is significantly below that of the tissue. For this reason, transparency of tissue is not as great as with the synthetic resins, and microscopic evaluation is difficult with a 45x or higher objective.	131
44	c	Transparency of the sections decreases if the mounting medium becomes too thick; cloudiness of the section may result from thickened mounting medium or too much mounting medium between the section and the cover glass.	131
45	a	Because formalin primarily binds with the -NH2 group, leaving fewer of these groups to develop positive charges and bind with eosin, the cytoplasm will take up less eosin and thus become more basophilic	10

ISBN 978-089189-6401

Question	Answer	Discussion	*Histotechnology* Page
46	b	At a pH between 4.6 and 5.0, eosin is negatively charged and can only combine with a positively charged group such as -NH3+	116
47	a	Large amounts of cane sugar added to aqueous mounting media, such as gum arabic and glycerol gelatin prevent diffusion of basic aniline dyes into the surrounding medium.	131
48	c	The pH of the staining solution is critical and ideally should be adjusted for different fixatives. Sheehan and Hrapchak recommended a pH between 6.4 and 6.9.	131
49	d	Ferric chloride is serves as both a mordant and strong oxidizer in Weigert hematoxylin. The solution will be overoxidized within a few days and ceases to be an effective stain.	114
50	a	Because of an abundance of ribosomes, rough endoplasmic reticulum will cause the cytoplasm to show increased basophilia; the Golgi apparatus does not stain, and mitochondria and lysosomes do not affect cytoplasmic staining.	108
51	F	Basic dyes are cationic, or positively charged dyes.	110
52	T	Oxidizers are sometimes used for differentiation, as with potassium ferrocyanide (second differentiating solution) in the Weil myelin stain.	111
53	T	Eosin is differentiated by the dehydrating alcohols, especially the lower alcohols (70%).	199
54	T	In most cases, effective staining is determined by developing different charges on the tissue and the dye, and a change in ph of the staining solution can dramatically alter tissue or dye charges.	111
55	T	Because additive fixatives combine with different tissue groups, they will affect dye uptake by those groups. For example, formalin decreases eosin binding with the -NH2 group, but Zenker solution does not affect eosin binding with that group, so that cytoplasm of sections fixed in Zenker solution will be much more acidophilic than that fixed with formalin.	10, 22
56	T	Ferric chloride is both the mordant and the oxidizer in some hematoxylins such as Weigert solution	115
57	F	Gill hematoxylin is an aluminum mordanted hematoxylin solution.	114

ISBN 978-089189-6401

Question	Answer	Discussion	*Histotechnology* Page
58	T	An increase in temperature will increase the rate of staining by increasing the diffusion rate of the dye molecules, and will also cause swelling of tissue components thus allowing better dye penetration.	111
59	T	Metachromatic dyes such as toluidine blue are frequently used to stain frozen sections because of the rapidity of staining; however, these stains lose metachromasia if dehydrated, cleared, and mounted with synthetic resins. Hence they are not permanent.	121
60	F	Resinous mounting media have an index of refraction very close to that of the tissue.	131
61	T	Resinous mounting media are commonly dissolved in toluene; if slides are mounted from xylene, a resinous mounting media dissolved in xylene is a better choice. Resinous mounting media dissolved in xylene substitutes are also available.	131
62	F	When too much mounting medium is between the cover glass and the tissue, cloudiness may result and clarity is lost.	132
63	F	The nucleolus (RNA) is stained red with the pyronin in the MGP stain.	128
64	F	Bouin solution is not a good fixative for tissue to be stained with the Feulgen stain because it hydrolyzes the nuclei excessively during fixation .	127
65-1	A	Mayer hematoxylin is always used progressively, Harris may be use progressively, but is more often used regressively.	114
65-2	A	Mayer is recommended for nuclear staining in immunohistochemical stains that might be adversely affected by alcohol, because it does not contain alcohol.	114
65-3	C	Both contain ammonium or potassium aluminum sulfate	113-114
65-4	B	The original formula for Harris hematoxylin specified mercuric oxide as the oxidizing agent.	113
65-5	A	Mayer hematoxylin traditionally adjusted the pH with citric acid, and Harris adjusted it with ascetic acid. Most commercial Mayer hematoxylin solutions are adjusted with acetic acid.	1113,114
66-1	B	Natural resins will yellow with age, synthetic resins will not	131
66-2	B	Natural resins are acidic and cause fading of stains with prolonged storage; synthetic resins are neutral.	131

Question	Answer	Discussion	*Histotechnology* Page
66-3	A	One advantage of synthetic resins is that they dry quickly.	131
66-4	D	Neither natural nor synthetic resins are dissolved in water; they are dissolved in either toluene or xylene.	131
66-5	C	All of the resinous mounting media will cause a gradual fading of the blue component of the Romanowsky stains.	129131
67-1	C	DNA is demonstrated by both the Feulgen and the methyl green-pyronin techniques.	126-128
67-2	B	Only the methyl green-pyronin technique will demonstrate RNA.	125-128
67-3	B	Because of the content of RNA, rough endoplasmic reticulin will be demonstrated only by the methyl green-pyronin technique.	128
67-4	A	Hydrolysis is involved only in the Feulgen technique, and the timing is critical.	125
67-5	B	Cytoplasm is not stained by the Feulgen technique, but is stained red by the methyl green-pyronin if the cytoplasm contains a large amount of RNA.	125-128
68-1	D	Neither of the listed chemicals is used in Weigert hematoxylin.	115
68-2	A	Hematoxylin is oxidized by sodium iodate to hematein; ammonium aluminum sulfate is a mordant.	113
68-3	B	Ammonium aluminum sulfate is a mordant for aluminum hematoxylin solutions	113
68-4	C	Both of the listed chemicals are used in Mayer hematoxylin	114
68-5	D	Neither of these compounds are used to adjust the pH of hematoxylin solutions.	113
69-1	C	Both ammonium aluminum sulfate and ferric chloride are mordants used in hematoxylin solutions	112-115
69-2	B	Only ferric chloride will oxidize hematoxylin solutions	115
69-3	B	Only ferric chloride is used in Weigert hematoxylin	112-115
69-4	A	Only ammonium aluminum sulfate is used in Harris hematoxylin	112
69-5	A	Only the aluminum hematoxylins are considered stable, iron hematoxylins can be used for only a few days.	112-115
70-1	B	Hematin is formed during fixation in formalin if the pH is below 6.0.	11

ISBN 978-089189-6401

Question	Answer	Discussion	*Histotechnology* Page
70-2	A	Hematein is the oxidation product of hematoxylin and may be formed by the action of air and light or by chemical oxidation.	112
70-3	B	Hematin is more commonly seen in bloody tissues.	11
70-4	B	Hematin is an artifact formed during formalin fixation.	11
70-5	D	Neither is formed by combining with aluminum salts; aluminum salts serve as mordants, not oxidizers.	112
71	c	Water is present in the mounted section indicating that the section was not completely dehydrated before clearing and mounting.	133
72.	b	Water must be removed from this section, and because the reagents are most likely contaminated, the coverslip should be removed and the section redehydrated and recleared with fresh reagents.	132
73		The bubbles seen in this section are water due to incomplete dehydration of the section.	132
74	d	The white areas in this section indicated incomplete removal of the paraffin preventing stain penetration.	121
75.	c	If drying of the slide is incomplete before removal of of the paraffin, the water will prevent complete deparaffinization, and incomplete staining will result.	121
76	c	Removing the coverslip, treating with xylene and alcohols, and then decolorizing and restaining would correct the problem seen in this image.	121
77	a	The epithelium in this section of skin shows a complete lack of contrast between the nuclei and cytoplasm indicating that the section was inadequately differentiated after staining with hematoxylin.	122
78	a	This section of bone marrow has been stained with the Giemsa stain.he overstaining with hematoxylin could be corrected in the future by decreasing the staining time in hematoxylin or increasing the time in the differentiating solution.	122
79.	a	It is very difficult to overstain sections with Mayer hematoxylin.	114
80	c	The tissue shown in image C is skin	122
81	d	The epithelium is keratinizing stratified squamous.	122
82	d	The mounting medium may retract if it has been thinned too much and the solvent has evaporated to some extent.	135

ISBN 978-089189-6401

Question	Answer	Discussion	*Histotechnology* Page
83	c	Warped cover glasses, as well as the use of mounting medium that is too thin, will cause retraction of the mounting medium.	135
84	d	Freshly opened mounting medium would be of the correct consistency to provide mounting with the least problems; thinning the mountant is likely to cause problems, as is the use of mounting medium that has thickened from evaporation.	135
85	a	Plasma cells will show intense pink cytoplasmic staining with the methyl green-pyronin stain.	128
86	b	The stain shown in image E the methyl green-pryonin as indicated by the red staining of RNA (rough endoplasmic reticulin) and the blue-green staining of DNA (nuclei).	128
87	d	Because of the ribosomes (RNA) present, rough endoplasmic reticulum will stain intensely red with pyronin	128
88	b	Deoxyribonucleic acid has been stained blue-green by methyl green in the methyl green-pyronin stain.	128
89	d	Pyronin gives the rose-red color in image E.	128
90	a	Erythrocytes are stained red in this Giemsa stain; because of the absence of rough endoplasmic reticulum in mature RBCs, they will show the most intense staining with the Giemsa stain and with eosin	130
91	d	This section of bone marrow has been stained with the Giemsa stain.	130
92.	a	The tissue is bone marrow.	130
93	c	The counterstain in ths image shows basically one shade of eosin; with correct staining, eosin should show three shades.	124
94	c	Eosin should be well differentiated by the dehydrating alcohols, with the most differentiation occurring in the lower (70%) alcohol.	124
95	a	The tissue structure is a blood vessel.	168
96	d	There is mounting medium on top of the coverslip from poor mounting technique; microscopic focusing in these areas will be impossible.	133
97	c	Removing the coverslip and applying a new one, carefully avoiding getting mounting medium on top of the coverslip, will correct the problem seen.	132
98	b	A problem known as "cornflaking" is seen in this section, due to drying of the tissue before applying the coverslip.	134

ISBN 978-089189-6401

Question	Answer	Discussion	*Histotechnology* Page
99	c	The tissue is pancreas; an islet of Langerhans is seen in the middle left.	108
100	d	An abundance of rough endoplasmic reticulin will increase the uptake of hematoxylin, giving a more basophilic staining of the cell cytoplasm, or an increased hematoxylin binding.	108
101	c	The tissue shown in this image is kidney, specifically a kidney glomerulus	124
102	b	Only two shade of eosin can be seen in this section, three shades should be seen with optimum eosin staining.	124
103	b	The red staining of the nuclei in this image is due to the presence of deoxyribonucleic acid.	127
104	a	The Feulgen reaction is demonstrated in this image.	127
105	c	Bouin solution hydrolyzes the nuclei excessively during fixation, therefore, tissue fixed in Bouin solution is contraindicated for the Feulgen stain.	127
106	c	Incomplete removal of the bluing agent will result in poor uptake of the eosin due to an improper pH. Also eosin with too little acid (too high pH) will also cause the same problem.	122
107	b	Overripened hematoxylin will stain nuclei reddish brown instead of blue.	122
108	c	If paraffin is incompletely removed, staining will be impeded and some areas will most likely remain unstained.	121
109	c	If the water following the rehydrating alcohols turns milky, it indicates that xylene is carried over into the water; the alcohols should be changed to correct this.	124
110	d	If the slide dries before applying the mounting medium and coverslip, glossy black nuclei, cornflaking, and brown pigment-like stippling may result.	134
111	c	Inadequate differentiation will result in very dark nuclear staining and also some bluish staining of the cytoplasm. Mayer hematoxylin is a very weak hematoxylin solution, and it is almost impossible to overstain.	122
112	b	Three shades of eosin should be seen in a correctly stained section; any less than that indicates poor differentiation of the eosin.	124

ISBN 978-089189-6401

Question	Answer	Discussion	*Histotechnology* Page
113	a	On standing, most hematoxylin solutions will develop a metallic sheen of oxidized dye, actually aluminum-hematein; this may cause a precipitate on stained sections if the solution is not filtered.	114,124
114	c	If dehydration is not complete, water bubbles will be seen in the mounted section and the section clarity will also be impaired.	133
115	b	Mounting medium on top of the cover glass will make it impossible to microscopically focus on the tissue.	133
116	a	Since the two blocks were processes at different times but stained together, the problem is likely caused by a difference in fixation or processing. Too much heat on the processor will cause hazy blue nuclear staining.	37
117	c	Bouin solution hydrolyzes the nuclei excessively during fixation; therefore, Feulgen stains are unsatisfactory after Bouin fixation. Tissue fixed in another solution should be requested if available.	127
118	a	Hematoxylin can best be removed by an acid alcohol solution.	114
119	c	Eosin is differentiated, or removed, by the lower concentrations of alcohol; therefore, if the last dehydrating alcohol is very pink, it most likely contains water.	116
120	d	It is most economical, and the best decision, to rotate solutions on a stainer depending on the number of slides going through the solution.	119
121	b	The pH of the staining solution is critical in the Giemsa stain, and the pH may need to be changed if the fixative has changed.	131
122	c	If the slide dries before mounting, an artifact known as "cornflaking will most likely be produced.	134

Histotechnology Workbook 3e
ISBN 978-089189-6401

Carbohydrates Questions

1-20. The following are multiple choice questions. Please circle the letter in front of the correct answer. There is only 1 best answer.

1. Glycogen is best demonstrated by the use of:
    a. crystal violet colloidal iron
    b. Mayer mucicarmine
    c. PAS with and without diastase
    d. alcian blue with and without hyaluronidase

2. Amyloid can be demonstrated with:
    a. Congo red
    b. Mayer mucicarmine
    c. cresyl echt violet
    d. alcian blue

3. The Schiff reaction demonstrates:
    a. hyaluronic acid
    b. aldehydes
    c. basophilic compounds
    d. amphoteric tissue components

4. A good control for the Mayer mucicarmine stain is:
    a. kidney
    b. appendix
    c. spleen
    d. liver

5. A good control for glycogen is:
    a. kidney
    b. appendix
    c. lung
    d. liver

6. To increase the specificity for amyloid, Congo red stains should be examined by which of the following types of microscopy?
    a. phase contrast
    b. dark field
    c. polarizing
    d. electron

7. Of the following, which is the best fixative for glycogen?
    a. Zenker
    b. Orth
    c. acetic acid
    d. absolute alcohol

8. Periodic acid is used in the PAS technique as a/an:
   a. mordant
   b. stain
   c. reducer
   d. oxidizer

9. The crystal violet stain for amyloid is a/an:
   a. polarization technique
   b. physical reaction
   c. impregnation method
   d. polychromatic stain

10. Acid mucopolysaccharides are demonstrated by:
   a. alcian blue
   b. alizarin red
   c. Congo red
   d. acid fuchsin

11. The reliability of the Schiff reagent may be checked by adding which of the following to a small aliquot of the Schiff solution?
   a. sodium iodate
   b. formaldehyde
   c. potassium metabisulfite
   d. diastase

12. A fluorescent dye used for the demonstration of amyloid is:
   a. crystal violet
   b. auramine O
   c. colloidal iron
   d. thioflavin T

13. The alcian blue stain performed at pH 0 demonstrates:
   a. all acid mucopolysaccharides
   b. carboxylated acid mucopolysaccharides
   c. sulfated acid mucopolysaccharides
   d. neutral mucopolysaccharides

14. Substances stained positive with the colloidal iron procedure will be:
   a. red
   b. blue
   c. apple green
   d. violet

15. Schiff reagent is a/an:
   a. reduced solution of basic fuchsin
   b. oxidized solution of basic fuchsin
   c. reduced solution of acid fuchsin
   d. oxidized solution of acid fuchsin

16. Diastase digestion increases specificity for:
   a. mucin
   b. amyloid
   c. carbohydrates
   d. glycogen

ISBN 978-089189-6401

17. Colloidal iron is used for the demonstration of:
    a. amyloid
    b. glycogen
    c. acid mucopolysaccharides
    d. neutral mucopolysaccharides

18. Which of the following methods will demonstrate glycogen?
    a. Congo red
    b. Giemsa
    c. Mayer mucicarmine
    d. Best carmine

19. Adjacent sections are stained with PAS, one with and one without diastase digestion. A positive result on the one without digestion and a negative result on the one with digestion indicates the presence of:
    a. carboxylated mucosubstances
    b. sulfated mucosubstances
    c. hyaluronic acid
    d. glycogen

20. Which of the following fungi are well demonstrated with the colloidal iron stain?
    a. *Histoplasma capsulatum*
    b. *Cryptococcus neoformans*
    c. *Candida albicans*
    d. *Coccidioides immitis*

21-31. The following statements are either true or false. Circle T if the statement is true, circle F if the statement is false.

21. Glucose, sucrose, and other oligopolysaccharides can be demonstrated easily in tissue sections. **[T\F]**

22. Hyaluronidase is used to digest some connective tissue mucins. **[T\F]**

23. The routine alcian blue stain is done at pH 1.5. **[T\F]**

24. Good Schiff reagent should be light pink. **[T\F]**

25. The end product in the colloidal iron method is Prussian blue. **[T\F]**

26. Amyloid shows a yellow birefringence following staining with Congo red. **[T\F]**

27. Glutaraldehyde is one of the recommended fixatives for the PAS reaction. **[T\F]**

28. The Schiff reaction may show false positivity following chromate-containing fixatives. **[T\F]**

29. Glycogen-containing tissue fixed in Bouin solution may show resistance to diastase digestion. **[T\F]**

30. The addition of acid to the crystal violet staining solution reduces background staining. **[T\F]**

31. 4 to 6 µm sections are recommended for crystal violet stains. **[T\F]**

ISBN 978-089189-6401

32. Match the following tissue components on the left with the reagents used on the right. Do not select counterstains. Some reagents may not be matched, or some techniques may be matched with >1 reagent.

Tissue components	Reagents used
____A. Acid mucopolysaccharides	a. alcian blue, pH 1.0
____B. Amyloid	b. alcian blue, pH 2.5
____C. Carboxylated acid mucopolysaccharides	c. colloidal iron
____D. Glycogen	d. Congo red
____E. Neutral polysaccharides	e. crystal violet
____F. Sulfated (only) acid mucopolysaccharides	f. diastase
	g. iron hematoxylin
	h. periodic acid
	i. Schiff reagent
	j. thioflavin T
	k. mucicarmine

33-36 Each of the following numbered words or phrases is associated with one, both, or neither of the headings listed as A or B above it. Within the parentheses on the right, place the appropriate letter for that word or phrase. Write:
A, if the numbered phrase is associated with A only
B, if the numbered phrase is associated with B only
C, if the numbered phrase is associated with both A and B
D, if the numbered phrase is associated with neither A nor B

33.

A. PAS
B. Alcian blue, pH 2.5
C. both
D. neither

1. Demonstrates neutral polysaccharides [ ]
2. Demonstrates acid mucosubstances [ ]
3. Reacts with aldehyde groupings [ ]
4. May give false positive staining after glutaraldehyde fixation [ ]
5. Used in the demonstration of sulfated (only) mucosubstances [ ]

34.

A. Alcian blue, pH 2.5
B. Alcian blue, pH 1.0
C. both
D. neither

1. Demonstrates sulfated acid mucopolysaccharides [ ]
2. Demonstrates carboxylated acid mucopolysaccharides [ ]
3. Demonstrates glycogen [ ]
4. Sometimes used following hyaluronidase [ ]
5. Demonstrates sulfated sialomucins [ ]

35.

A. Congo red
B. Thioflavin T
C. both
D. neither

1. Used for the demonstration of amyloid [ ]
2. Shows green birefringence in amyloid deposits [ ]
3. Is primarily a fluorescence technique [ ]
4. Best on 4 to 5 μm sections [ ]
5. Orth fixation preferred [ ]

36.

A. Diastase
B. Hyaluronidase
C. both
D. neither

1. Used in demonstrating specific carbohydrates [ ]
2. Digests glycogen [ ]
3. Removes connective tissue mucin [ ]
4. Often combined with the alcian blue technique [ ]
5. Used to demonstrate amyloid [ ]

ISBN 978-089189-6401

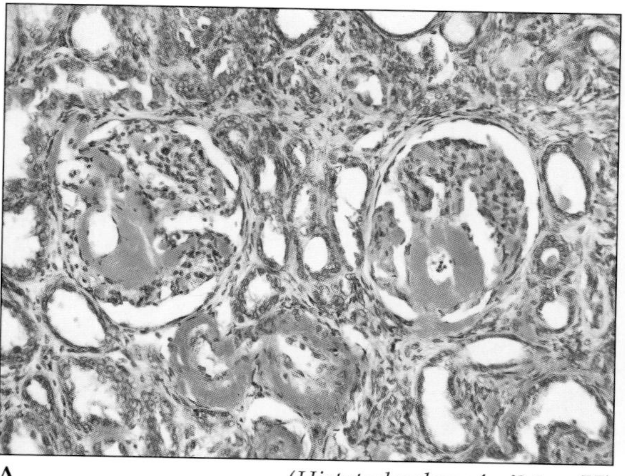

A (*Histotechnology 4e*, **i3.1**, p 55)

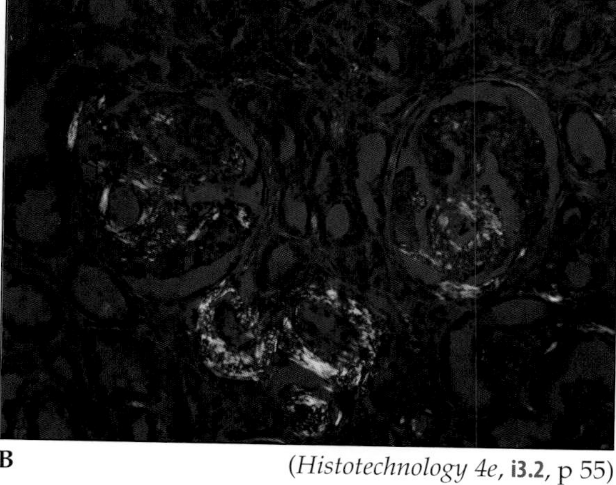

B (*Histotechnology 4e*, **i3.2**, p 55)

37-82. The following questions relate to images A-K as specified.

37. The staining technique shown in image A is most likely:
    a. Congo red
    b. PAS
    c. mucicarmine
    d. oil red O

38. The substance stained red in image A is:
    a. an acid mucopolysaccharide
    b. an epithelial mucin
    c. glycogen
    d. amyloid

39. Another technique that might be used to demonstrate the substance stained red in image A is:
    a. PAS
    b. thioflavin T
    c. Sudan black B
    d. alcian blue

40. Sections for the technique shown in image A should be cut at:
    a. 2 μm to 3 μm
    b. 4 μm to 5 μm
    c. 8 μm to 10 μm
    d. 12 μm to 15 μm

41. What type of microscopy is demonstrated in image B?
    a. polarizing
    b. fluorescence
    c. electron
    d. phase contrast

42. The technique shown in image B is most likely:
    a. thioflavin T
    b. Congo red
    c. auramine-rhodamine
    d. indirect immunofluorescence

ISBN 978-089189-6401

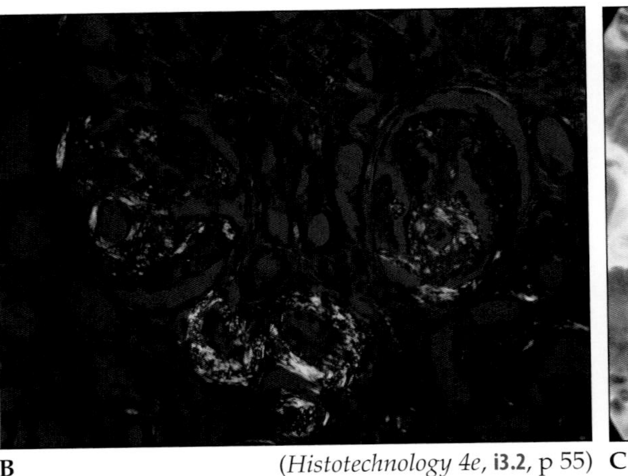

B (*Histotechnology 4e*, **i3.2**, p 55)

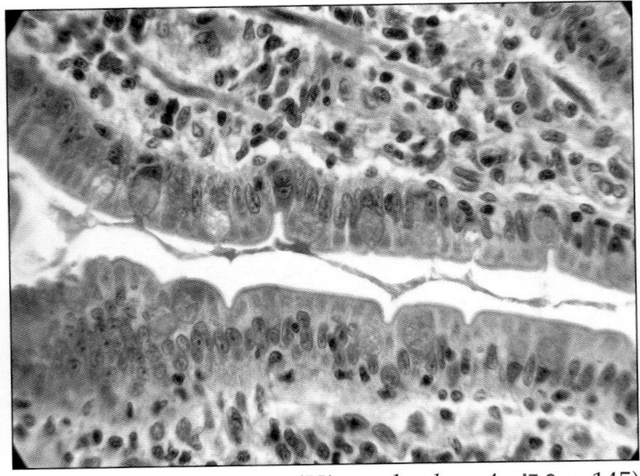

C (*Histotechnology 4e*, **i7.8**, p 145)

43. Another technique that could be used to demonstrate the apple green-colored substance in image B is:
    a. mucicarmine
    b. alcian blue
    c. auramine-rhodamine
    d. crystal violet

44. Control slides for the technique shown in image B may give poor results if:
    a. tissue containing newly formed deposits is used
    b. the slides have been cut and stored for a long time
    c. the sections are cut at 8 µm
    d. the tissue was fixed in absolute alcohol

45. The technique shown in image C is most likely:
    a. mucicarmine
    b. PAS
    c. Congo red
    d. oil red O

46. The tissue cells stained red in image C are:
    a. Paneth
    b. adipose
    c. goblet
    d. enterochromaffin

47. A good control for the technique shown in image C is:
    a. esophagus
    b. stomach
    c. small intestine
    d. umbilical cord

48. The nuclear counterstain most likely used in the technique shown in image C is:
    a. kernechtrot
    b. brazilin
    c. aluminum hematoxylin
    d. iron hematoxylin

ISBN 978-089189-6401

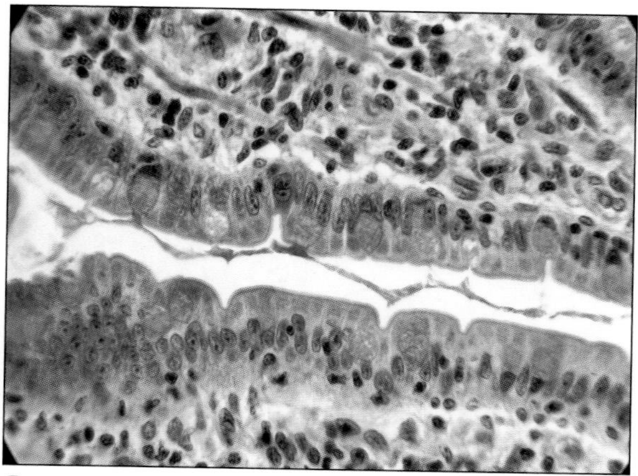

C (*Histotechnology 4e*, **i7.8**, p 145)

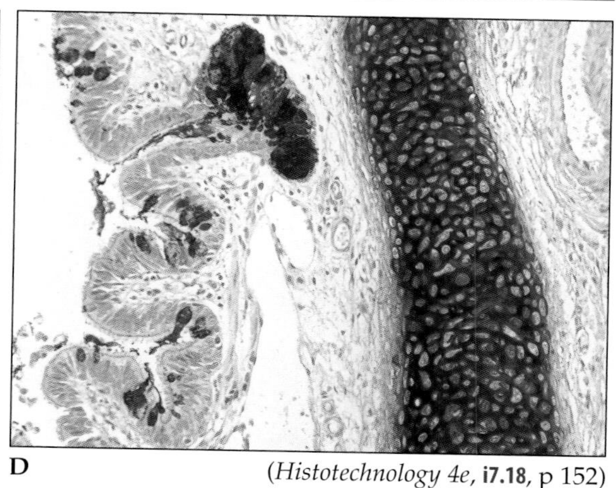

D (*Histotechnology 4e*, **i7.18**, p 152)

49. The substance stained red in image C is:
    a. glycogen
    b. mucin
    c. fat
    d. amyloid

50. Of the following, the technique shown in image D is most likely:
    a. Schmorl technique for reducing substances
    b. PAS
    c. alcian blue, pH 1.0
    d. colloidal iron

51. The substance stained blue in image D is most likely:
    a. an acid mucopolysaccharide
    b. a neutral mucosubstance
    c. glycogen
    d. chitin

52. Another technique that would look almost identical to the technique shown in image D is:
    a. PAS
    b. alcian blue, pH 2.5
    c. alcian blue, pH 1.0
    d. mucicarmine

53. The end product of the technique shown in image D is:
    a. Turnbull blue
    b. Prussian blue
    c. colloidal iron
    d. ferrous iron

54. The technique shown in image D demonstrates:
    a. both carboxylated and sulfated mucosubstances
    b. carboxylated mucosubstances only
    c. sulfated mucosubstances only
    d. neutral mucosubstances

ISBN 978-089189-6401

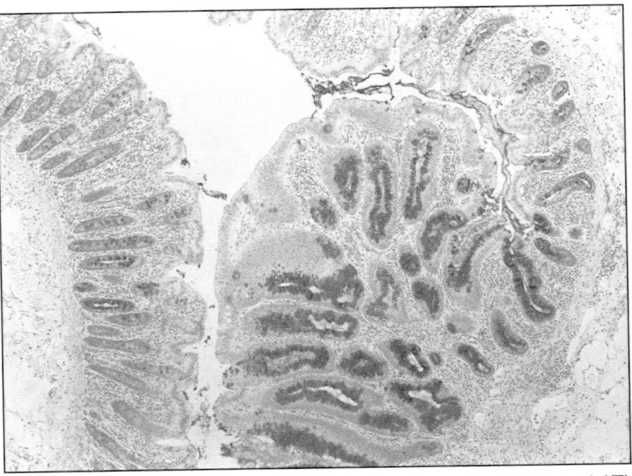

E (*Histotechnology 4e*, **i7.13**, p 147)

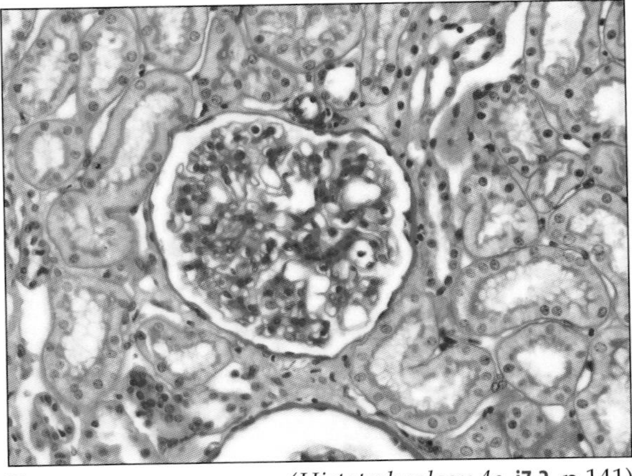

F (*Histotechnology 4e*, **i7.2**, p 141)

55. Of the following, the technique shown in image E is most likely:
    a. Schmorl technique for reducing substances
    b. PAS
    c. alcian blue, pH 2.5
    d. crystal violet

56. Another technique that would look almost identical to the technique shown in image E is:
    a. PAS
    b. colloidal iron
    c. alcian blue, pH 1.0
    d. mucicarmine

57. The technique shown in image E demonstrates:
    a. both carboxylated and sulfated mucosubstances
    b. carboxylated mucosubstances only
    c. sulfated mucosubstances only
    d. neutral mucosubstances

58. The staining technique shown in image F is the:
    a. Congo red
    b. Mayer mucicarmine
    c. PAS
    d. colloidal iron

59. The tissue shown in image F is:
    a. lymph node
    b. liver
    c. pancreas
    d. kidney

60. The component/structure stained red in image F is:
    a. epithelial mucin
    b. an acid mucopolysaccharide
    c. basement membrane
    d. amyloid

ISBN 978-089189-6401

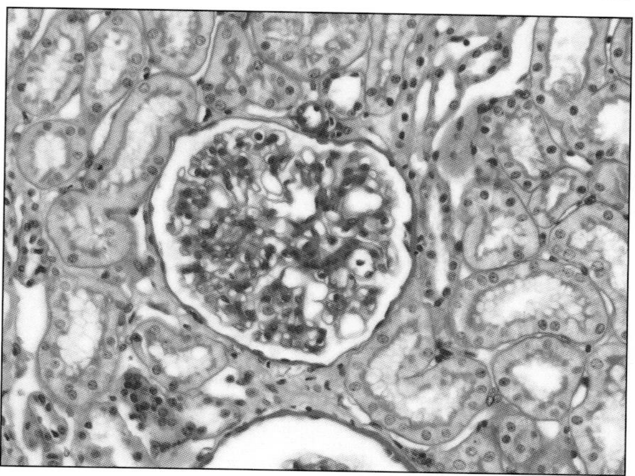

F (*Histotechnology 4e*, **i7.2**, p 141)

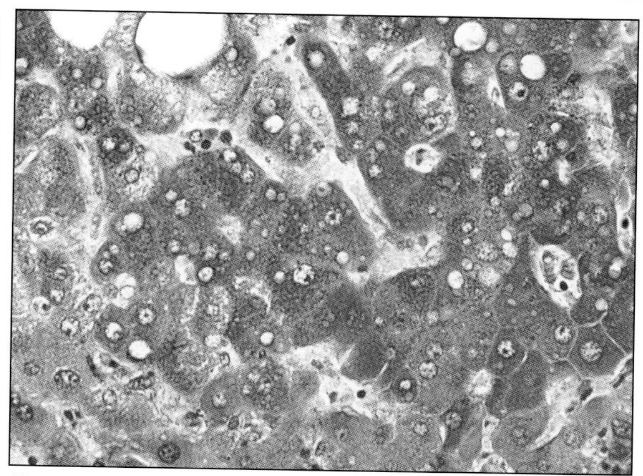

G (*Histotechnology 4e*, **i7.4**, p 142)

61. Another technique that could be used to demonstrate the same tissue component as that stained rose in image F is:
    a. alcian blue
    b. colloidal iron
    c. Congo red
    d. methenamine silver

62. The technique shown in image F depends upon the presence of:
    a. ketones
    b. aldehydes
    c. sulfated compounds
    d. carboxylated compounds

63. For this technique, the tissue shown in image F should be sectioned at:
    a. 1 µm to 2 µm
    b. 3 µm to 4 µm
    c. 5 µm to 6 µm
    d. 7 µm to 8 µm

64. The technique shown in image G is the best stain for the demonstration of:
    a. glycogen
    b. amyloid
    c. sulfated mucopolysaccharides
    d. carboxylated mucopolysaccharides

65. The substance demonstrated in image G is:
    a. amyloid
    b. lipid
    c. glycogen
    d. an acid mucosubstances

ISBN 978-089189-6401

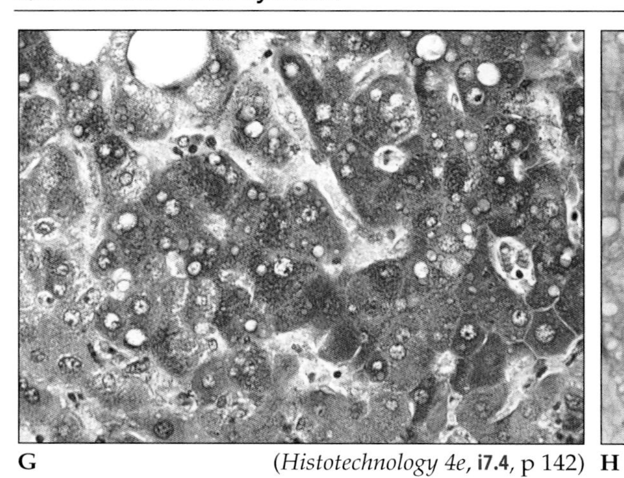

G (*Histotechnology 4e*, **i7.4**, p 142)

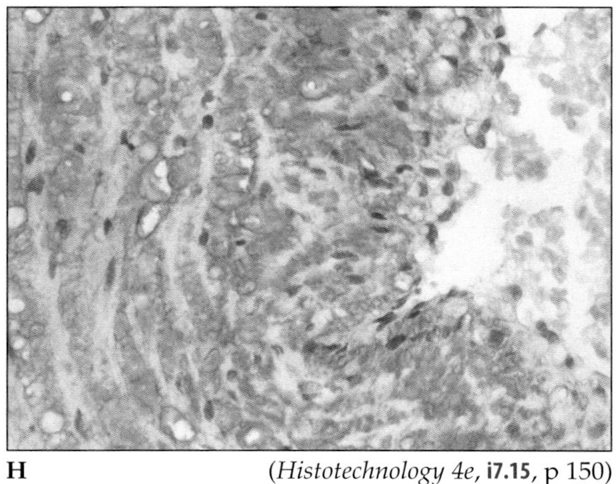

H (*Histotechnology 4e*, **i7.15**, p 150)

66. The substance demonstrate in image G could be removed by:
    a. hyaluronidase
    b. alcohol
    c. lipase
    d. α-amylase

67. The tissue shown in image G is:
    a. kidney
    b. liver
    c. esophagus
    d. spleen

68. In the section of umbilical cord seen in image H, the blue staining is due to:
    a. epithelial mucin
    b. connective tissue mucin
    c. glycogen
    d. nonspecific staining

69. The tissue stained blue in image H would show decreased or absent staining if treated with:
    a. hyaluronidase
    b. lipase
    c. diastase
    d. α-amylase

ISBN 978-089189-6401

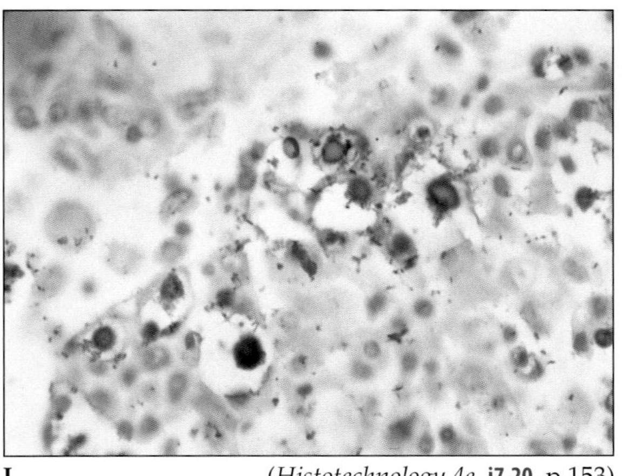

I (*Histotechnology 4e*, **i7.20**, p 153)

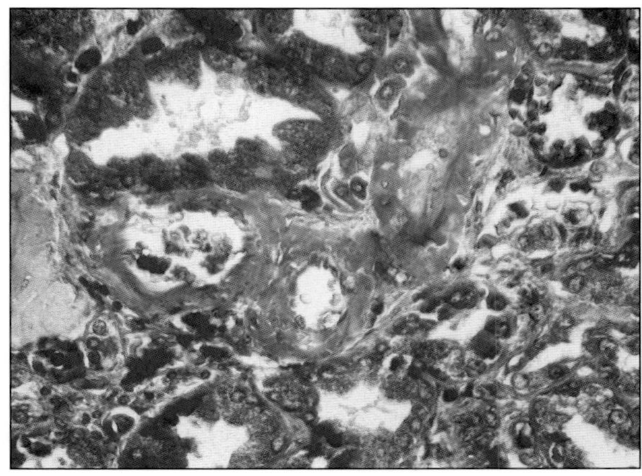

J (*Histotechnology 4e*, **i7.25**, p 155)

70. The fungal organisms seen in image I are most likely:
    a. *Histoplasma capsulatum*
    b. *Cryptococcus neoformans*
    c. *Candida albicans*
    d. *Coccidioides immitis*

71. Which staining technique was most likely used in image I?
    a. Schmorl
    b. Grocott
    c. colloidal iron
    d. methylene blue

72. Another technique that is frequently used to aid in the identification of the organisms stained blue in image I is:
    a. Congo red
    b. Warthin-Starry
    c. carbol fuchsin
    d. mucicarmine

73. The substance demonstrated in image J is:
    a. glycogen
    b. amyloid
    c. an aldehyde
    d. an acid mucosubstances

74. The stain demonstrated in image J is the:
    a. Congo red
    b. aldehyde fuchsin
    c. PAS
    d. crystal violet

75. Another stain that could be used to differentially demonstrate the substance stained rose in image J is:
    a. PAS
    b. Best carmine
    c. Congo red
    d. Giemsa

ISBN 978-089189-6401

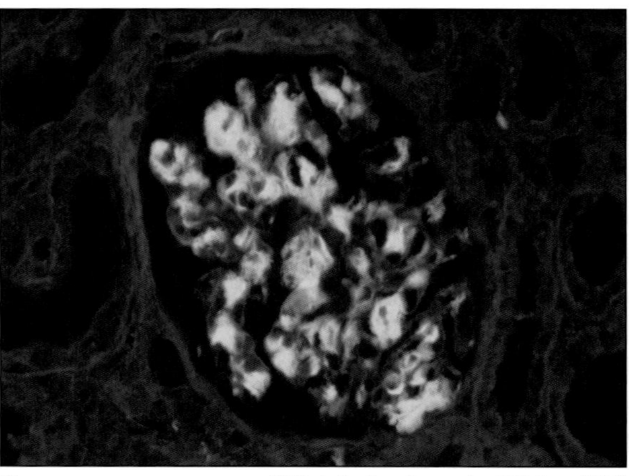

K (*Histotechnology 4e*, **i7.26**, p 157)

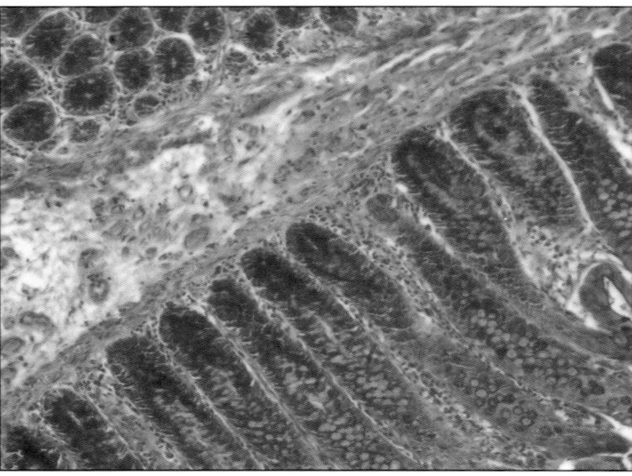

L (*Histotechnology 4e*, **i7.21**, p 153)

76. What type of microscope is used for the technique shown in image K?
    a. polarizing
    b. fluorescent
    c. light
    d. electron

77. The substance demonstrated in image K is most likely:
    a. amyloid
    b. fungi
    c. glycogen
    d. an acid mucosubstances

78. The dye used for the technique demonstrated in image K is most likely:
    a. auramine O
    b. rhodamine
    c. thioflavin T
    d. metanil yellow

79. The stain shown in image L is most likely:
    a. methylene blue
    b. alcian blue, pH 1.0
    c. colloidal iron
    d. toluidine blue

80. Everything in image L is incorrectly stained EXCEPT:
    a. goblet cells
    b. collagen
    c. muscle
    d. lamina propria

81. The problem shown in image L could most likely be corrected by:
    a. prolonging dehydration
    b. preparing fresh colloidal iron solution
    c. increasing the decolorization time
    d. letting the colloidal iron solution age

ISBN 978-089189-6401

82. One possible cause of the problem shown in image L is:
    a. prolonged decolorization
    b. unripened colloidal iron solution
    c. pH is too high
    d. dehydration too brief

73-88. The following are problem solving questions.

83. No staining of the glomerular basement membrane can be seen microscopically on a control section of kidney. This may be the result of:
    a. inadequate oxidation
    b. prolonged treatment with Schiff reagent
    c. thickening of the basement membrane
    d. lack of treatment with sodium metabisulfite

84. Marked nonspecific background staining is noted on a section stained with the PAS technique. This could be the result of:
    a. overoxidation of the section
    b. prolonged washing with water
    c. fixation with glutaraldehyde
    d. fixation with Zenker solution

85. Very weak staining is noted on a PAS stained control section of liver. One problem-solving action is to:
    a. check the Schiff reagent with formaldehyde
    b. verify the use of potassium metabisulfite
    c. shorten the oxidation time
    d. decrease the washing time

86. Sections of small intestine show orange goblet cells that are partially obscured by the yellow background. This is most likely the result of:
    a. prolonged staining with mucicarmine
    b. overstaining with metanil yellow
    c. improper use of iron hematoxylin
    d. a poor choice of control tissue

87. Control sections stained with Congo red show only yellow, and no green, birefringence. This could probably be corrected in the future by:
    a. reducing the time in the Congo red
    b. using iron hematoxylin for the nuclear stain
    c. ensuring that the sections are cut at 8 µm to 10 µm
    d. using only control tissue fixed in formalin

88. Make 8 copies of the following worksheet and complete 1 copy (try to do this without referring to the text) for each of the following techniques:
    a. PAS (example given in answers)
    b. Mayer mucicarmine
    c. Alcian blue, pH 2.5
    d. Alcian blue, pH 1.0
    e. Colloidal iron
    f. Congo red
    g. Crystal violet
    h. Thioflavin T
    i. Best carmine

ISBN 978-089189-6401

No answers are given for this exercise. The text must be used to check for correctness.

Staining technique ______________________________

Preferred fixative ______________________________

Preferred thickness ______________________________

Microscope used ______________________________

Control tissue ______________________________

Major reagents **Purpose**

Principle of the technique ______________________________

Purpose of stain ______________________________

Results ______________________________

Sources of error ______________________________

ISBN 978-089189-6401

Carbohydrates *Answers*

Question	Answer	Discussion	*Histotechnology* Page
1	c	Glycogen is dissolved by diastase, so the section stained with the PAS without diastase will stain positive and the one with diastase will be negative.	141-142
2	a	The Congo red stain demonstrates amyloid; the other stains listed will not.	154
3	b	Aldehydes are demonstrated by Schiff reaction.	139
4	b	Acidic mucins are present in the goblet cells of the appendix epithelium; therefore, it is a good control for the mucicarmine stain. The other tissues listed do not contain mucin.	144-145
5	d	Liver provides a good control for glycogen. Cervix also provides a good control because it contains both glycogen (ectocervix) and mucin (endocervix); diastase will digest the glycogen but leave the mucin positively stained. The other tissues listed do not contain glycogen.	141,143
6	c	Congo red stains followed by polarization provide one of the most specific techniques for amyloid.	154
7	d	Although other fixatives may be used satisfactorily, absolute alcohol is considered the best fixative for glycogen.	24
8	d	Periodic acid oxidizes certain tissue groups (most commonly 1, 2 glycol) to aldehydes.	139
9	d	Crystal violet and methyl violet have been shown to be mixtures of basic dyes. Therefore, it is more likely that the amyloid selectively reacts with 1 of the dye components, while the background stains with the other dyes, and is thus a polychromatic rather than a metachromatic stain.	156
10	a	Of the stains listed, only alcian blue will stain acid mucopolysaccharides.	147
11	b	Since formaldehyde is an aldehyde, Schiff reagent will react with it and turn rapidly reddish purple if good.	139
12	d	Thioflavin is a fluorescent dye used to demonstrate amyloid. Crystal violet and colloidal iron are not fluorescent dyes; auramine O is fluorescent but is used to demonstrate mycobacteria.	157
13	c	Alcian blue at a pH of 1.0 will demonstrate only sulfated acid mucopolysaccharides, while at 2.5 it will demonstrate both carboxylated and sulfated mucopolysaccharides; it does not demonstrate neutral mucopolysaccharides.	147-149

ISBN 978-089189-6401

Question	Answer	Discussion	*Histotechnology* Page
14	b	Substances stained positive with the colloidal iron procedure will be blue.	152
15	a	Basic fuchsin is reduced by sulfurous acid, forming Schiff reagent.	139
16	d	Diastase digestion effectively removes glycogen from tissue sections by depolymerizing it into smaller sugar units that are washed out of the section. This is one of the most specific techniques for the demonstration of glycogen.	141
17	c	Colloidal iron is used for the demonstration of acid mucopolysaccharides.	151-152
18	d	Best carmine is a stain for glycogen, but it is not as reliable as the PAS with diastase digestion. The PAS with diastase is the method of choice for glycogen.	144
19	d	Glycogen is the only substance listed that is sensitive to diastase digestion.	141
20	b	Because of the mucinous capsule, *Cryptococcus neoformans* is well demonstrated by colloidal iron, alcian blue, and mucicarmine; the other organisms do not have the mucinous capsule and are not demonstrated by these stains.	148 153
21	F	These compounds are extremely soluble in aqueous solution and therefore cannot be demonstrated in tissue sections.	138
22	T	Hyaluronidase will digest some connective tissue mucins such as hyaluronic acid, chondroitin sulfates A, and chondroitin C.	149-150
23	F	The routine alcian blue stain is done at a pH of 2.5.	147
24	F	Good Schiff reagent should be colorless to straw colored.	139
25	T	The end product in the colloidal iron method is $Fe_4[Fe(CN)_6]_3\downarrow$ or Prussian blue.	151
26	F	Amyloid should show an apple green birefringence following Congo red staining.	155
27	F	Because glutaraldehyde is a dialdehyde, 1 aldehyde may not be involved in protein cross-linking during fixation, but may be left free to react with the Schiff reagent, thus giving a false reaction.	140
28	F	A chromate-containing fixative may overoxidize reactive groups during fixation, and the Schiff reaction may be weak.	141

Question	Answer	Discussion	*Histotechnology* Page
29	T	Glycogen fixed in picric acid-containing fixatives may be more resistant to diastase digestion than when digestion follows other fixatives.	143
30	T	The addition of acid to the staining solution will prevent overstaining of cytoplasmic components.	156
31	F	Sections for crystal violet staining of amyloid should be cut thicker, between 10 µm and 12 µm.	156
32A	a, b, c, k	Acid mucopolysaccharides are stained by alcian blue, pH 1.0 and pH 2.5, by colloidal iron, and by mucicarmine.	144-152
32B	d, e, j	Congo red, crystal violet, and thioflavin are all stains for amyloid.	154-157
32C	b, c	Carboxylated acid mucopolysaccharides will be demonstrated by both the alcian blue, pH2.5, and colloidal iron methods, but not by alcian blue, pH 1.0.	144-148,151
32D	f, h, i	Diastase, periodic acid, and Schiff reagent are all used in the PAS stain for glycogen.	141-142
32E	h, i	Periodic acid and Schiff reagent are used in the PAS stain that will demonstrate neutral polysaccharides.	139-141
32F	a	Alcian blue, pH 1.0, will demonstrate only sulfated acid mucopolysaccharides.	148-149
33-1	A	The PAS demonstrates neutral polysaccharides.	139
33-2	B	Alcian blue, pH 2.5, demonstrates acid mucosubstances.	147
33-3	A	Only the PAS reacts with aldehyde groupings.	139
33-4	A	Because glutaraldehyde is a dialdehyde, 1 aldehyde may not be involved in protein cross-linking during fixation, but may be left free to react with the Schiff reagent, thus giving a false reaction.	140
33-5	D	Neither of these methods is used to demonstrate only sulfated mucosubstances.	139, 147
34-1	C	Alcian blue at both pH 2.5 and at 1.0 will demonstrate sulfated acid mucopolysaccharides.	147-148
34-2	A	Only alcian blue at pH 2.5 will demonstrate carboxylated acid mucopolysaccharides, they will not be demonstrated at pH 1.0.	147-148
34-3	D	Neither stain demonstrates glycogen.	147-148
34-4	A	Alcian blue, pH 2.5, with hyaluronidase digestion is used to demonstrate connective tissue mucins.	149
34-5	C	Both will stain sialomucins.	147-148

ISBN 978-089189-6401

Question	Answer	Discussion	*Histotechnology* Page
35-1	C	Both methods are used for the demonstration of amyloid.	154,157
35-2	A	Only the Congo red method shows apple green birefringence in amyloid deposits.	155
35-3	B	The thioflavin T is primarily a fluorescence technique.	157
35-4	D	The Congo red method is best on 8 µm to 10 µm sections and the thioflavin T method is best on 6 µm to 10 µm sections.	154,157
35-5	D	Fixation in Orth solution is not preferred for either method.	153,157
36-1	C	Both are used in the demonstration of specific carbohydrates, diastase for the demonstration of glycogen, and hyaluronidase for the demonstration of connective tissue mucins.	141,149
36-2	A	Only diastase will digest glycogen.	141
36-3	B	Only hyaluronidase removes connective tissue mucin.	149
36-4	B	Only hyaluronidase digestion is combined with the alcian blue technique.	149
36-5	D	Neither is used in the demonstration of amyloid.	154-157
37	a	The staining technique is Congo red.	55, 154
38	d	Congo red has stained amyloid deposits red in this slide.	55,154
39	b	Thioflavin will also demonstrate amyloid.	157
40	c	Unless sections are cut at 8 µm to 10 µm, they will not show apple green birefringence.	155
41	a	Polarizing microscopy is used in image B.	55
42	b	The Congo red stain seen by light microscopy in image A has been polarized in image B.	55
43	d	Crystal violet can also be used to demonstrate amyloid, although it is not very specific.	156
44	b	The intensity of staining with Congo red has been reported to decrease with the age of the cut sections; therefore, polarization would also show less intensity.	154
45	a	The mucin in goblet cells has been stained red by the Mayer mucicarmine technique.	145
46	c	The cells stained red are goblet cells present in epithelium of the small intestine.	145

ISBN 978-089189-6401

Question	Answer	Discussion	*Histotechnology* Page
47	c	A good control for the Mayer mucicarmine stain is small intestine.	144
48	d	Iron hematoxylin is used because the nuclei will not be decolorized by the acidity of the solutions that follow.	115,145
49	b	Mucin has been stained red in this image.	145
50	d	Of the techniques listed, the technique is most likely the colloidal iron.	153
51	a	The cartilage, goblet cells, and mucin secreting gland all contain acid mucopolysaccharides that are stained blue in this image.	152
52	b	The alcian blue would give the same results as the colloidal iron, although the stain might be slightly less intense.	147,153
53	b	The end product in the colloidal iron method is $Fe_4[Fe(CN)_6]_3\downarrow$, or Prussian blue.	151
54	a	The colloidal iron stain demonstrates both carboxylated and sulfated mucosubstances.	151
55	c	Mucin has been stained by the alcian blue, pH 2.5, in this image.	147
56	b	The colloidal iron stain would look almost identical to the alcian blue stained section shown in image E.	152
57	a	Alcian blue, pH 2.5 demonstrates both carboxylated and sulfated mucosubstances.	147
58	c	A section stained with the PAS technique is shown in image F.	141
59	d	A section of kidney is shown in image F.	141
60	c	The glomerular basement membrane is demonstrated by the PAS stain.	141
61	d	The glomerular basement membrane could also be demonstrated by the methenamine silver technique.	180-182
62	b	Schiff reagent reacts with aldehydes; this is the basis of the PAS technique.	140
63	a	For the best demonstration of the glomerular basement membrane, sections should be cut at 1 µm to 2 µm.	139
64	a	The stain is the PAS and, with diastase digestion, is the best stain for the demonstration of glycogen	141
65	c	Glycogen is demonstrated in image G.	141142
66	d	α-amylase or diastase will remove glycogen.	141
67	b	A section of liver is shown in image G.	142

ISBN 978-089189-6401

Question	Answer	Discussion	*Histotechnology* Page
68	b	Connective tissue mucin is stained blue by alcian blue, pH 2.5.	149-150
69	a	Hyaluronidase digestion would markedly decrease the blue staining seen in image H.	149
70	b	The stains for acid mucopolysaccharides stain *Cryptococcus neoformans*, aiding in differentiating it from other fungal organisms.	146,153
71	c	The colloidal iron stain was used to demonstrate *Cryptococcus neoformans.*	153
72	d	Mucicarmine is also used to aid in the identification of *Cryptococcus neoformans.*	146
73	b	The substance deposited around the blood vessels in image J is amyloid.	156
74	d	Amyloid has been stained by crystal violet in this image.	156
75	c	Congo red could also be used to stain the substance stained by crystal violet in this image.	154
76	b	A fluorescent microscope has been used for the technique shown in image K.	157
77	a	Amyloid deposits in a section of kidney have been stained with thioflavin T.	157
78	c	Thioflavin T has been used to stain amyloid deposits in a section of kidney.	157
79	c	The stain in image L is the colloidal iron.	153
80	a	The only correct staining is in goblet cells. All other staining is nonspecific background staining.	153
81	b	Repeating the stain with freshly prepared colloidal iron solution would most likely correct the problem.	153
82	c	If the pH is above 2.0, nonspecific background staining may occur.	153
83	a	Inadequate oxidation of the tissue reactive groups (primarily 1, 2 glycol) to aldehydes will result in very weak or no staining with Schiff reagent.	139
84	c	Because glutaraldehyde is a dialdehyde, 1 aldehyde may not be involved in protein cross-linking during fixation, but may be left free to react with the Schiff reagent, thus giving a false reaction.	140

ISBN 978-089189-6401

Question	Answer	Discussion	*Histotechnology* Page
85	a	The viability of Schiff reagent is readily checked by adding a few drops of Schiff reagent to 10 mL of 37%-40% formaldehyde; the rapid development of a reddish purple indicates a good reagent.	139
86	b	If the goblet cells are orange and the background an intense yellow, it indicates overstaining with metanil yellow.	146
87	c	Sections for Congo red staining for amyloid must be cut at 8 µm to 10 µm, or the correct apple green birefringence will not be realized.	154

ISBN 978-089189-6401

88. Staining Technique: PAS

Preferred Fixative: 10% neutral-buffered formalin or Bouin

Preferred Thickness: Kidney 1-2 μm, all others 4-5 μm

Microscope Used: Light

Control Tissue: Kidney (most sensitive), liver, or cervix (with endo- and ecto-)

Major reagents	Purpose
Periodic acid	Oxidizes adjacent 1,2 glycols and other reactive groups to aldehydes
Schiff reagent	Chemically combines with aldehydes
Metabisulfite rinse	Removes excess Schiff reagent, prevents false colorization due to adsorbed reagent.
Running water	Promotes restoration of the quinoid structure in dye bound by the aldehydes
Harris hematoxylin	Counterstain for nuclei

Principle of the Technique: Certain tissue elements are oxidized to aldehydes by periodic acid. Schiff reagent is used to demonstrate these aldehydes.

Purpose of Stain: Demonstration of polysaccharides, neutral mucosubstances, and basement membranes.

Results: Sites of aldehyde formation: bright rose. Some positive substances are glycogen, neutral mucosubstances, basement membranes, and fungal walls.

Sources of Error: Overused or old reagents are the most common source of error.

ISBN 978-089189-6401

Connective & Muscle Tissues *Questions*

1-3. Fill in the blanks.

1. List 3 connective tissue fibers and suggest 1 stain for each.

Fiber	Stain
1. ____________	____________
2. ____________	____________
3. ____________	____________

2. List 4 connective tissue cells and suggest 1 stain for each (unless not normally demonstrated).

Cell	Stain
1. ____________	____________
2. ____________	____________
3. ____________	____________
4. ____________	____________

3. List the 3 types of muscle fibers.

   1. ________________________
   2. ________________________
   3. ________________________

ISBN 978-089189-6401

4-32. The following are multiple choice questions. There is only 1 best answer.

4. With both the Masson and Gomori trichrome procedures, muscle stains:
   a. red
   b. green
   c. blue
   d. yellow

5. Which of the following methods best demonstrates elastic tissue?
   a. Verhoeff-van Gieson
   b. Silver impregnation
   c. Gomori trichrome
   d. PAS

6. The first step in most reticulin methods is:
   a. silver impregnation
   b. sensitization
   c. reduction
   d. oxidation

7. The Verhoeff method differentiates with:
   a. an acid
   b. a base
   c. an oxidizer
   d. excess mordant

8. Van Gieson solution stains collagen:
   a. green
   b. blue
   c. red
   d. yellow

9. Bouin solution functions in the Masson trichrome stain as a/an:
   a. oxidizer
   b. decolorizer
   c. reducer
   d. mordant

10. The components of van Gieson solution are:
    a. picric acid and basic fuchsin
    b. picric acid and acid fuchsin
    c. aniline blue and Biebrich scarlet
    d. light green and acid fuchsin

11. Gomori aldehyde fuchsin solution contains:
    a. basic fuchsin, hydrochloric acid, and paraformaldehyde
    b. acid fuchsin, hydrochloric acid, and paraldehyde
    c. basic fuchsin, hydrochloric acid, and paraldehyde
    d. acid fuchsin, picric acid, and acetic acid

ISBN 978-089189-6401

12. Most silver stains use which of the following as a toning agent?:
    a. sodium thiosulfate
    b. formaldehyde
    c. uranyl nitrate
    d. gold chloride

13. The reducing agent in most reticulin stains is:
    a. formaldehyde
    b. periodic acid
    c. uranyl nitrate
    d. sodium thiosulfate

14. Mallory PTAH stain is:
    a. polychromatic
    b. orthochromatic
    c. metachromatic
    d. apochromatic

15. A good control for reticulin stains is:
    a. kidney
    b. blood vessel
    c. liver
    d. skin

16. Toluidine blue is used to demonstrate which of the following cells?
    a. plasma
    b. mast
    c. fibroblasts
    d. macrophages

17. The component of basement membranes that is usually demonstrated with special stains is:
    a. protein
    b. carbohydrate
    c. laminin
    d. collagen

18. A stain that might be used to demonstrate cirrhosis of the liver is the:
    a. orcein
    b. Verhoeff-van Gieson
    c. Masson trichrome
    d. methenamine silver

19. In the Masson trichrome, Biebrich scarlet is removed from collagen by:
    a. acetic acid
    b. aniline blue
    c. picric acid
    d. phosphotungstic acid

ISBN 978-089189-6401

20. Iron hematoxylin, rather than aluminum hematoxylin, is usually used to stain nuclei in trichrome procedures because:
    a. subsequent staining solutions are acidic
    b. of the staining solution stability
    c. the stain is more easily prepared
    d. the mounted sections are more permanent

21. The preferred fixative for the Masson trichrome stain is:
    a. Bouin solution
    b. 10% neutral buffered formalin
    c. Zenker solution
    d. absolute alcohol

22. Silver impregnation stains for reticulin depend on the formation of which of the following chemical groups?
    a. quinoid
    b. aldehyde
    c. carboxyl
    d. amino

23. The diamine silver complex is formed by a reaction between silver and:
    a. formaldehyde
    b. uranium nitrate
    c. ammonium hydroxide
    d. periodic acid

24. Sections for the demonstration of basement membranes should be cut at:
    a. 2 µm
    b. 4 µm
    c. 6 µm
    d. 8 µm

25. The oil red O stain requires which of the following sections?
    a. paraffin
    b. celloidin
    c. frozen
    d. plastic

26. The oil red O stain might be used to demonstrate:
    a. rhabdomyosarcomas
    b. leiomyosarcomas
    c. liposarcomas
    d. adenocarcinomas

ISBN 978-089189-6401

27. Which of the following methods is an example of physical staining?
    a. toluidine blue
    b. Verhoeff-van Gieson
    c. methenamine silver
    d. oil red O

28. Fat is chemically fixed and maintained in tissue by:
    a. osmium tetroxide
    b. mercuric chloride
    c. calcium formol
    d. Carnoy solution

29. Plasma cells can be demonstrated with:
    a. methyl green-pyronin
    b. Verhoeff-van Gieson
    c. toluidine blue
    d. PAS

30. When ferric ammonium sulfate is used in a silver stain for reticulin, it functions as the:
    a. oxidizer
    b. sensitizer
    c. reducer
    d. toner

31. Mallory PTAH solution is ripened for immediate use by:
    a. air
    b. light
    c. sodium iodate
    d. potassium permanganate

32. When used in a silver stain for reticulin, phosphomolybdic acid functions as the:
    a. oxidizer
    b. sensitizer
    c. reducer
    d. toner

ISBN 978-089189-6401

33. Fill in the following chart:

Type of muscle	Number of nuclei per fiber	Location of nuclei	Striated (yes/no)	Voluntary (yes/no)
Skeletal				
Cardiac				
Smooth				

34. Place the letter of the PREFERRED fixative on the right in front of each method listed on the left. Letters denoting the fixative may be used more than once.

Connective tissue method

____A. Aldehyde fuchsin
____B. Gomori trichrome
____C. Masson trichrome
____D. Oil red O
____E. Paraffin processed fat
____F. Phosphotungstic acid-hematoxylin
____G. Gomori reticulin
____H. Verhoeff-van Gieson

Fixative

a. B-5
b. Bouin solution
c. 10% neutral buffered formalin
d. osmium tetroxide
e. Zenker solution

35. Match the following reagents on the left with the procedure(s) on the right in which they are commonly used (letters may be used more than once or not at all):

Reagent

____A. Acid fuchsin
____B. Aniline blue
____C. Basic fuchsin
____D. Biebrich scarlet
____E. Chromotrope 2R
____F. Diamine silver
____G. Iodine
____H. Pyronin
____I. Paraldehyde

Procedure

a. aldehyde fuchsin
b. MGP
c. Gomori trichrome
d. Gordon and Sweets
e. Masson trichrome
f. van Gieson
g. Verhoeff, primary stain

ISBN 978-089189-6401

36-42. Each of the following numbered words or phrases is associated with one, both, or neither of the headings listed as A or B above it. Within the parentheses on the right, place the appropriate letter for that word or phrase. Write:
A, if the numbered phrase is associated with A only
B, if the numbered phrase is associated with B only
C, if the numbered phrase is associated with both A and B
D, if the numbered phrase is associated with neither A nor B

36.

A. Gomori reticulin	1. Requires an oxidation step	[ ]
B. Periodic acid-methenamine silver	2. Based on carbohydrate demonstration	[ ]
C. both	3. Uses a separate formaldehyde reduction step	[ ]
D. neither	4. Zenker fixation is preferred	[ ]
	5. Kidney provides the best control tissue	[ ]

37.

A. Verhoeff	1. Uses acid differentiation	[ ]
B. Aldehyde fuchsin	2. Uses ferric chloride as a mordant	[ ]
C. both	3. Is a stain for elastic tissue	[ ]
D. neither	4. Primary stain is stable for months	[ ]
	5. Uses paraldehyde in the primary stain	[ ]

38.

A. Masson trichrome	1. Stains collagen red	[ ]
B. van Gieson	2. Stains muscle red	[ ]
C. both	3. Is used to demonstrate elastic tissue	[ ]
D. neither	4. Uses a saturated solution of picric acid in the primary stain	[ ]
	5. Differentiates collagen from smooth muscle	[ ]

39.

A. Adipose cells	1. Demonstrated by oil red O	[ ]
B. Mast cells	2. Granules stain metachromatically	[ ]
C. both	3. Are connective tissue cells	[ ]
D. neither	4. Demonstration requires frozen sections	[ ]
	5. Fixation in Carnoy is preferred	[ ]

40.

A. Methyl green-pyronin	1. Demonstrates mast cells metachromatically	[ ]
B. Toluidine blue	2. Demonstrates DNA	[ ]
C. both	3. Stains the cytoplasm of plasma cells rose	[ ]
D. neither	4. Used for the demonstration of connective tissue cells	[ ]
	5. Used for the demonstration of fibroblasts	[ ]

ISBN 978-089189-6401

41.

A. Acid fuchsin	1. Used in aldehyde fuchsin	[ ]
B. Basic fuchsin	2. Used in the Masson trichrome	[ ]
C. both	3. Used in the Gordon and Sweets technique	[ ]
D. neither	4. Used in van Gieson stain	[ ]
	5. Is also known as pararosaniline	[ ]

42.

A. Phosphotungstic acid-hematoxylin	1. Stains muscle blue	[ ]
B. Masson trichrome	2. Stains collagen reddish orange	[ ]
C. both	3. Used to demonstrate cross-striations	[ ]
D. neither	4. Is considered a connective tissue stain	[ ]
	5. Used to demonstrate elastic tissue	[ ]

ISBN 978-089189-6401

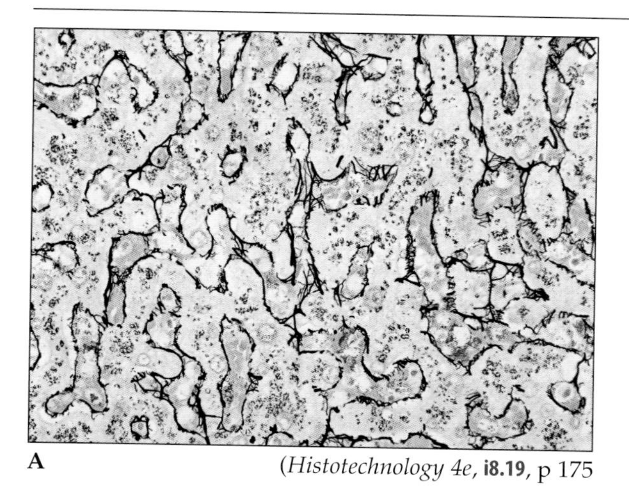

A (*Histotechnology 4e*, **i8.19**, p 175

43-93. The following questions apply to images A-J as specified.

43. The tissue component stained black in image A is:
    a. collagen
    b. elastic fibers
    c. reticulin
    d. nerve fibers

44. The technique shown in image A requires the use of:
    a. diamine silver
    b. methenamine silver
    c. silver chloride
    d. silver proteinate

45. Formaldehyde is used in the technique shown in image A as a/an:
    a. oxidizer
    b. sensitizer
    c. reducer
    d. accelerator

46. The tissue shown in image A was most likely stained by the method of:
    a. Verhoeff
    b. Gomori
    c. Mallory
    d. Masson

47. The control used for the technique shown in image A is:
    a. kidney
    b. small intestine
    c. spleen
    d. liver

48. The technique in image A depends on the presence of:
    a. carbohydrates
    b. lipids
    c. proteins
    d. hyaluronic acid

ISBN 978-089189-6401

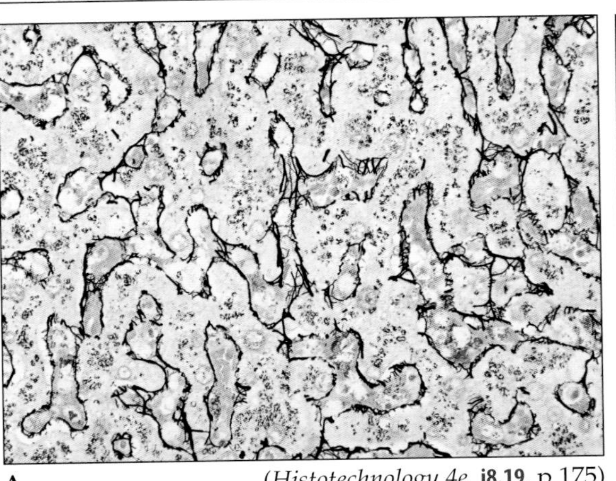

A (*Histotechnology 4e*, **i8.19**, p 175)

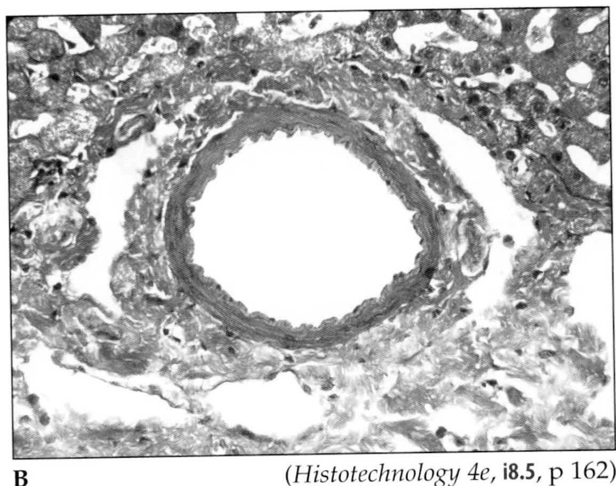

B (*Histotechnology 4e*, **i8.5**, p 162)

49. The tissue shown in image B was most likely stained by the method of:
    a. Nasher and Shanklin
    b. van Gieson
    c. Movat
    d. Masson

50. The tissue component stained blue in image B is:
    a. epithelium
    b. collagen
    c. smooth muscle
    d. skeletal muscle

51. The red stained circular tissue component seen in image B is:
    a. epithelium
    b. collagen
    c. smooth muscle
    d. elastic tissue

52. The preferred fixative for the technique shown in image B is:
    a. formalin
    b. Bouin solution
    c. Carnoy solution
    d. Zenker solution

53. A modification of the technique shown in image B stains collagen:
    a. green
    b. red
    c. yellow
    d. purple

54. The technique shown in image C is:
    a. progressive
    b. regressive
    c. a silver impregnation
    d. a metallic substitution

ISBN 978-089189-6401

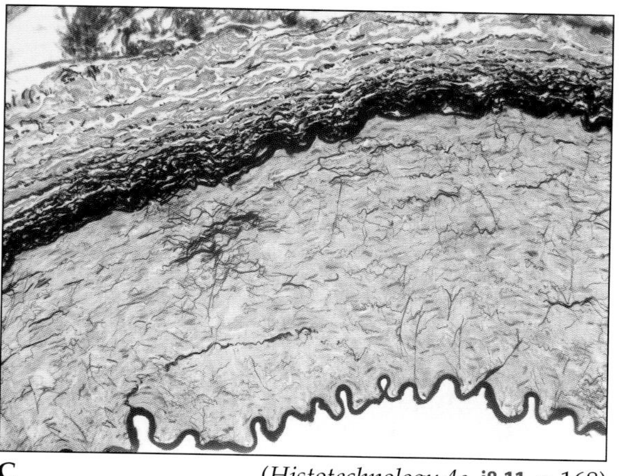

C (*Histotechnology 4e*, **i8.11**, p 168)

55. The technique demonstrated in image C is the:
    a. Verhoeff-van Gieson
    b. phosphotungstic acid-hematoxylin
    c. aldehyde fuchsin
    d. Masson trichrome

56. The tissue shown in image C is a section of a/an:
    a. aorta
    b. muscular artery
    c. large vein
    d. arteriole

57. Another method for demonstrating the tissue component stained black in image C is:
    a. phosphotungstic acid-hematoxylin
    b. methenamine silver
    c. toluidine blue
    d. aldehyde fuchsin

58. The tissue component stained red in image C is:
    a. elastic tissue
    b. smooth muscle
    c. collagen
    d. reticulin

59. The tissue component stained black in image C is:
    a. elastic fibers
    b. smooth muscle
    c. collagen
    d. reticulin

60. A chemical used in the technique shown in image C for both oxidation and differentiation is:
    a. iodine
    b. hematoxylin
    c. picric acid
    d. ferric chloride

ISBN 978-089189-6401

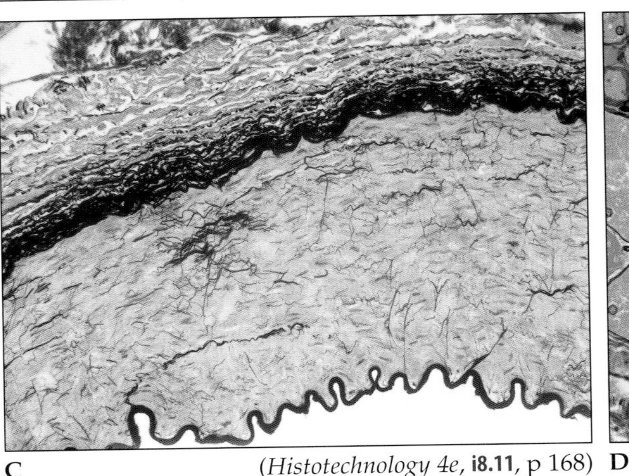

C (*Histotechnology 4e*, **i8.11**, p 168)

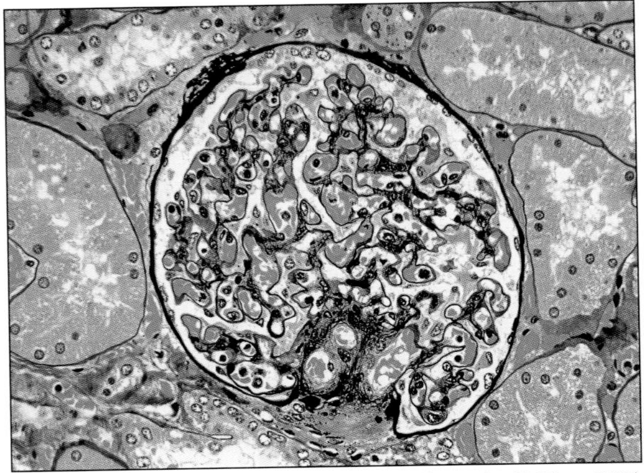

D (*Histotechnology 4e*, **i8.27**, p 181)

61. The solution responsible for the staining of the muscle in image C contains:
    a. basic fuchsin
    b. picric acid
    c. hematoxylin
    d. Biebrich scarlet

62. The tissue demonstrated in image D is:
    a. kidney
    b. thymus
    c. liver
    d. tonsil

63. The technique demonstrated in image D uses:
    a. methenamine silver
    b. diamine silver
    c. silver chloride
    d. silver protein

64. The tissue component(s) stained black in image D is/are:
    a. reticulin
    b. elastic fibers
    c. collagen fibers
    d. basement membrane

65. Another technique for demonstrating the tissue component stained black in image D is:
    a. alcian blue, pH 2.5
    b. PAS
    c. aldehyde fuchsin
    d. colloidal iron

66. The technique shown in image D depends on the:
    a. formation of aldehydes
    b. presence of amino groups
    c. presence of carboxyl groups
    d. formation of a diamine silver complex

ISBN 978-089189-6401

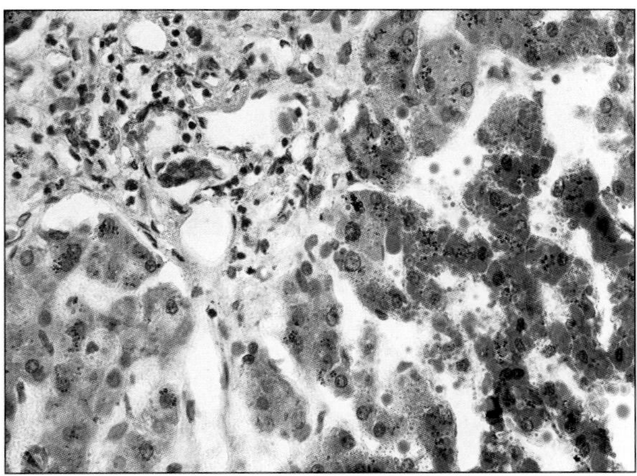

E (*Histotechnology 4e*, **i8.33**, p 184)

67. The oxidizer used in the technique shown in image D is:
    a. potassium permanganate
    b. sodium iodate
    c. periodic acid
    d. phosphomolybdic acid

68. The technique shown in image E is the:
    a. PAS
    b. oil red O
    c. alizarin red
    d. Masson trichrome

69. The preferred fixative for the technique shown in image E is:
    a. formalin
    b. Bouin
    c. B-5
    d. alcohol

70. The sections used for the technique shown in image E must be:
    a. embedded in glycol methacrylate
    b. embedded in paraffin
    c. freeze-dried
    d. frozen

71. The section shown in image E was most likely:
    a. a paraffin section
    b. removed from the stain prematurely
    c. coverslipped improperly by mashing on the coverglass
    d. coverslipped with a synthetic resin mountant

72. The component stained red in image E is:
    a. calcium
    b. lipid
    c. glycogen
    d. collagen

ISBN 978-089189-6401

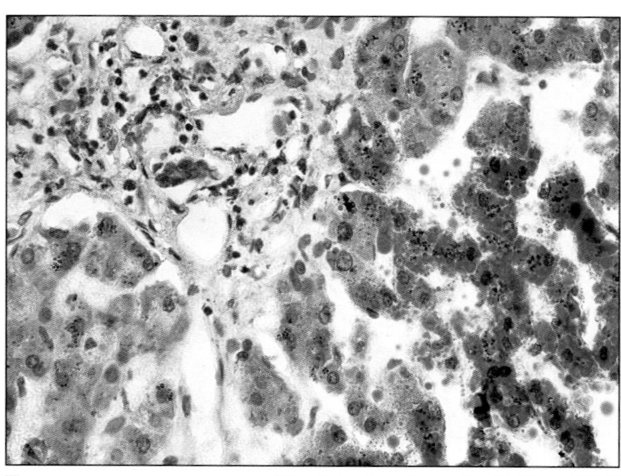

E (*Histotechnology 4e*, **i8.33**, p 184)

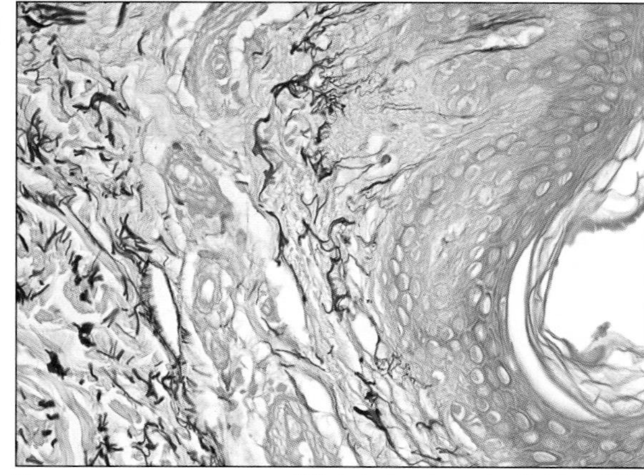

F (*Histotechnology 4e*, **i8.14**, p 170)

73. The technique shown in image E is a/an:
    a. physical method
    b. chemical method
    c. impregnation
    d. substitution

74. Another technique that could be used to demonstrate the substance stained red in image E is the:
    a. PAS
    b. Masson
    c. Sudan black B
    d. Verhoeff

75. The tissue shown in image F is:
    a. esophagus
    b. cervix
    c. skin
    d. tonsil

76. The technique demonstrated in image F is the:
    a. aldehyde fuchsin
    b. toluidine blue
    c. methenamine silver
    d. Verhoeff

77. The component stained purple in image F is/are:
    a. nerve
    b. reticular fibers
    c. basement membrane
    d. elastic fibers

78. A good substitute for 1 of the chemicals in the primary staining solution used to stain the purple fibers in image F is:
    a. formaldehyde
    b. acetaldehyde
    c. paraformaldehyde
    d. glutaraldehyde

ISBN 978-089189-6401

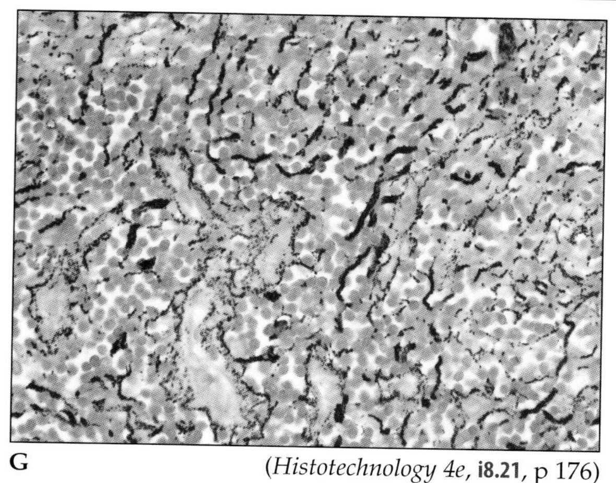

G (*Histotechnology 4e*, **i8.21**, p 176)

79. The technique shown in image G demonstrates:
    a. reticulin
    b. collagen
    c. elastin
    d. cross-striations

80. The stain shown in image G has stained reticulin in:
    a. the correct granular pattern
    b. the correct linear pattern
    c. an incorrect granular pattern
    d. an incorrect linear pattern

81. The stain shown in image G probably results from:
    a. old sensitizing reagent
    b. incorrect toning
    c. incomplete removal of silver
    d. a properly done stain

82. The counterstain used in the technique shown in image G is most likely:
    a. basic fuchsin
    b. alizarin red
    c. nuclear fast red
    d. Biebrich scarlet

83. The cells with the rose-violet cytoplasm shown in image H are most likely:
    a. lymphocytes
    b. adipose cells
    c. fibroblasts
    d. mast cells

84. The stain shown in image H is most likely:
    a. methyl green-pyronin
    b. toluidine blue
    c. crystal violet
    d. Feulgen

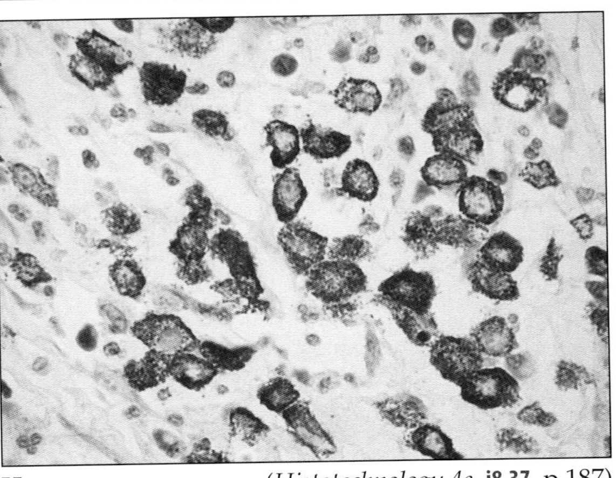

H (*Histotechnology 4e*, **i8.37**, p 187)

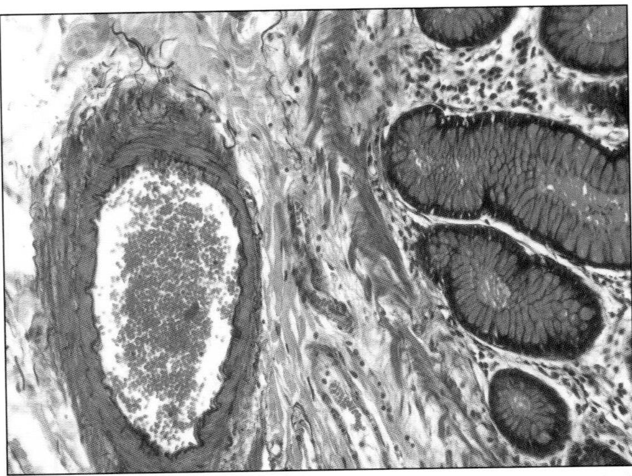

I (*Histotechnology 4e*, **i8.16**, p 172)

85. The rose-red staining shown in image H is:
    a. orthochromatic
    b. polychromatic
    c. metachromatic
    d. physical

86. The cells with rose-violet cytoplasm shown in image H belong to which of the following tissue types?
    a. epithelial
    b. connective tissue
    c. muscle
    d. nerve

87. The technique shown in image I is most likely that of:
    a. Movat
    b. Gomeri
    c. Masson
    d. Verhoeff

88. Collagen is stained yellow in image I by:
    a. metanil yellow
    b. safran
    c. picric acid
    d. gold chloride

89. Elastic fiber are demonstrated in the method shown in image I by:
    a. aluminum hematoxylin
    b. iron hematoxylin
    c. aldehyde fuchsin
    d. monastral fast blue

90. The technique shown in image J is most likely the:
    a. phosphotungstic acid hematoxylin
    b. Movat pentachrome
    c. Congo red
    d. aldehyde fuchsin

ISBN 978-089189-6401

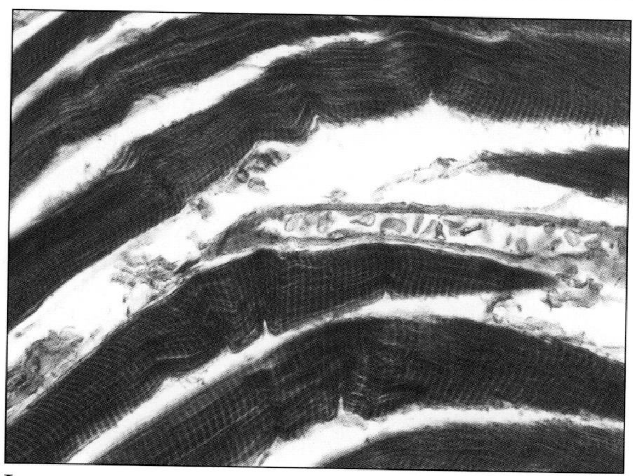

J (*Histotechnology 4e*, **i8.24**, p 179)

91. The technique shown in image J is:
    a. orthochromatic
    b. polychromatic
    c. metachromatic
    d. physical

92. The blue stained tissue component in image J is:
    a. collagen
    b. smooth muscle
    c. skeletal muscle
    d. fibrin

93. The orange stained tissue component in image J is:
    a. amyloid
    b. elastic tissue
    c. smooth muscle
    d. collagen

ISBN 978-089189-6401

94-104. The following are problem solving questions.

94. The Verhoeff-van Gieson shows both orange collagen and orange muscle. This most likely could be corrected in the future by:
    a. differentiating longer in 95% alcohol
    b. ensuring that the picric acid solution is saturated
    c. increasing the concentration of the acid fuchsin
    d. mordanting the section in Bouin solution

95. The Masson trichrome stain shows only a faint grayish pink staining of the muscle. This could most likely be prevented in the future by:
    a. increasing the concentration of the phosphotungstic acid
    b. using a mixture of phosphotungstic and phosphomolybdic acids
    c. using fresh acid fuchsin-Biebrich scarlet solution
    d. ensuring that the sections are acidic at the end of the stain

96. A black precipitate is noted on a periodic acid-methenamine silver stained section that has been on the pathologist's desk for about a month. The stain did not have any precipitate originally. This indicates that most likely the:
    a. section was not properly toned
    b. silver nitrate solution was old
    c. glassware may not have been chemically cleaned
    d. sodium thiosulfate step may have been omitted

97. Fat droplets are seen in the tissue spaces of an oil red O stained section. This most likely resulted from:
    a. dissolving the stain in propylene glycol
    b. using glycerine jelly for mounting the sections
    c. pressing on the coverglass to remove air bubbles
    d. a displacement of fat during paraffin processing

98. Formalin fixed tissue shows very faded blue staining with the Masson trichrome technique. The most likely explanation is that the sections were:
    a. left too long in the final acetic acid solution
    b. stained with old acid fuchsin
    c. fixed in Bouin solution
    d. dried in a hot dryer

99. Microscopic examination of a section stained with the Gomori reticulin stain and counterstained with nuclear fast red shows cloudiness of both the section and the slide. This is most likely the result of:
    a. improper oxidation of the reticulin
    b. incomplete removal of the unreduced silver
    c. inadequate washing after the nuclear fast red
    d. the use of old ammonium hydroxide solution

100. Granular deposition of the silver is seen on the control stained with the Gordon and Sweets reticulin method. One possible explanation is that:
    a. this is the normal result of the Gordon and Sweets method
    b. the reagents may have been old
    c. the sections were not properly toned
    d. the sections are too thick

ISBN 978-089189-6401

101. Black precipitate is seen on sections stained with the Gomori method for reticulin. This is most likely the result of:
    a. overrinsing the slide prior to the formaldehyde
    b. leaving the slides too long in gold chloride
    c. using glassware that was not chemically clean
    d. inadequately rinsing the slide after nuclear fast red

102. A Masson stain has been requested and the supply of phosphomolybdic acid has been depleted. The best action is to substitute:
    a. phosphotungstic acid
    b. hydrochloric acid
    c. picric acid
    d. acetic acid

103. The connective tissue has failed to stain yellow with the Movat pentachrome stain. One possible cause is that the:
    a. metanil yellow is too dilute
    b. safran solution contains water
    c. phosphotungstic acid was removed with acetified water
    d. tissue was fixed in an acetic-formalin mercury solution

104. The goblet cells in a section of small intestine fail to show any blue staining with the Movat pentachrome stain. This could possibly be the result of:
    a. not removing the alkaline alcohol completely
    b. inadequate staining with crocein scarlet-acid fuchsin
    c. treating the slides with alkaline alcohol too briefly
    d. the presence of acetic acid in the alcian blue solution

ISBN 978-089189-6401

105. Make 13 copies of the worksheet that follows, and complete 1 copy for each of the following techniques (try to do this without referring to the text):

a. Masson trichrome
b. Gomori trichrome
c. van Gieson
d. Verhoeff-van Gieson
e. Aldehyde fuchsin
f. Russell modification of the Movat pentachrome
g. Gomori reticulin
h. Gordon and Sweets reticulin
i. Phosphotungstic acid–hematoxylin
j. oil red O
k. Sudan Black B
l. Osmium tetroxide
m. Toluidine blue

ISBN 978-089189-6401

No answers are given for this exercise. The text must be used to check for correctness.

Staining technique ________________

Preferred fixative ________________

Preferred thickness ________________

Microscope used ________________

Control tissue ________________

Major reagents	**Purpose**
Periodic acid	
Schiff reagent	
Metabisulfite rinse	
Running water	
Harris hematoxylin	

Principle of the technique ________________

Purpose of stain ________________

Results ________________

Sources of error ________________

ISBN 978-089189-6401

Connective & Muscle Tissues
Answers

Question	Answer	Discussion		*Histotechnology* Page
1	*Fiber*		*Stain*	
	Collagen		Masson or Gomori trichrome	160-177
	Elastic		Verhoeff-van Gieson, aldehyde fuchsin, orcein, Miller, or resorcin-fuchsin	
	Reticulin		Gomori or Gordon & Sweets (others not included in text are Wilder, Snook, Laidlaw, Nasher & Shanklin)	
2	Adipose		oil red O, Sudan black B, osmium tetroxide	160, 184-188
	Fibroblast		Not routinely demonstrated	
	Mast cell		Toluidine blue	
	Macrophage		Not routinely demonstrated	
	Mesenchymal cell		Not routinely demonstrated	
	Plasma cell		Methyl green pyronin (MGP)	
	Other blood cells		Not routinely demonstrated in soft tissue, Giemsa if requested	
3		Skeletal (striated, voluntary) Cardiac (striated, involuntary, found in heart) Smooth (nonstriated, involuntary)		161
4	a	On paraffin sections, muscle stains red with both the Masson and Gomori trichrome procedures; it will stain bluish green on unfixed frozen tissue.		162-165, 312-314
5	a	Of the stains listed, the Verhoeff-van Gieson is the only one that demonstrates elastic tissue; other stains for elastic tissue are the orcein, Miller, and resorcin fuchsin.		168-170
6	d	Oxidation is the first step in most reticulin methods; this is followed by sensitization, silver impregnation, reduction, toning, and removing any unreduced silver.		173
7	d	In the Verhoeff method, elastic tissue is differentiated with ferric chloride, the mordant in the stain.		167
8	c	Collagen stains red and muscle yellow with the van Gieson stain.		166
9	d	Formalin fixed tissue stains poorly with the Masson trichrome stain; therefore, paraffin sections should be mordanted in Bouin solution prior to staining.		162-164
10	b	Van Gieson solution contains picric acid and acid fuchsin.		166

ISBN 978-089189-6401

Question	Answer	Discussion	*Histotechnology* Page
11	c	Gomori aldehyde fuchsin solution contains basic fuchsin, hydrochloric acid, and paraldehyde. Acetaldehyde may be used instead of paraldehyde.	169-179
12	d	Gold chloride is used as a toner in many silver methods; the gold replaces the silver, giving a more stable compound. Section clarity and contrast are also improved.	173
13	a	Formaldehyde is used in all reticulin methods to reduce the silver diamine ions to metallic silver at the original sites of the reticulin sugar molecules.	373
14	a	The PTAH stain is polychromatic; 1 solution gives 2 major colors.	178
15	c	Liver provides a very good control for reticulin stains.	1174
16	b	Mast cells will stain metachromatically with toluidine blue; that is, they will stain a different color from the rest of the tissue.	187
17	b	The carbohydrate component of basement membranes is oxidized to aldehydes and then demonstrated with methenamine silver or the PAS reaction.	1 80-182
18	c	The Masson trichrome is frequently used to identify increases in collagenous tissue in cirrhosis of the liver.	162
19	d	Phosphotungstic and/or phosphomolybdic acids are used to remove Biebrich scarlet (or other red dyes) from collagen. Collagen is then counterstained with either aniline blue or light green.	162-164
20	a	Iron hematoxylin is normally used in trichrome procedures because the subsequent acid solutions would tend to decolorize aluminum hematoxylin stained nuclei.	164
21	a	Bouin solution is the preferred fixation for tissue to be stained with Masson trichrome; formalin fixed tissue does not differentially stain as well.	164
22	b	Carbohydrates (hexose sugars) present in reticulin must be oxidized to aldehydes for silver impregnation.	1173
23	c	Ammonium hydroxide reacts with silver nitrate to form the diamine silver complex.	173

ISBN 978-089189-6401

Question	Answer	Discussion	*Histotechnology* Page
24	a	Sections should be cut at 2 μm for glomerular basement membrane studies.	180
25	c	Frozen sections must be used for fat demonstration by the oil red O technique.	183
26	c	Tumors arising from fat cells (liposarcomas) can be demonstrated with the oil red O technique.	183
27	d	The oil red O technique is a physical method of staining; that is, it is absorbed by and soluble in the fat.	183
28	a	Osmium tetroxide solutions chemically fix fat, blackening it in the process. This is the only method for fat that is chemical. Osmium fixed tissue may be processed routinely, although the sections must be thin for fixation because of the poor penetration of osmium tetroxide solutions.	185
29	a	Plasma cells can be demonstrated with the methyl green-pyronin technique; the RNA in the cytoplasm will stain rose with pyronin.	188
30	b	Ferric ammonium sulfate is used as a sensitizer in some reticulin methods.	173
31	d	Potassium permanganate may be used to ripen Mallory PTAH solutions immediately.	178
32	a	Phosphomolybdic acid is used in the Wilder reticulin stain as the oxidizer.	173
33		(see table below)	161
34A	c	10% neutral buffered formalin is preferred; chromate fixatives should be avoided.	169
34B	b	Bouin solution is preferred; if formalin is used, the paraffin sections must be mordanted in Bouin solution.	165

Question 33:

Type of muscle	Number of nuclei per fiber	Location of nuclei	Striated (yes/no)	Voluntary (yes/no)
Skeletal	Many	Peripheral	Yes	Yes
Cardiac	1	Central	Yes	No
Smooth	1	Central	No	No

Histotechnology Workbook 3e
ISBN 978-089189-6401

Question	Answer	Discussion	*Histotechnology* Page
34C	b	Bouin solution is preferred; if formalin is used, the paraffin sections must be mordanted in Bouin solution.	164
34D	c	10% neutral buffered formalin is preferred; solutions containing alcohol should be avoided.	183
34E	d	Osmium tetroxide will fix fat in thin sections so that they may be processed.	185
34F	c, e	Zenker fixed tissue is best, but 10% neutral buffered formalin may be used, and the paraffin sections mordanted in either Zenker or Bouin solution.	178-179
34G	c	10% neutral buffered formalin is preferred.	174
34H	c, e	Neutral buffered formalin or Zenker solution is preferred.	167
35A	e, f	Acid fuchsin is used in both the Masson trichrome and van Gieson stains.	163, 167
35B	c, e	Although fast green is normally found in the Gomori trichrome stain, aniline blue or light green may be used; aniline blue is also the most used counterstain for the Masson technique.	162,165
35C	a	Basic fuchsin is used in the aldehyde fuchsin stain; it should be pararosaniline and not rosaniline.	169-170
35D	e	Biebrich scarlet is used in the Biebrich scarlet solution for the Masson trichrome stain.	163
35E	c	Chromotrope 2R is the red dye in the Gomori trichrome stain.	165
35F	d	Diamine silver is the impregnating solution in the Gordon and Sweets reticulin stain.	173, 177
35G	g	Iodine is one of the components of the Verhoeff elastic staining solution.	167
35H	b	Pyronin stains RNA red in the methyl green-pyronin stain.	188
35I	a	Paraldehyde is used in the preparation of the aldehyde fuchsin staining solution for elastic fibers.	169
36-1	C	Both methods require oxidation of carbohydrate components to aldehydes.	174, 1180
36-2	C	Both methods are based on carbohydrate demonstration.	174, 180
36-3	A	Only the reticulin method uses a separate formaldehyde reduction step.	174,180
36-4	D	Formalin fixation is preferred for both methods; mercury-containing fixatives are not recommended for the periodic acid-methenamine silver method.	174, 180

ISBN 978-089189-6401

Question	Answer	Discussion	*Histotechnology* Page
36-5	B	Kidney is the best control for the periodic acid-methenamine silver method; liver is the best control for reticulin methods.	174,180
37-1	D	Neither method used acid differentiation; Verhoeff is differentiated with excess mordant, and aldehyde fuchsin is differentiated with 70% alcohol.	167, 169
37-2	A	Ferric chloride is the mordant for the iron hematoxylin solution and also serves as the differentiating solution.	167
37-3	C	Both are stains for elastic tissue.	167,169
37-4	D	Neither stain is stable for months; Verhoeff solution should be prepared fresh each time, and aldehyde fuchsin is stable for a maximum of 2 months unless frozen.	167,170
37-5	B	Paraldehyde is used in the preparation of the aldehyde fuchsin primary stain.	169
38-1	B	The van Gieson stains collagen red and muscle yellow.	166
38-2	A	The Masson trichrome stains muscle red and collagen blue or green.	162-163
38-3	D	Neither is used for the demonstration of elastic tissue.	162,166
38-4	B	Only the van Gieson procedure uses picric acid in the primary stain.	162,166
38-5	C	Both will differentiate collagen from smooth muscle.	162,166
39-1	A	Oil red O is used to demonstrate fat (adipose cells).	183
39-2	B	The granules of mast cells stain metachromatically.	187
39-3	C	Both adipose cells and mast cells are connective tissue cells.	160
39-4	A	The demonstration of adipose cells requires frozen sections unless the tissue is fixed with osmium tetroxide, as fat is dissolved by alcohol and xylene during processing.	183,185
39-5	D	10% neutral buffered formalin is preferred; Carnoy solution would dissolve adipose cells.	183,187
40-1	B	The granules of mast cells stain metachromatically with toluidine blue.	187
40-2	A	DNA is stained blue-green with the methyl green-pyronin stain.	188
40-3	A	Because of the RNA content, the cytoplasm of plasma cells stains rose with the methyl green-pyronin stain.	188

ISBN 978-089189-6401

Question	Answer	Discussion	*Histotechnology* Page
40-4	C	Plasma cells and mast cells (both connective tissue cells) are demonstrated with these 2 techniques.	187-188
40-5	D	Neither technique is used for the demonstration of fibroblasts.	187-188
41-1	B	Basic fuchsin, along with paraldehyde and hydrochloric acid, are used to prepare aldehyde fuchsin.	169
41-2	A	Acid fuchsin and Biebrich scarlet are combined for the red staining solution in the Masson trichrome stain.	162-163
41-3	D	Neither of these dyes is used in the Gordon and Sweets reticulin technique.	176-177
41-4	A	Acid fuchsin is combined with a saturated solution of picric acid to form van Gieson solution.	167
41-5	B	Basic fuchsin, CI 42500, is also known as pararosaniline. Basic fuchsin, CI 42510, is known as rosaniline.	169-170
42-1	A	Phosphotungstic acid-hematoxylin stains muscle blue.	178-179
42-2	A	Phosphotungstic acid-hematoxylin stains collage reddish orange.	178-179
42-3	A	Phosphotungstic acid-hematoxylin beautifully demonstrates cross-striations.	178-179
42-4	B	The Masson trichrome method is considered a connective tissue stain; the phosphotungstic acid-hematoxylin method is primarily for the demonstration of muscle cross-striations, and muscle is not a connective tissue.	160-162
42-5	D	Neither stain is used for the demonstration of elastic tissue.	162-163, 180-181
43	c	Reticulin is stained impregnated by an ammoniacal or diamine silver complex, and then reduced and toned, resulting in black fibers.	175
44	a	A diamine silver complex is used to impregnate reticulin fibers; methenamine silver is used in the GMS and periodic acid-methenamine silver stain for basement membranes; silver proteinate is used in the Bodian stain for nerve fibers; silver chloride is insoluble in water and not used in staining.	173, 181, 193,
45	c	Formaldehyde is the reducer in all reticulin methods.	173

ISBN 978-089189-6401

Question	Answer	Discussion	*Histotechnology* Page
46	b	Gomori is the only reticulin stain listed, and image A shows a reticulin stained section; Verhoeff stains elastic tissue; Masson stains collagen and muscle; Mallory stains muscle striations.	174
47	d	Liver is the control tissue shown in image A; the sinusoids are well outlined by the reticulin stain.	15
48	a	Adjacent glycol groups of the hexose sugar molecules (carbohydrate) present in reticulin are oxidized to aldehydes for reaction with the diamine silver complex.	174
49	d	A Masson stain, differentiating between muscle (red) and collagen (blue) is shown in image B.	162
50	b	Collagen is stained blue by the Masson technique.	162
51	c	Smooth muscle is stained red by the Masson technique.	162
52	b	Bouin solution is the preferred fixative for tissue to be stained with the Masson trichrome stain.	162
53	a	Light green may also be used in the Masson technique, staining collagen green.	163
54	b	The Verhoeff technique is regressive; excess mordant is the method of differentiation.	167
55	a	The method demonstrated in image C is the Verhoeff-van Gieson for elastic tissue.	168
56	b	The tissue is a section of a muscular artery.	168
57	d	Aldehyde fuchsin could be used to demonstrate the tissue stained black (elastic tissue) in image C.	170
58	c	Collagen is stained red by the van Gieson solution.	168
59	a	Elastic tissue is stained black by iron hematoxylin.	168
60	d	Ferric chloride is used to oxidize the iron hematoxylin solution and also to differentiate the overstained elastic fibers.	167-168
61	b	Muscle is stained yellow by the picric acid in van Gieson solution.	168
62	a	The tissue shown in image D is kidney, specifically a kidney glomerulus.	181
63	a	Methenamine silver is used to stain the glomerular basement membrane; diamine silver complex is used to impregnate reticulin fibers; silver proteinate is used in the Bodian stain for nerve fibers; silver chloride is insoluble in water and not used in staining.	173,181, 193

ISBN 978-089189-6401

Question	Answer	Discussion	*Histotechnology* Page
64	d	The glomerular basement membrane is stained black in image D.	181
65	b	The PAS technique also can be used to demonstrate the basement membrane.	141, 183
66	a	The carbohydrate component of the basement membrane is oxidized to aldehydes, which then bind the methenamine silver complex and reduce the silver to its metallic form.	180
67	c	Periodic acid is used to oxidize the carbohydrates to aldehydes.	180
68	b	An oil red O stain is shown in image E.	184
69	a	Formalin is the preferred fixative for tissue to be stained by the oil red O technique.	183
70	d	Tissue to be stained with oil red O must be frozen; fat is dissolved during paraffin and glycol methacrylate processing.	183
71	c	The section shown in image E was most likely coverslipped improperly by mashing on the coverglass; this has displaced the fat droplets.	184
72	b	Lipid has been stained red by oil red O in image E.	184
73	a	Oil red O staining of lipid is a physical method of staining; the dye is absorbed by and dissolved in the fat.	183
74	c	Sudan black B also can be used to demonstrate fat; this also requires frozen sections.	184
75	c	Skin is shown in image F; a small amount of keratin can be seen covering the epidermis.	170
76	a	The aldehyde fuchsin technique has been used to demonstrate elastic tissue.	170
77	d	Elastic tissue is stained purple in image F.	169
78	b	The aldehyde fuchsin staining solution contains basic fuchsin, paraldehyde, and hydrochloric acid, but acetaldehyde may be substituted for paraldehyde; it is cheaper and does not require a DEA number.	169
79	a	Reticulin is stained black in image G.	175
80	c	The reticulin has stained in an irregular granular pattern instead of the correct linear pattern.	175
81	a	Granular reticulin stain most likely results from old sensitizing reagent.	175
82	c	The counterstain shown in image G is most likely nuclear fast red (Kernechtrot).	174

ISBN 978-089189-6401

Question	Answer	Discussion	*Histotechnology* Page
83	d	Mast cell granules have stained rose-violet in this image.	187
84	b	Toluidine blue has been used to stain the mast cell granules.	186
85	c	The staining of the mast cell granules by toluidine blue is a metachromatic stain; that is, the granules have stained a different color from the dye solution and the background.	186
86	b	Mast cells are connective tissue cells.	160
87	a	The Movat pentachrome stain is shown in image I.	172
88	b	Safran is used to stain muscle yellow in the Movat pentachrome stain.	171-172
89	b	Iron hematoxylin is used to stain the elastic tissue fibers in the Movat pentachrome stain.	171-172
90	a	The phosphotungstic acid hematoxylin (PTAH) stain is shown in image J.	179
91	b	The PTAH stain is polychromatic (a single dye solution stains tissue components different colors by a phenomenon other than metachromasia).	178
92	c	Skeletal muscle has been stained blue in image J; close inspection will reveal cross-striations in the fibers.	179
93	d	The red-brown stained tissue component in image J is collagen.	179
94	b	The preparation of van Gieson solution is critical; if the picric acid solution is not saturated, then collagen, muscle, and cell cytoplasm may all stain the same color.	168
95	c	Decreased red staining usually indicated that the staining solution has aged or been overused and should be discarded.	164
96	d	Sodium thiosulfate is used to remove unreduced silver, If this step is omitted, any unreduced silver remaining in the section may be reduced over time by exposure to light.	1173
97	c	Fat is very mobile, and pressing on the coverglass during the mounting step may result in displacement.	184
98	a	If the blue staining appears faded in the Masson trichrome stain, it is most likely that the slides have been overdifferentiated with acetic acid.	164

ISBN 978-089189-6401

Question	Answer	Discussion	*Histotechnology* Page
99	c	When nuclear fast red is used as a counterstain, slides must be washed well with water before transfer to the dehydrating solutions, or cloudiness will develop that can be removed only by backing up to water.	176
100	b	Old reagents, especially old uranium nitrate, may cause a granular deposition of silver during reticulin staining.	176
101	c	If the glassware used in silver staining procedures is not chemically clean, the result may be nonspecific silver precipitation on the section and the slide.	176
102	a	Phosphotungstic acid is used alone if light green is used for the counterstain; also in the Gomori procedure only phosphotungstic acid is used.	163-165
103	b	For proper staining of the collagen, the safran solution must not contain water. It must be tightly capped to prevent hydration and evaporation.	171
104	c	Alkaline alcohol converts the alcian blue to monastral fast blue, which is insoluble; complete conversion is necessary or the alcian blue will be decolorized during the remainder of the procedure. Complete removal of the alkaline alcohol is also important, for any remaining in the tissue will affect subsequent staining, not the alcian blue staining.	171-172

ISBN 978-089189-6401

Nerve *Questions*

1-14. The following are multiple choice questions. Please circle the letter in front of the correct answer. There is only 1 best answer.

1. Nissl substance is present in:
   a. astrocytes
   b. neurons
   c. Schwann cells
   d. microglia

2. A neuron is a:
   a. phagocytic cell
   b. myelin producing cell
   c. nerve cell
   d. neuroglial cell

3. Nissl substance is composed of:
   a. rough endoplasmic reticulum
   b. neurofilaments
   c. glial fibers
   d. microtubules

4. Nissl substance is demonstrated by which of the following methods?
   a. Luxol fast blue
   b. Cresyl echt violet
   c. Silver techniques
   d. Phosphotungstic acid-hematoxylin

5. Astrocytes are demonstrated by which of the following procedures?
   a. Luxol fast blue
   b. Cresyl echt violet
   c. Weil
   d. Cajal

6. The preferred fixative for sections to be stained by the Cajal technique is:
   a. formalin ammonium bromide
   b. 10% neutral buffered formalin
   c. 10% aqueous formalin
   d. alcoholic formalin

7. Sections to be stained for myelin should be cut at:
   a. 4 µm to 5 µm
   b. 6 µm to 8 µm
   c. 10 µm to 15 µm
   d. 20 µm to 30 µm

ISBN 978-089189-6401

8. In the Holzer technique, glial fibers are stained with:
   a. phosphotungstic acid-hematoxylin
   b. cresyl echt violet
   c. silver nitrate
   d. crystal violet

9. A method that can be used to demonstrate senile plaques is that of:
   a. Holzer
   b. Weil
   c. Bielschowsky
   d. Cajal

10. Neuron cell bodies are found primarily in:
   a. gray matter of the central nervous system
   b. white matter of the central nervous system
   c. peripheral nerve
   d. the ependyma

11. Spinal cord is an excellent control for which of the following techniques?
   a. Bielschowsky
   b. Weil
   c. Holzer
   d. Bodian

12. The preferred fixative for the Bodian technique is:
   a. formalin ammonium bromide
   b. neutral buffered formalin
   c. Bouin solution
   d. B-5

13. Glial fibers are stained blue by:
   a. thionin
   b. cresyl echt violet
   c. Luxol fast blue
   d. phosphotungstic acid-hematoxylin

14. Macroscopic (naked eye) evaluation can be used to judge the quality of which of the following techniques?
   a. Holmes
   b. Weil
   c. Holzer
   d. Sevier-Munger

ISBN 978-089189-6401

15. List 2 techniques for demonstrating myelin.

    a. ______________________________

    b. ______________________________

16. State the 2 solutions for differentiation in the Weil procedure.

    a. ______________________________

    b. ______________________________

17. List the reagents contained in the staining solution used in the Weil method.

    a. ______________________________

    b. ______________________________

18. Suggest 2 methods for demonstrating nerve cell processes.

    a. ______________________________

    b. ______________________________

19. Myelin is found in the ______________ matter.

20. Match the following. Each reagent on the left may be used in the demonstration of 1 or more tissue components on the right. Some components may be demonstrated by >1 of the reagents listed.

Reagent	Component
____A. Borax-ferricyanide	a. myelin
____B. Cresyl echt violet	b. astrocytes
____C. Crystal violet	c. nerve fibers
____D. Gold sublimate	d. glial fibers
____E. Iron hematoxylin	e. Nissl substance
____F. Luxol fast blue	
____G. Protargol	
____H. Phosphotungstic acid-hematoxylin	

ISBN 978-089189-6401

21-38. The following statements are either true or false. Circle T if the statement is true, circle F if the statement is false.

21. Functionally, the autonomic nervous system is under voluntary control. **[T\F]**

22. A neuron has only 1 axon. **[T\F]**

23. Nissl substance is composed of clumps of DNA. **[T\F]**

24. In the central nervous system, myelin is made by the astrocytes. **[T\F]**

25. Ependymal cells are epithelial cells. **[T\F]**

26. Myelin is responsible for the color of the white matter. **[T\F]**

27. Stains for Nissl substance can be used to identify the presence of neurons in tumor tissue. **[T\F]**

28. A colorless background indicates a problem with the cresyl echt violet stain. **[T\F]**

29. Peripheral nerve is a good control for the Bodian stain. **[T\F]**

30. Copper is used in the Bodian impregnating solution to increase the differentiation between neural and connective tissues. **[T\F]**

31. The Holmes technique is an argentaffin method. **[T\F]**

32. Prolonged washing of sections stained with PTAH will enhance the red staining of certain tissue components. **[T\F]**

33. The Weil technique uses both excess mordant and an oxidizer for the differentiation steps. **[T\F]**

34. Luxol fast blue is a water soluble dye. **[T\F]**

35. Gray matter is practically colorless in a correctly performed Luxol fast blue stain. **[T\F]**

36. When used as a counterstain for Luxol fast blue, cresyl echt violet must be used in an acid solution. **[T\F]**

37. When the Luxol fast blue stain is combined with the Holmes silver nitrate stain, both glial fibers and myelin are demonstrated. **[T\F]**

38. Aniline oil used in the Holzer technique is very toxic and rated by NIOSH as neoplastic. **[T\F]**

ISBN 978-089189-6401

39-42. Each of the following numbered words or phrases is associated with one, both, or neither of the headings listed as A or B above it. Within the parentheses on the right, place the appropriate letter for that word or phrase. Write:

A, if the numbered phrase is associated with A only
B, if the numbered phrase is associated with B only
C, if the numbered phrase is associated with both A and B
D, if the numbered phrase is associated with neither A nor B

39.

A. Weil	1. Demonstrates myelin	[ ]
B. Luxol fast blue	2. Demonstrates glial cells	[ ]
C. both	3. Differentiated with excess mordant	[ ]
D. neither	4. Differentiation is begun with an alkaline solution	[ ]
	5. Is a regressive method of staining	[ ]

40.

A. Bodian	1. Demonstrates axons	[ ]
B. Holzer	2. Will stain a component of the peripheral nervous system	[ ]
C. both	3. Will demonstrate gliosis	[ ]
D. neither	4. Used for the demonstration of Nissl substance	[ ]
	5. Will demonstrate astrocytic processes	[ ]

41.

A. Bielschowsky	1. Used for the demonstration of neurofibrillary tangles	[ ]
B. Cresyl echt violet	2. Demonstrates rough endoplasmic reticulum in neurons	[ ]
C. both	3. Used for the demonstration of astrocytic processes	[ ]
D. neither	4. Will identify chromatolysis	[ ]
	5. Aids in the diagnosis of Alzheimer disease	[ ]

42.

A. Cajal	1. Is used for the demonstration of myelin	[ ]
B. Holmes	2. Fixation in formalin ammonium bromide is preferred	[ ]
C. both	3. Requires frozen sections	[ ]
D. neither	4. Is a silver impregnation method	[ ]
	5. Will demonstrate nerve fibers	[ ]

ISBN 978-089189-6401

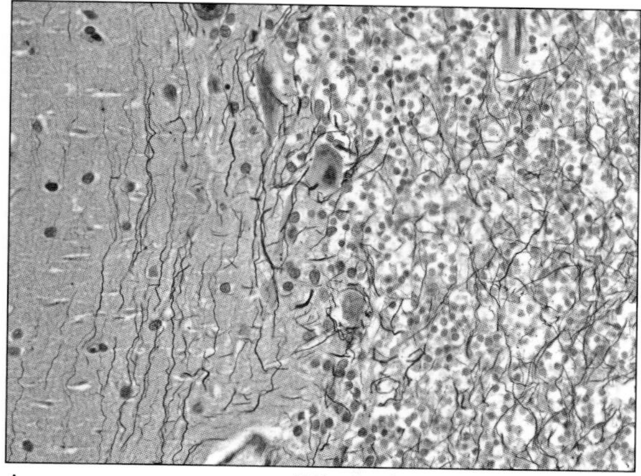

A (*Histotechnology 4e*, **i9.4**, p 194)

43-72. The following questions relate to the images A-G as specified.

43. The stain demonstrated in image A is most likely the:
    a. Holzer
    b. Weil
    c. Bodian
    d. Luxol fast blue

44. The structures stained black in image A are:
    a. reticulin fibers
    b. nerve fibers
    c. astrocytic processes
    d. myelin sheaths

45. The nervous tissue in image A is:
    a. peripheral nerve
    b. cerebral cortex
    c. choroid plexus
    d. cerebellum

46. The preferred fixative for the technique demonstrated in image A is:
    a. B-5
    b. Bouin
    c. formalin ammonium bromide
    d. neutral buffered formalin

47. The impregnating solution used in the technique shown in image A contains:
    a. iron hematoxylin
    b. silver protein
    c. mercuric chloride
    d. aniline blue

ISBN 978-089189-6401

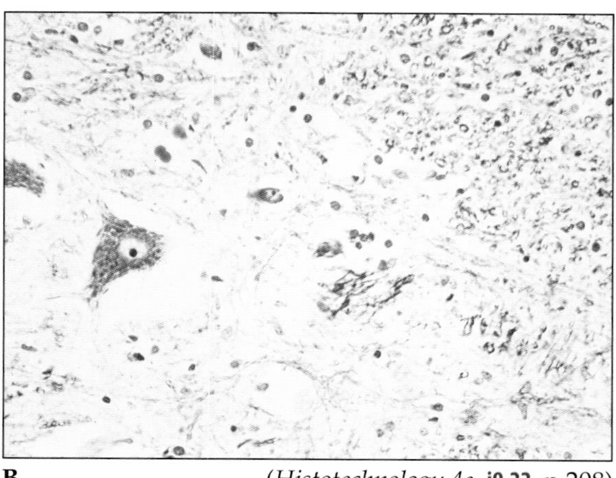

B (*Histotechnology 4e*, **i9.22**, p 208)

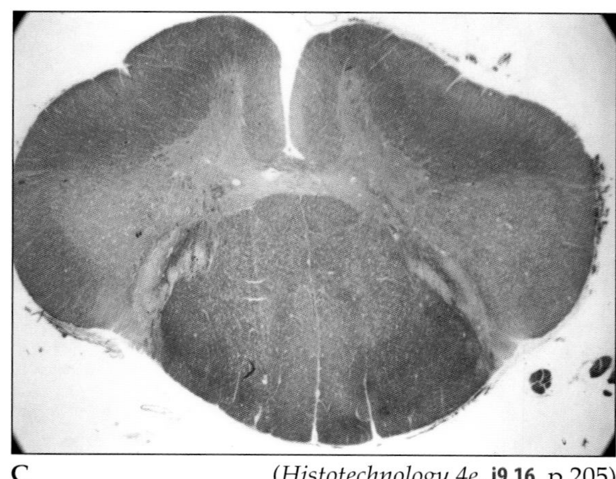

C (*Histotechnology 4e*, **i9.16**, p 205)

48. The large rose stained structure shown in image B is a/an:
    a. neuron
    b. astrocyte
    c. plasma cell
    d. senile plaque

49. The cytoplasmic material stained rose shown in image B is:
    a. amyloid
    b. neurofibrillary tangles
    c. DNA
    d. rough endoplasmic reticulum

50. The structures stained blue in image B are:
    a. astrocytic processes
    b. nerve fibers
    c. neurofibrillary tangles
    d. myelin sheaths

51. The rose staining in image B is due to staining with which of the following solutions?
    a. cresyl echt violet
    b. crystal violet
    c. basic fuchsin
    d. Schiff reagent

52. The tissue shown in image C is:
    a. spinal cord
    b. medulla
    c. cerebral cortex
    d. cerebellum

53. The sections for the technique shown in image C should be cut at:
    a. 4 µm to 6 µm
    b. 6 µm to 8 µm
    c. 10 µm to 15 µm
    d. 15 µm to 20 µm

ISBN 978-089189-6401

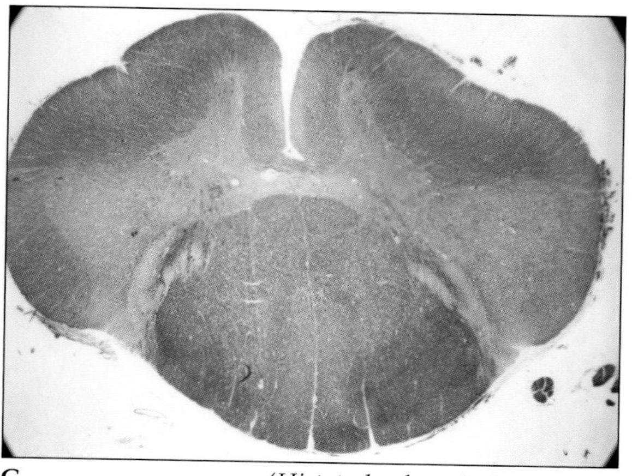

C (*Histotechnology 4e*, **i9.16**, p 205)

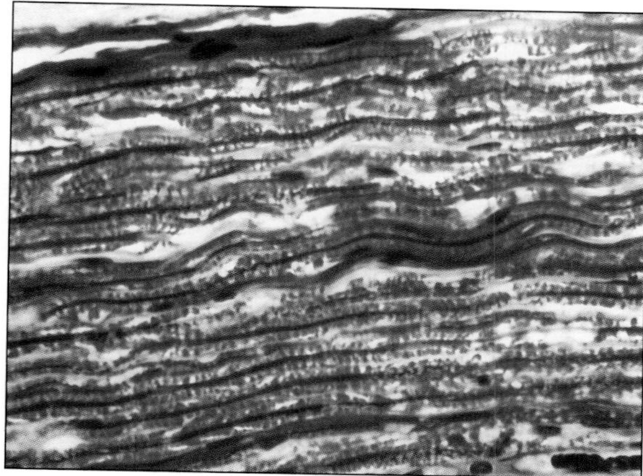

D (*Histotechnology 4e*, **i9.25**, p 210)

54. The technique shown in image C is most likely the:
    a. Weil
    b. Bodian
    c. Holzer
    d. phosphotungstic acid-hematoxylin

55. The primary staining solution used in the technique shown in image C is:
    a. silver protein
    b. crystal violet
    c. iron hematoxylin
    d. methenamine silver

56. Another technique that can be used to demonstrate the substance stained black in image C is:
    a. Bodian
    b. Holzer
    c. Cajal
    d. Luxol fast blue

57. The tissue component(s) stained blue-black in image C is/are:
    a. myelin
    b. nerve fibers
    c. glial fibers
    d. neurofibrillary tangles

58. The tissue shown in image D is:
    a. cerebral cortex
    b. cerebellum
    c. peripheral nerve
    d. spinal cord

59. The structure(s) stained black in image D is/are:
    a. reticulin
    b. axons
    c. myelin
    d. glial fibers

ISBN 978-089189-6401

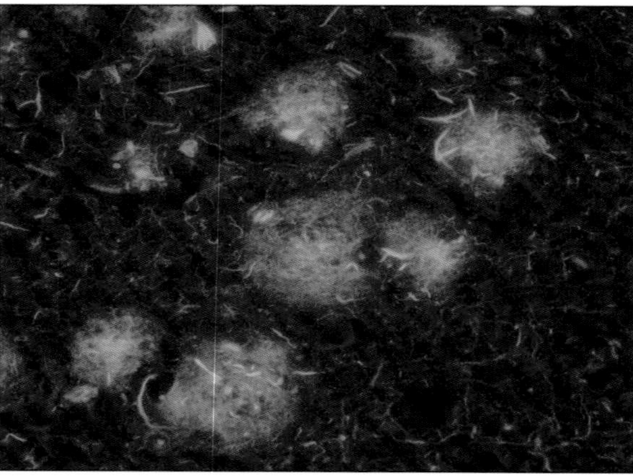

E (*Histotechnology 4e*, **i9.12**, p 201)

60. The material stained blue in image D is:
    a. reticulin
    b. axons
    c. myelin
    d. glial fibers

61. The blue staining in image D is due to:
    a. aniline blue
    b. alcian blue
    c. methylene blue
    d. Luxol fast blue

62. The preferred micrometer thickness for sections to be stained by the technique shown in image D is:
    a. 4-5
    b. 6-8
    c. 10-15
    d. 20-25

63. The type of microscopy used in image E is:
    a. polarizing
    b. fluorescence
    c. dark field
    d. phase contrast

64. The bright structures seen in image E are most likely due to:
    a. astrocytes
    b. microglia
    c. senile plaques
    d. gliosis

65. The stain used in image E is most likely:
    a. thioflavin S
    b. rhodamine
    c. auramine
    d. fluorescein isothiocyanate

ISBN 978-089189-6401

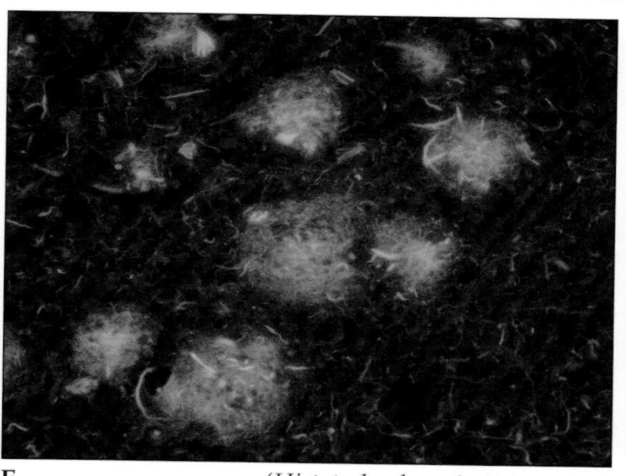

E (*Histotechnology 4e*, **i9.12**, p 201)

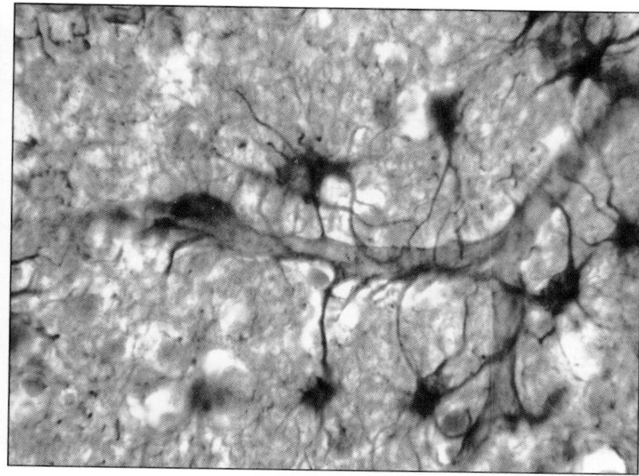

F (*Histotechnology 4e*, **i9.15**, p 204)

66. Another stain that could be used to demonstrate the bright structures in image E is:
    a. Weil
    b. Holzer
    c. Cajal
    d. Bielschowski

67. The black structures seen in image F are:
    a. ependymal cells
    b. neurons
    c. astrocytes
    d. microglia

68. The stain most likely used in image F was:
    a. Cajal
    b. Holzer
    c. Grimelius
    d. Bielschowski

69. The sections for the stain shown in image F must be:
    a. paraffin cut at 10 μm15 μm
    b. paraffin cut at 4 μm5 μm
    c. frozen cut at 10 μm15 μm
    d. frozen cut at 20 μm30 μm

ISBN 978-089189-6401

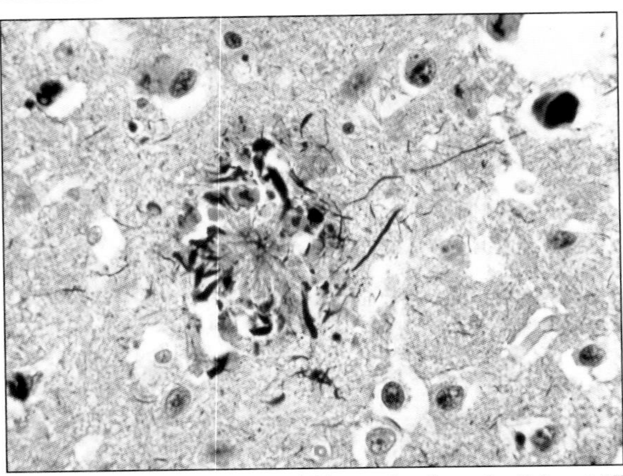

G (*Histotechnology 4e*, **i9.8**, p 197

70. The stain shown in image G is most likely the:
    a. Grimelius
    b. Bielschowski
    c. Holzer
    d. Holmes

71. The black stained structure in the center of image G is a/an:
    a. astrocyte
    b. area of gliosis
    c. senile plaque
    d. oligodendroglial cell

72. The structure in the center of image G indicates:
    a. multiple sclerosis
    b. gliosis
    c. Neiman-Pick disease
    d. Alzheimer disease

ISBN 978-089189-6401

73-80. The following are problem solving questions.

73. Bodian stained sections show marked precipitation on the sections. This could probably be prevented in the future by:
    a. using chemically cleaned glassware
    b. decreasing the amount of copper
    c. substituting sodium sulfite in the reducer
    d. increasing the time in the oxalic acid

74. Bodian stained sections show light gray nerve fibers. One possible explanation is that the sections were left too long in:
    a. Protargol
    b. gold chloride
    c. oxalic acid
    d. sodium thiosulfate

75. Sections stained with PTAH show blue glial fibers, but the neurons are unstained. One possible cause is that:
    a. the sections were washed too long before clearing and mounting
    b. the PTAH staining was done at room temperature
    c. naturally ripened stain was used
    d. sections were cut too thin

76. Sections stained using the Holzer technique show marked purple crystalline precipitate. This precipitate could most likely be removed by:
    a. allowing the slides to air dry before mounting
    b. treating with straight aniline oil
    c. prolonging the clearing step
    d. using a Coplin jar for the crystal violet stain

77. Weil stained sections show blue-black white matter and brown gray matter. This indicates that the sections were:
    a. overstained in iron hematoxylin
    b. left in dilute ammonia water too long
    c. left too long in ferric ammonium sulfate
    d. inadequately treated with borax-ferricyanide

78. Luxol fast blue stained sections show dark blue gray matter and a lighter blue white matter. This can be most easily corrected by:
    a. continuing the differentiation step
    b. returning the slide to the Luxol fast blue
    c. prolonging the clearing step of staining
    d. repeating the stain on a new section

ISBN 978-089189-6401

79. Sections stained with the Luxol fast blue-cresyl echt violet technique show bluish purple myelin and a diffuse rose-purple background. The most likely explanation is that the:
    a. myelin differentiation step was inadequate
    b. sections were cut too thick
    c. cresyl echt violet was not acidified
    d. Luxol fast blue was not the correct concentration

80. Sections stained with the Luxol fast blue-Holmes silver nitrate technique show very pale blue myelin and gray axons. The most likely explanation is that the:
    a. myelin differentiation step was shortened
    b. sections were cut too thin
    c. volume of staining solution was too large
    d. sections were overtoned with gold chloride

ISBN 978-089189-6401

81. Make 10 copies of the worksheet that follows, and complete 1 copy (try to do this without referring to the text) for each of the following techniques:

a. Cresyl echt violet
b. Bodian
c. Holmes silver nitrate
d. Bielschowsky
e. Sevier-Munger
f. Phosphotungstic acid-hematoxylin
g. Holzer
h. Cajal
i. Weil
j. Luxol fast blue
k. Thioflavin S

No answers are given for this exercise. The text must be used to check for correctness.

Preferred fixative ______________________________

Preferred thickness ______________________________

Microscope used ______________________________

Control tissue ______________________________

Major reagents	Purpose
Periodic acid	
Schiff reagent	
Metabisulfite rinse	
Running water	
Harris hematoxylin	

Principle of the technique ______________________________

Purpose of stain ______________________________

Results ______________________________

Sources of error ______________________________

ISBN 978-089189-6401

Nerve *Answers*

Question	Answer	Discussion	*Histotechnology* Page
1	b	Nissl substance is basophilic material in the cytoplasm of neurons. Ultrastructurally, Nissl substance can be identified as large aggregates of rough endoplasmic reticulum.	190
2	c	Neurons are nerve cells.	190
3	a	Nissl substance consists of large aggregates of rough endoplasmic reticulum, with the RNA content providing the basis for demonstration by special light microscopic techniques.	190
4	b	Nissl substance is sharply stained with basic aniline dyes such as cresyl echt violet and thionin.	190
5	d	Astrocytes are demonstrated by the Cajal stain.	204
6	a	Formalin ammonium bromide is the preferred fixative for tissue to be stained with the Cajal procedure. This may be used as a secondary fixative following 10% neutral buffered formalin.	203
7	c	Sections to be stained for myelin should be cut at 10 µm to 15 µm. This provides the best contrast between the gray and white matter.	204-206
8	d	A crystal violet solution is used to stain glial fibers in the Holzer technique.	202-203
9	c	The Bielschowsky is one method for the demonstration of senile plaques; others are Sevier-Munger and thioflavin S.	196-201
10	a	Neuron cell bodies are found primarily in gray matter of the central nervous system.	205-208
11	b	Spinal cord is an excellent control for myelin stains, as it shows a sharp differentiation between gray and white matter. Since most nerve fibers are cut in cross-section, spinal cord is not a good control for the Bodian technique. Controls for senile plaques and astrocytes are usually from the cerebral cortex.	193, 204-206
12	b	10% neutral buffered formalin is the preferred fixative for the Bodian technique.	193
13	d	Glial fibers are stained blue by phosphotungstic acid-hematoxylin; thionin and cresyl echt violet stain Nissl substance, and Luxol fast blue stains myelin.	202

ISBN 978-089189-6401

Question	Answer	Discussion	*Histotechnology* Page
14	b	The quality of myelin stains (Weil and Luxol fast blue) can be determined macroscopically (naked eye) with the gray and white matter easily distinguished; on a good myelin stain, it is frequently easier to determine the areas of demyelination with the naked eye than with the microscope.	206
15	a b	Weil Luxol fast blue	204-206
16	a b	Ferric ammonium sulfate Borax ferricyanide	205
17	a b	Ferric ammonium sulfate Hematoxylin	205
18	a b c d	Bodian Holmes Bielschowsky Sevier-Munger	193-199
19	White	Myelin is a fatty, nonliving substance that is responsible for the color of the white matter.	204-211
20A	a	Borax-ferricyanide is used in the Weil technique for myelin.	205
20B	e	Cresyl echt violet is used to stain Nissl substance.	191-192
20C	b, d	Crystal violet is used in the Holzer technique for glial fibers. The Holzer technique will also stain astrocytes, but is not primarily used for this purpose.	202-203
20D	b	Gold sublimate is used in the Cajal method for astrocytes.	203-204
20E	a	Iron hematoxylin is used in the Weil technique for myelin.	205
20F	a	Luxol fast blue is used for staining myelin.	206
20G	c	Protargol is used in the Bodian technique for nerve fibers.	197-198
20H	a, d	Phosphotungstic acid-hematoxylin is will stain both glial fibers and myelin, but is not the preferred method for either.	201-202
21	F	The autonomic nervous system is involuntary.	193
22	T	A neuron has only 1 axon, but may have many dendrites.	190
23	F	Nissl substance is composed of clumps of rough endoplasmic reticulin. Ribosomes (RNA) are attached to channels of endoplasmic reticulin.	190
24	F	In the central nervous system, myelin is made by oligodendroglia.	190

ISBN 978-089189-6401

Question	Answer	Discussion	*Histotechnology* Page
25	T	Ependymal cells are epithelial cells that line the ventricles and spinal canal.	191
26	T	Myelin is a fatty substance responsible for the color of the white matter.	190,207
27	T	Neurons in tumor tissue can be identified by stains for Nissl substance.	191
28	F	A good cresyl echt violet stain for Nissl substance should have a colorless background.	191-192
29	T	Peripheral nerve is a good control for the Bodian stain, because the nerve fibers present longitudinally.	193
30	T	Copper is used in the Bodian technique to destain connective tissue, thus allowing a greater degree of differentiation between neural and connective tissue elements.	193
31	F	The Holmes method requires an external reducer; thus it is an argyrophil method.	194-195
32	F	Components will lose their red-brown color after water or prolonged alcohol washing.	201
33	T	Ferric ammonium sulfate is differentiation with excess mordant differentiator and borax-ferricyanide is differentiation with an oxidizing agent.	204-205
34	F	Luxol fast blue is alcohol soluble, not water soluble like alcian blue.	206
35	T	Gray matter is practically colorless in a correctly performed Luxol fast blue stain.	208
36	T	If not acidified for the Luxol fast blue stain, cresyl echt violet will stain the background as well as Nissl substance.	208
37	F	The combination of the Holmes and Luxol fast blue techniques will demonstrate nerve fibers and myelin; glial fibers are not demonstrated.	209-210
38	T	Aniline oil has a permissible exposure limit of 5 ppm, is a sensitizer, and is toxic by skin absorption. It is rated by NIOSH to be neoplastic.	203
39-1	C	Both the Weil and Luxol fast blue techniques will demonstrate myelin.	204-207
39-2	D	Neither technique will demonstrate glial cells.	204-207
39-3	A	Weil stain is differentiated with excess mordant (ferric ammonium sulfate).	204-205
39-4	B	Differentiation of the Luxol fast blue stain is done with an alkaline solution (lithium carbonate).	206

ISBN 978-089189-6401

Question	Answer	Discussion	*Histotechnology* Page
39-5	C	Both stains are regressive or require differentiation.	204-205
40-1	A	Axons are demonstrated by the Bodian stain.	193-194
40-2	A	The Bodian technique will demonstrate axons in the peripheral nervous system.	193-194
40-3	B	The Holzer technique demonstrates glial fibers and areas of gliosis.	202
40-4	D	Neither technique will demonstrate Nissl substance.	193-194,202
40-5	B	The Holzer technique will demonstrate astrocyte (a glial cell) processes.	203
41-1	A	The Bielschowsky is useful in the demonstration of neurofibrillary tangles and senile plaques.	196
41-2	B	Cresyl echt violet will demonstrate rough endoplasmic reticulum (Nissl substance) in neurons.	190-191
41-3	D	Neither stain will demonstrate astrocytic processes	190-191,203-204
41-4	B	Cresyl echt violet will demonstrate chromatolysis, or the loss of Nissl substance, in neurons.	191
41-5	A	The Bielschowsky is useful in the diagnosis of Alzheimer disease.	196
42-1	D	Neither technique will demonstrate myelin.	194-196,203-204
42-2	A	Fixation in formalin ammonium bromide is preferred for tissue to be stained by the Cajal technique.	203
42-3	A	The Cajal technique requires free floating, frozen sections.	203
42-4	B	Only the Holmes technique is a silver impregnation method.	199-200
42-5	B	Only the Holmes demonstrates nerve fibers; the Cajal demonstrates astrocytes (glial cells).	194-196,203-204
43	c	The stain demonstrated in image A is the Bodian.	193-194
44	b	Nerve fibers are stained black in image A.	193-194
45	d	The presence of Purkinje cells and a granular layer aid in identifying this tissue as cerebellum.	199
46	d	10% neutral buffered formalin is the preferred fixative for tissues to be stained with the Bodian stain.	193-194
47	b	Silver protein (Protargol) is used in the impregnating solution for the Bodian technique.	193-194
48	a	The rose stained structure shown in image B is a neuron.	207
49	d	Rough endoplasmic reticulin (Nissl substance) is responsible for the rose staining shown in image B.	190,208

ISBN 978-089189-6401

Question	Answer	Discussion	*Histotechnology* Page
50	d	Myelin sheaths are stained blue in image B.	208
51	a	Cresyl echt violet is responsible for the rose stained Nissl substance in image B.	208
52	a	The tissue shown in image C is spinal cord.	205
53	c	Sections to be stained for myelin should be cut at 10 µm15 µm.	205
54	a	The Weil stain is shown in image C.	205
55	c	The primary stain used for the Weil stain (image C) is iron hematoxylin.	205
56	d	Luxol fast blue can also be used to stain myelin.	206
57	a	Myelin (white matter) is stained blue-black in image C.	205
58	c	Peripheral nerve is shown in image D.	210
59	b	Axons are stained black in image D.	210
60	c	Myelin is stained blue in image D.	210
61	d	Luxol fast blue is responsible for the blue stained myelin seen in image D.	210
62	c	Sections for the stain shown in image D should be cut at 10-15µm.	210
63	b	Fluorescence microscopy was used for the stain shown in image E.	201
64	c	The fluorescent structures seen in image E are senile plaques.	201
65	a	Thioflavin S is a fluorescent dye that will stain senile plaques; although the others are fluorescent dyes, they will not demonstrate senile plaques.	200-201
66	d	The Bielschowski stain can also be used to stain senile plaques.	196
67	c	The black structures are astrocytes. Note their perivascular feet attached to the basement membrane of a capillary.	204
68	a	The stain demonstrated in image F is that of Cajal.	204
69	d	Free-floating frozen sections are cut at 20 µm to 30 µm for the Cajal stain.	204
70	b	The stain shown in image G is the Bielschowski.	197
71	c	The black stained structure in the center of image G is a senile plaque.	197
72	d	The structure in the center of image G indicates Alzheimer disease.	197

ISBN 978-089189-6401

Question	Answer	Discussion	*Histotechnology* Page
73	a	The Bodian stain is a silver technique and chemically cleaned glassware must be used.	196-197
74	c	The oxalic acid treatment must not be prolonged because overtreatment will ruin the silver proteinate reaction.	197-197
75	a	Sections stained with the PTAH must be rapidly dehydrated and cleared or the brownish red colors will disappear.	201
76	b	Crystal violet precipitate in the Holzer technique may be removed with straight aniline oil.	203
77	d	The gray matter should be no darker than a light tan; brown gray matter indicates that the differentiation with borax ferricyanide was insufficient.	205-206
78	a	The gray matter should be colorless with the Luxol fast blue technique, and differentiation should be continued until that is achieved.	206-207
79	c	If the cresyl echt violet is not acidified, the background will stain diffusely with the dye.	208
80	b	Sections should be cut at 10 µm to 15 µm for myelin stains, and thinner sections will be pale and not show good differentiation between the gray and white matter.	204-206

Microorganisms *Questions*

1-29. The following are multiple choice questions. Please circle the letter in front of the correct answer. There is only 1 best answer.

1. Acid-fast stains may be negative if the tissue was fixed in:
   a. 10% formalin
   b. B-5 solution
   c. Carnoy solution
   d. Zenker solution

2. In the Fite method, the organisms stain:
   a. red
   b. blue
   c. green
   d. black

3. After Schiff reagent, tissues are rinsed in a sulfite solution to:
   a. fix the stain in the tissue
   b. differentiate the stain
   c. remove the excess leucofuchsin
   d. oxidize the tissue

4. In the Brown-Hopps modification of the Gram stain for tissues, Gram+ organisms appear:
   a. bright red
   b. blue-black
   c. yellow-orange
   d. green

5. The property on which the acid-fast stain depends is its:
   a. affinity for anionic dyes
   b. capability for reducing silver
   c. failure to stain with a dye other than basic fuchsin
   d. ability to resist decolorization with dilute acids

6. Which of the following is a method for the demonstration of fungi?
   a. Ziehl-Neelsen
   b. Warthin-Starry
   c. Giemsa
   d. PAS

7. The best stain for the demonstration of *Mycobacterium leprae* is the:
   a. Fite
   b. PAS
   c. Kinyoun
   d. Gram

ISBN 978-089189-6401

8. The PAS stain differs from the Gridley technique in the:
   a. use of Schiff reagent
   b. organism demonstrated
   c. oxidizer used
   d. section thickness required

9. Artifactual precipitate seen in the Grocott stain may be the result of using:
   a. plastic forceps
   b. gelatin in the water bath
   c. glassware that was not chemically cleaned
   d. excess time in the gold chloride solution

10. Spherical or ovoid bacteria are classified as:
    a. rickettsiae
    b. bacilli
    c. spirochetes
    d. cocci

11. A medically important protozoan is:
    a. *Staphylococcus aureus*
    b. *Giardia lamblia*
    c. *Candida albicans*
    d. *Clostridium tetani*

12. The basic structure of filamentous fungi is the:
    a. hypha
    b. bud
    c. endospore
    d. spherule

13. The carbol-fuchsin methods are specific for:
    a. mycobacteria
    b. dimorphic fungi
    c. diplococci
    d. spore-forming bacilli

14. The auramine-rhodamine technique will demonstrate:
    a. *Staphylococcus aureus*
    b. *Mycobacterium tuberculosis*
    c. *Candida albicans*
    d. *Clostridium tetani*

15. Carbol-fuchsin contains:
    a. acid fuchsin and hydrochloric acid
    b. acid fuchsin and phenol
    c. basic fuchsin and hydrochloric acid
    d. basic fuchsin and phenol

16. Stains for the demonstration of spirochetes are based on their property of:
    a. argentophilia
    b. argyrophilia
    c. metachromasia
    d. acid-fastness

ISBN 978-089189-6401

17. The term "mycosis" is used to describe a disease caused by:
    a. fungi
    b. viruses
    c. bacteria
    d. rickettsiae

18. The differential staining achieved with the Gram stain is due to differences in the bacterial:
    a. size
    b. shape
    c. cell wall
    d. nucleus

19. Which of the following is a fluorescence technique?
    a. Ziehl-Neelsen
    b. Warthin-Starry
    c. auramine-rhodamine
    d. Brown & Brenn

20. The PAS reaction will demonstrate fungi, because the cell wall contains:
    a. lipids
    b. carbohydrates
    c. reducing substances
    d. argyrophilic protein

21. The Gridley stain uses:
    a. periodic acid and methenamine silver
    b. periodic acid and Schiff reagent
    c. chromic acid and methenamine silver
    d. chromic acid and Schiff reagent

22. In the Hotchkiss-McManus modification of the PAS technique, aldehydes are formed by:
    a. periodic acid
    b. chromic acid
    c. potassium permanganate
    d. sodium bisulfite

23. The preferred fixative for the Warthin-Starry technique is:
    a. Carnoy
    b. Zenker
    c. B-5
    d. 10% buffered formalin

24. The "developer" in the Warthin-Starry stain is:
    a. gelatin
    b. hydroquinone
    c pyridine
    d. uranyl nitrate

25. Which of the following techniques will demonstrate *Pneumocystis jiroveci*?
    a. Grocott
    b. Gridley
    c. PAS
    d. Kinyoun

ISBN 978-089189-6401

26. If fungi are to be demonstrated, a good counterstain for the PAS technique is:
    a. nuclear fast red
    b. van Gieson
    c. light green
    d. eosin

27. In the Gridley procedure, the aldehyde fuchsin stain will attach to:
    a. aldehydes
    b. Schiff reagent
    c. chromic acid
    d. periodic acid

28. To differentiate *Cryptococcus neoformans* from other yeastlike fungi, which of the following should be performed?
    a. PAS
    b. Gridley
    c. Grocott
    d. Mayer mucicarmine

29. The difference between *Cryptococcus neoformans* and other yeastlike fungi is that only *Cryptococcus neoformans* has a capsule containing:
    a. glycogen
    b. mucin
    c. aldehydes
    d. lipid

30-45. The following statements are either true or false. Circle T if the statement is true, circle F if the statement is false.

30. Gram+ organisms CANNOT be decolorized once stained with crystal violet. **[T\F]**

31. A problem may result from allowing the slides to dry during the Gram staining process. **[T\F]**

32. The stains for spirochetes are argyrophil techniques. **[T\F]**

33. Rod shaped bacteria are called bacilli. **[T\F]**

34. Viral organisms are easily demonstrated with special histochemical stains. **[T\F]**

35. A good Grocott methenamine silver stain shows organisms with a crisp black cell wall and a visible internal structure. **[T\F]**

36. Mercurial fixatives are satisfactory when stains for spirochetes are to be done. **[T\F]**

37. Tissue containing *Helicobacter pylori* is a satisfactory control for the Diff-Quik Giemsa modification. **[T\F]**

38. The Gridley stain is more intense than the PAS. **[T\F]**

ISBN 978-089189-6401

39. The mordant is applied after the primary dye in the Gram stain. **[T\F]**

40. Peanut oil is used in the Ziehl-Neelsen method. **[T\F]**

41. Acid-fast stains are satisfactory on tissue fixed in Carnoy solution. **[T\F]**

42. Iodine serves as a mordant in the Gram stain. **[T\F]**

43. *Helicobacter pylori* is a spirochete. **[T\F]**

44. *Helicobacter pylori* is readily demonstrated by a Romanowsky type stain. **[T\F]**

45. The Giemsa stain will differentially stain the different types of bacteria. **[T\F]**

46. Match the following reagents on the right with the procedure on the left in which they are used. Letters may be used more than once or not at all.

Procedure	**Reagent**
______A. Gridley	a. acetone
______B. Grocott	b. acid-alcohol
______C. Kinyoun	c. chromic acid
______D. PAS	d. crystal violet
______E. Steiner & Steiner	e. hydroquinone
______F. Brown & Hopps	f. metanil yellow
	g. periodic acid
	h. picric acid

47. Match the organism on the right with the procedure on the left that is used for that organism. Letters may be used more than once or not at all.

Procedure	**Microorganism**
______A. Auramine-rhodamine	a. fungi
______B. Brown & Brenn	b. Gram+ bacteria
______C. Gridley	c. *Helicobacter pylori*
______D. Grocott	d. *Mycobacterium tuberculosis*
______E. Steiner & Steiner	e. *Pneumocystis jiroveci*
______F. Ziehl-Neelsen	f. *Treponema pallidum*
______G. PAS	g. viral inclusions

48. Match the following reagents on the left with their function on the right. Letters may be used more than once or not at all.

Reagents	**Function**
______A. Acid-alcohol	a. differentiation
______B. Chromic acid	b. impregnation
______C. Gold chloride	c. mordant
______D. Hydroquinone	d. oxidation
______E. Iodine	e. reduction
______F. Periodic acid	f. toning

ISBN 978-089189-6401

49-53. Each of the following numbered words or phrases is associated with one, both, or neither of the headings listed as A or B above it. Within the parentheses on the right, place the appropriate letter for that word or phrase. Write:

A, if the numbered phrase is associated with A only
B, if the numbered phrase is associated with B only
C, if the numbered phrase is associated with both A and B
D, if the numbered phrase is associated with neither A nor B

49.

A. Kinyoun	1. Staining solution contains phenol	[ ]
B. Auramine-rhodamine	2. Demonstrates mycobacteria	[ ]
C. both	3. Is a fluorescent technique	[ ]
D. neither	4. Results are easily contaminated by tap water	[ ]
	5. Demonstrates spirochetes	[ ]

50.

A. PAS	1. Used for the demonstration of mycobacteria	[ ]
B. CAS	2. Uses chromic acid oxidation	[ ]
C. both	3. Demonstrates the lipoid capsule of the organisms	[ ]
D. neither	4. Depends on the formation of aldehyde groups	[ ]
	5. Uses basic fuchsin as the dye	[ ]

51.

A. Gram	1. Will stain bacteria	[ ]
B. Giemsa	2. Often used for the demonstration of *Helicobacter pylori*	[ ]
C. both	3. Uses crystal violet	[ ]
D. neither	4. Differentiates between different types of bacteria	[ ]
	5. Preferred for the demonstration of *Legionella pneumophila*	[ ]

52.

A. Gridley	1. Demonstrates fungi	[ ]
B. Grocott	2. Depends on the formation of aldehydes	[ ]
C. both	3. Uses Schiff reagent	[ ]
D. neither	4. Uses chromic acid oxidation	[ ]
	5. Is a Romanowsky type stain	[ ]

53.

A. Fite	1. Used for the demonstration of mycobacteria	[ ]
B. Steiner & Steiner	2. Preferred for the demonstration of *Legionella pneumophila*	[ ]
C. both	3. Uses carbol-fuchsin	[ ]
D. neither	4. Is an argyrophil technique	[ ]
	5. Depends on the formation of aldehydes	[ ]

ISBN 978-089189-6401

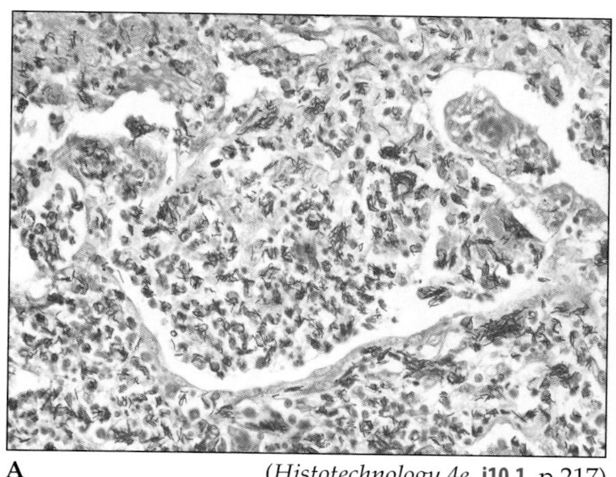

A (*Histotechnology 4e*, **i10.1**, p 217)

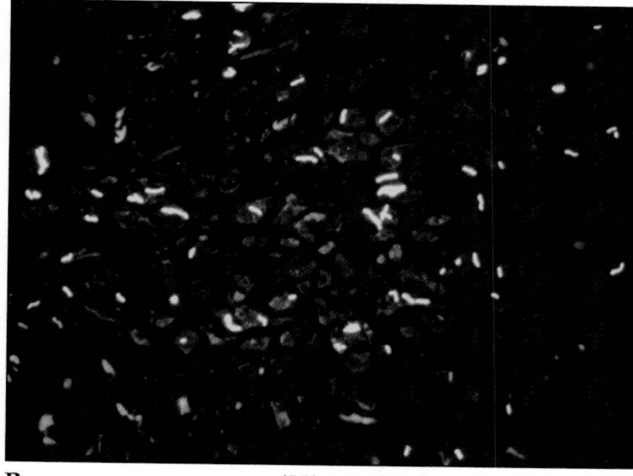

B (*Histotechnology 4e*, **i10.7**, p 222)

54-88. The following questions apply to images A-H as specified.

54. The stain demonstrated in image A is most likely the:
    a. auramine-rhodamine
    b. PAS
    c. Kinyoun
    d. Gridley

55. The primary stain used in the technique shown in image A is:
    a. aldehyde fuchsin
    b. carbol-fuchsin
    c. leucofuchsin
    d. acid fuchsin

56. The stain shown in image A may be unsatisfactory following fixation in:
    a. Carnoy solution
    b. Bouin solution
    c. B-5 solution
    d. 10% buffered formalin

57. The stain shown in image A is dependent on the organism's:
    a. waxy capsule
    b. carbohydrate component
    c. argyrophilic character
    d. internal structure

58. Organisms demonstrated by the technique shown in image A belong to the group known as:
    a. spirochetes
    b. bacilli
    c. mycobacteria
    d. fungi

59. The technique shown in image B is most likely the:
    a. auramine-rhodamine
    b. PAS
    c. Kinyoun
    d. thioflavin T

ISBN 978-089189-6401

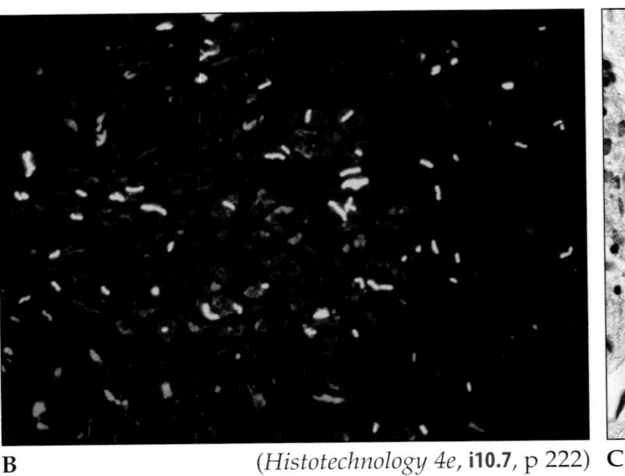

B (*Histotechnology 4e*, **i10.7**, p 222)

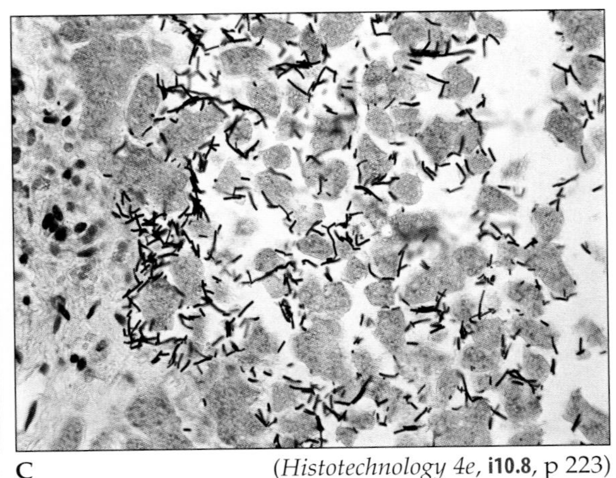

C (*Histotechnology 4e*, **i10.8**, p 223)

60. The stain shown in image B utilizes which of the following types of microscopy?
    a. polarizing
    b. transmission electron
    c. phase contrast
    d. fluorescence

61. The preferred fixative for the technique shown in image B is:
    a. 10% buffered formalin
    b. Carnoy solution
    c. absolute alcohol
    d. B-5 solution

62. The light source for the technique shown in image B is a/an:
    a. electron gun
    b. tungsten filament
    c. halogen lamp
    d. fluorescent tube

63. Organisms demonstrated by the technique shown in image B belong to the group known as:
    a. mycobacteria
    b. bacilli
    c. spirochetes
    d. fungi

64. Another technique that could be used to demonstrate the organisms shown in image B is the:
    a. Brown & Hopps
    b. Gridley
    c. Ziehl-Neelsen
    d. Dieterle

65. The organisms demonstrated in image C are:
    a. Gram+
    b. Gram–
    c. acid-fast
    d. argentaffin

ISBN 978-089189-6401

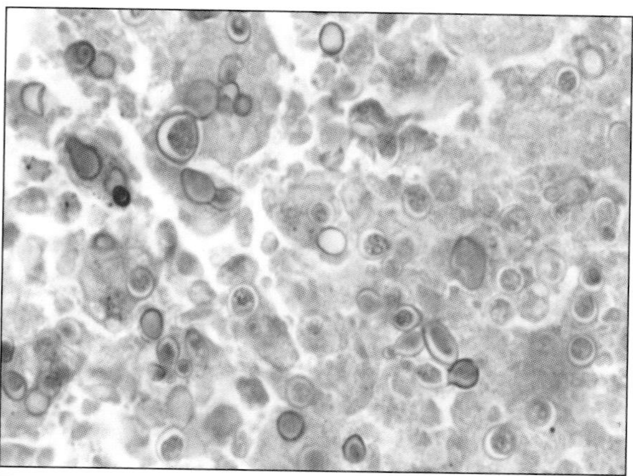

D (*Histotechnology 4e*, **i10.13**, p 227)

66. The organisms demonstrated in image C are:
    a. bacilli
    b. diplococci
    c. spirochetes
    d. mycobacteria

67. The reagent that stains the organisms demonstrated in image C is:
    a. basic fuchsin
    b. Gallego solution
    c. methylene blue
    d. crystal violet

68. The stain demonstrated in image C is the:
    a. Gridley
    b. Giemsa
    c. Gram
    d. Grocott

69. The technique shown in image D is most likely the:
    a. Congo red
    b. PAS
    c. Fite
    d. Feulgen

70. The reaction shown in image D depends on the presence of:
    a. ketones
    b. amino groups
    c. lipoproteins
    d. aldehydes

71. The reaction shown in image D depends on oxidation by:
    a. periodic acid
    b. phosphomolybdic acid
    c. potassium permanganate
    d. sodium iodate

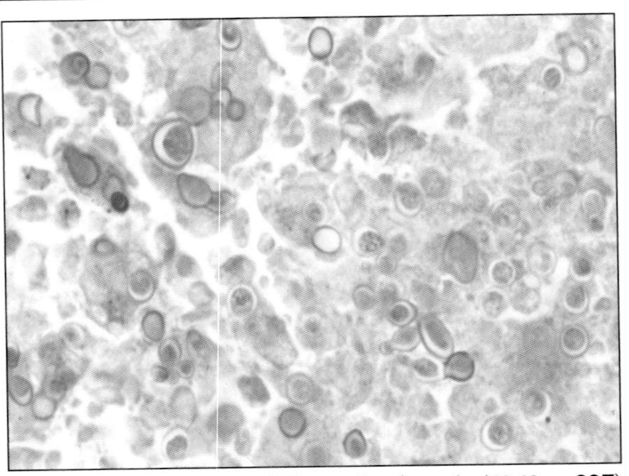

D (*Histotechnology 4e*, **i10.13**, p 227)

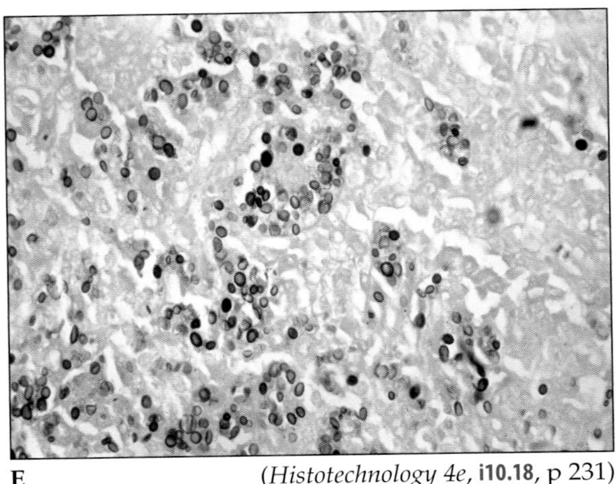

E (*Histotechnology 4e*, **i10.18**, p 231)

72. Another stain that is frequently used to demonstrate the structures stained rose by the technique shown in image D is the:
    a. Fite
    b. Grocott
    c. Giemsa
    d. Gram

73. The control for the stain shown in image D must contain:
    a. mycobacteria
    b. bacteria
    c. diplococci
    d. fungi

74. The technique shown in image E is most likely the:
    a. Dieterle
    b. Warthin-Starry
    c. Steiner & Steiner
    d. Grocott

75. The technique shown in image E depends on the presence in the organism's cell wall of:
    a. lipids
    b. carbohydrates
    c. amino acids
    d. hyaluronic acid

76. The impregnating solution for the technique shown in image E contains:
    a. methenamine
    b. Protargol
    c. hydroquinone
    d. pyridine

77. Stained black by the technique shown in image E are:
    a. Gram+ bacteria
    b. calcium spherules
    c. urate crystals
    d. fungal organisms

ISBN 978-089189-6401

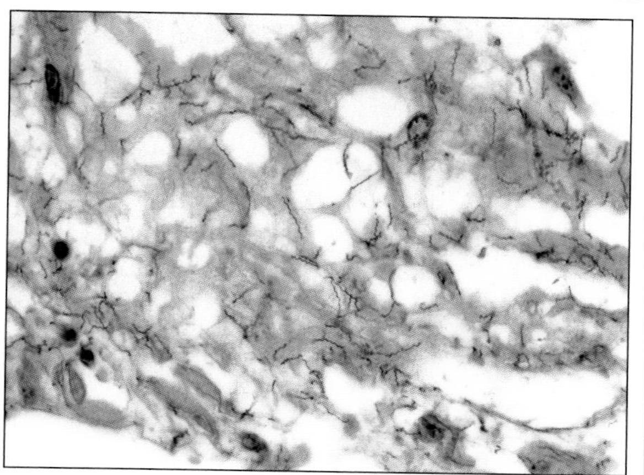

F (*Histotechnology 4e*, **i10.24**, p 235)

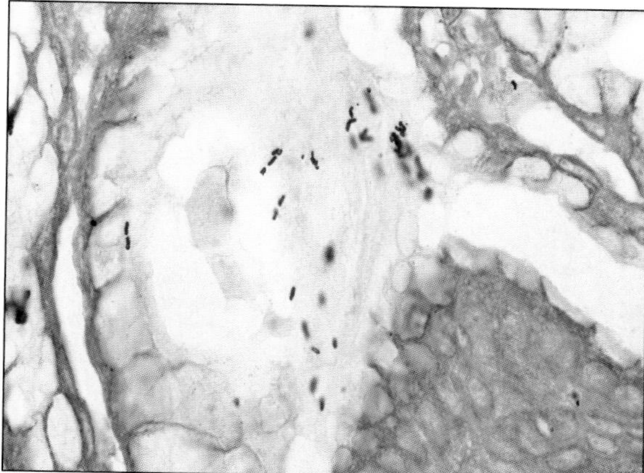

G (*Histotechnology 4e*, **i10.28**, p 239)

78. The technique shown in image F is most likely:
    a. argyrophilic
    b. argentaffin
    c. metallic substitution
    d. simultaneous coupling

79. The technique shown in image F is which of the following?
    a. Giemsa
    b. Grocott
    c. Warthin-Starry
    d. Brown & Hopps

80. The organisms demonstrated in image F are most likely:
    a. *Legionella pneumophila*
    b. *Treponema pallidum*
    c. *Helicobacter pylori*
    d. *Staphylococcus aureus*

81. The "developer" used in the technique shown in image F contains:
    a. sodium metabisulfite
    b. acetic acid
    c. hydroquinone
    d. glycerine

82. The technique shown in image G is most likely the:
    a. Giemsa
    b. Grocott
    c. Brown & Hopps
    d. Steiner & Steiner

83. The organisms demonstrated in image G is most likely:
    a *Legionella pneumophila*
    b. *Treponema pallidum*
    c. *Helicobacter pylori*
    d. *Staphylococcus aureus*

ISBN 978-089189-6401

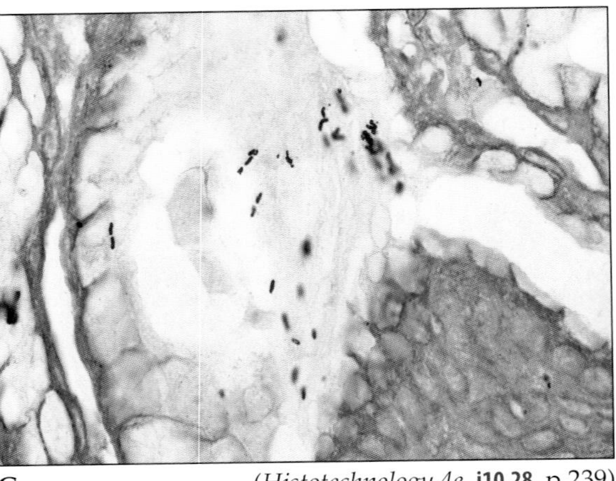

G (*Histotechnology 4e*, **i10.28**, p 239)

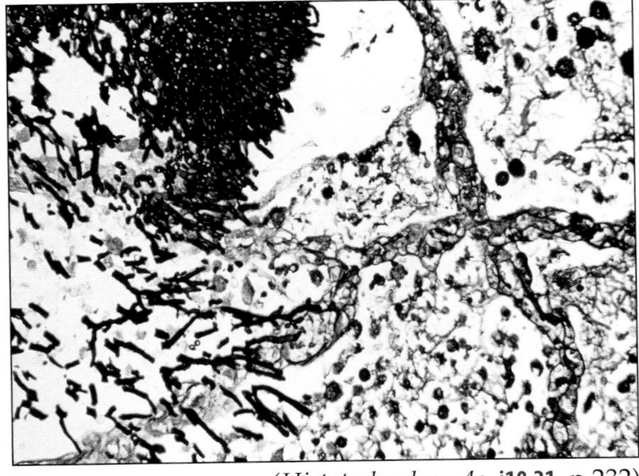

H (*Histotechnology 4e*, **i10.21**, p 232)

84. Which of the following terms best describes the technique shown in image G?
    a. argyrophilic
    b. argentaffin
    c. metallic substitution
    d. simultaneous coupling

85. For the technique shown in image G, the sections are sensitized with a solution of:
    a. potassium permanganate
    b. hydroquinone
    c. formaldehyde
    d. uranyl nitrate

86. The technique shown in image H is the:
    a. Steiner & Steiner
    b. Grocott
    c. Dieterle
    d. Giemsa

87. The section shown in image H has been:
    a. stained correctly
    b. overtoned with gold chloride
    c. improperly reduced with formaldehyde
    d. left in the impregnating solution too long

88. The black stained structures shown in image H are called:
    a. hyphae
    b. septae
    c. rickettsiae
    d. mycoplasmas

ISBN 978-089189-6401

89-100. The following are problem solving questions.

89. Acid-fast organisms are seen on a section of lung within normal alveolar sacs. They appear to lie slightly out of the plane of the section. This is most likely the result of:
    a. contamination from the flotation bath
    b. a section that is too thick
    c. poor mounting technique
    d. the disease process

90. The methylene blue counterstain is too heavy on the Kinyoun acid-fast stain, so that the organisms present are very difficult to locate. This problem could most likely be corrected by:
    a. cutting a new section and repeating the stain
    b. increasing the amount of light used for microscopic examination
    c. backing the section up into acid-alcohol, then recounterstaining removing the coverslip and repeating the entire procedure
    d. repeating with shortened impregnation

91. Grocott stained sections from the lung of a patient known to have *Histoplamsa capsulatum* show marked background staining, especially of reticulin and collagen. The most likely cause is:
    a. staining in a laboratory microwave
    b. oxidation with periodic acid
    c. oxidation with chromic acid
    d. prolonged treatment with gold chloride

92. Scattered patchy blue areas are seen on the Brown & Hopps Gram stain although the decolorization step was prolonged. This is most likely the result of:
    a. a section of uneven thickness
    b. drying of the section during the procedure
    c. inadequate mordanting of the section
    d. overtreatment with acetone

93. The background of a Brown & Hopps Gram stained section is an intense red. This could most likely be corrected in the future by changing the time in the:
    a. iodine solution
    b. Gallego solution
    c. picric acid-acetone
    d. crystal violet

94. The control section containing both Gram+ and Gram– organisms shows only Gram+ organisms when stained with the Brown & Hopps technique. This is most likely the result of:
    a. insufficient time in the Gallego solution
    b. improper application of the crystal violet
    c. insufficient time in the iodine solution
    d. overdifferentiation with picric acid-acetone

ISBN 978-089189-6401

95. A section of liver stained with the Grocott stain shows diffuse black staining over the entire section, making it difficult to see organisms. This could most likely be corrected in the future by treating liver sections with:
    a. decreased concentration of chromic acid
    b. diastase prior to beginning the stain
    c. a more dilute solution of methenamine silver
    d. a longer time in the gold chloride

96. A section of lung from a patient with sputum cultures positive for acid-fast organisms gave a negative result when stained with the Ziehl-Neelsen stain. To confirm that no organisms are present in the lung tissue, it would be best to stain new sections with:
    a. auramine-rhodamine
    b. Giemsa
    c. Gram
    d. Dieterle

97. The control section containing *Coccidioides immitis* shows very pale pink stained organisms on the PAS stain. This is most likely the result of:
    a. prolonged time in the Schiff reagent
    b. inadequate time in the sulfurous rinse solution
    c. too long in the running tap water
    d. old or overused reagents

98. The chromic acid keeps turning dark after using it only 2 or 3 times. This could most likely be corrected in the future by:
    a. allowing more time in the xylene
    b. increasing the time in the alcohols
    c. checking the concentration of the chromic acid solution
    d. ensuring the complete removal of alcohol prior to chromic acid

99. Grocott stained sections show reticulin and red cells stained black. This most likely is the result of:
    a. overimpregnation
    b. prolonged oxidation
    c. poor deparaffinization
    d. inadequate toning

100. Grocott stained sections from the lung of a patient with positive cultures of *Histoplasma capsulatum* do not reveal any organisms. The best course of action is to:
    a. stain new sections with the PAS
    b. ensure that chromic acid is used as the oxidizer
    c. repeat using fresh periodic acid
    d. omit the sodium thiosulfate step

ISBN 978-089189-6401

101. Make 12 copies of the worksheet that follows, and complete 1 copy (try to do this without referring to the text) for each of the following techniques:

a. Kinyoun and Ziehl-Neelsen carbol-fuchsin
b. Fite carbol-fuchsin
c. Auramine O-rhodamine B
d. Gram
e. Giemsa
f. Hotchkiss-McManus PAS
g. Gridley
h. Grocott methenamine silver
i. Mayer mucicarmine
j. Warthin-Starry
k. Dieterle
l. Steiner & Steiner

No answers are given for this exercise. The text must be used to check for correctness.

Staining technique ______________________________

Preferred fixative ______________________________

Preferred thickness ______________________________

Microscope used ______________________________

Control tissue ______________________________

Major reagents	Purpose
Periodic acid	
Schiff reagent	
Metabisulfite rinse	
Running water	
Harris hematoxylin	

Principle of the technique ______________________________

Purpose of stain ______________________________

Results ______________________________

Sources of error ______________________________

ISBN 978-089189-6401

Microorganisms *Answers*

Question	Answer	Discussion	*Histotechnology* Page
1	c	Fixation in Carnoy solution will make acid-fast organisms nonacid-fast.	217
2	a	Acid-fast organisms are stained red in the Fite method (a carbol fuchsin method).	220
3	c	The sulfite rinse following Schiff reagent is to remove any excess leucofuchsin. Any remaining Schiff reagent may be oxidized by highly chlorinated water and cause nonspecific staining.	140, 226
4	b	Gram+ organisms are stained blue-black in the Brown-Hopps Gram stain.	22-223
5	d	The ability of acid-fast stains to resist decolorization with dilute acid is a basic property of acid-fast organisms and one on which carbol-fuchsin stains depend.	216
6	d	Of the methods listed, only the PAS is a method for the demonstration of fungi.	226
7	a	In the Fite method, the acid-fastness of the leprosy organism is enhanced when the waxy capsule is protected by the mixture of peanut oil and xylene, and by the avoidance of dehydrating solutions.	220
8	c	The PAS uses periodic acid as an oxidizer, while the Gridley technique uses chromic acid.	226, 228
9	c	The Grocott fungus stain is a silver impregnation method, and the glassware must be chemically cleaned or a precipitate may result.	230-231
10	d	Cocci are spherical or ovoid.	214
11	b	The only protozoan of the listed organisms is *Giardia lamblia,* which causes an infection of the small intestine.	216
12	a	The basic structure of the filamentous fungi is the hypha; filamentous fungi are also called molds.	215
13	a	The carbol-fuchsin methods are specific for mycobacteria, the most important being *Mycobacterium tuberculosis* and *Mycobacterium leprae*. Also, *M avium* has become more important because of AIDS.	214
14	b	The auramine-rhodamine technique is a fluorescent method for *Mycobacterium tuberculosis*.	221-222
15	d	Carbol fuchsin contains basic fuchsin and phenol, known as carbolic acid in older literature.	216-217

ISBN 978-089189-6401

Question	Answer	Discussion	*Histotechnology* Page
16	b	Spirochetes have the ability to bind silver, but not to reduce it. A chemical reducer, hydroquinone, is used in a "developer" for that purpose; therefore spirochete stains are argyrophil.	234
17	a	The study of fungi is termed mycology, and a disease produced by fungi is known as mycosis.	214-215
18	c	Differences in bacterial cell walls account for the differential Gram+ and Gram– staining.	222
19	c	The auramine-rhodamine technique is a fluorescent method for *Mycobacterium tuberculosis*.	221-222
20	b	Fungal cell walls contain carbohydrates that may be demonstrated with the PAS, CAS, and GMS reactions.	226-232
21	d	Chromic acid oxidizes carbohydrates in the fungal cell walls to aldehydes, and the aldehydes are then reacted with Schiff reagent.	228
22	a	Periodic acid oxidizes the carbohydrates in the fungal cell walls to aldehydes in the Hotchkiss-McManus modification of the PAS.	226
23	d	10% buffered formalin is the preferred fixative for the Warthin-Starry technique.	234
24	b	Hydroquinone is the reducer in the "developer" used in the Warthin-Starry stain; although spirochetes can bind silver, they are unable to reduce silver to a visible metallic form.	234
25	a	*Pneumocystis jiroveci* organisms are demonstrated by a silver technique, the Grocott stain.	230-235
26	c	Light green provides the best contrast for fungi stained by the PAS technique.	227
27	b	Aldehyde fuchsin acts as an aldehyde and occupies uninvolved linkages of the Schiff reagent, thus reinforcing the depth of the stain.	228-229
28	d	Mayer mucicarmine, alcian blue, and colloidal iron may all be used to differentiate *Cryptococcus neoformans* from other yeastlike fungi.	234
29	b	Among the yeastlike fungi, only *Cryptococcus neoformans* has a mucoid capsule that can be demonstrated by the techniques used for acid mucosubstances.	234
30	F	The decolorization step is a relative one, and sections can be overdecolorized, removing stain from both Gram– and Gram+ organisms.	222
31	T	If sections are allowed to dry at any stage of the procedure, insoluble compounds may be formed that are difficult or impossible to decolorize.	224

ISBN 978-089189-6401

Question	Answer	Discussion	*Histotechnology* Page
32	T	Spirochetes have the ability to bind silver, but not to reduce it. A chemical reducer, hydroquinone, is used in a "developer" for that purpose; therefore spirochete stains are argyrophil.	234
33	T	Rod shaped bacteria are known as bacilli	214
34	F	Some viral organisms form inclusions that can be seen only with the electron microscope, but some form inclusions that can be seen with the light microscope. However, there is no histochemical stain for the virus itself. There are IHC and ISH stains that will demonstrate some viruses.	215
35	T	A good Grocott methenamine silver will show fungi with a crisp black cell wall and visible internal structure.	231
36	F	Mercurial and chromate fixatives should be avoided when staining for spirochetes; 10% buffered formalin is preferred.	234, 238
37	T	The Diff-Quik Giemsa modification is used for the demonstration of *Helicobacter pylori*.	224
38	F	Fungi stain less intensely with the Gridley stain than with the PAS.	228
39	T	Iodine (mordant) is applied after crystal violet (primary stain) in the Gram stain.	222-223
40	F	Peanut oil mixed with xylene is used in the Fite method for mycobacteria.	220-221
41	F	Carnoy solution should not be used to fix tissue on which acid-fast stains will be needed.	217
42	T	Iodine is the mordant in the Gram stain.	222-223
43	F	*Helicobacter pylori* is a Gram– bacillus.	225
44	T	The Romanowsky type dyes (eg, Diff-Quik) are used to demonstrate *Helicobacter pylori*.	224-225
45	F	The Giemsa stain will not differentially stain different types of bacteria; all stain the same color.	130
46A	c, f	Chromic acid (oxidizer) and metanil yellow (counterstain) are used in the Gridley stain.	228-229
46B	c, g	Chromic acid is the traditional oxidizer for the Grocott fungus stain; however some laboratories have had to substitute periodic acid. Most commercial kits also use periodic acid, although this is not as good as chromic acid; it is not as strong an oxidizer and may fail to oxidize *Histoplasma capsulatum* sufficiently for demonstration. It also leads to more background staining.	230-232
46C	b	Acid-alcohol is the decolorizer in the Kinyoun acid-fast technique.	216

ISBN 978-089189-6401

Question	Answer	Discussion	*Histotechnology* Page
46D	g	Periodic acid is the oxidizer in the PAS technique.	225-226,
46E	e	Hydroquinone is the reducer in the Steiner & Steiner technique for spirochetes.	238
46F	a, d, h	Acetone, crystal violet, and picric acid are all used in the Brown & Hopps Gram stain.	222-223
47A	d	Auramine-rhodamine is a fluorescence technique for acid-fast organisms.	221-222
47B	b	The Brown & Brenn technique is for both Gram+ and Gram– bacteria.	223
47C	a	Fungi may be stained with the Gridley fungus stain.	228-229
47D	a, e	Fungi and *Pneumocystis jiroveci* are stained with the Grocott methenamine silver technique.	230-234
47E	c, f	The Steiner & Steiner technique will demonstrate *Helicobacter pylori* and *Treponema pallidum.*	238-239
47F	d	*Mycobacterium tuberculosis* organisms are demonstrated by the Ziehl-Neelsen technique.	218
47G	a	Fungal organisms are demonstrated with the PAS technique.	226
48A	a	Acid-alcohol is used for differentiation in the carbol-fuchsin techniques.	216
48B	d	Chromic acid is an oxidizer used in the CAS, Gridley, and Grocott fungal techniques.	227-230
48C	f	Gold chloride is used for toning in many silver techniques (eg, Grocott methenamine silver).	230-231
48D	e	Hydroquinone is the reducer used in "developers" in the Warthin-Starry, Steiner & Steiner, and Dieterle technique.	234-239
48E	c	Iodine is the mordant in Gram stains.	222-223
48F	d	Periodic acid is used for oxidation in the PAS technique.	226-227
49-1	C	Both Kinyoun carbol-fuchsin and auramine-rhodamine solutions contain phenol.	220, 221
49-2	C	Both methods will demonstrate mycobacteria.	216-222
49-3	B	Auramine-rhodamine is a fluorescent technique for mycobacteria.	221-222
49-4	C	Nonpathogenic mycobacteria are present in tap water and may contaminate both stains.	216-222
49-5	D	Neither technique will demonstrate spirochetes. Spirochetes are demonstrated with silver methods.	234-239
50-1	D	Neither the PAS nor the CAS is used to demonstrate mycobacteria.	226-228

ISBN 978-089189-6401

Question	Answer	Discussion	*Histotechnology* Page
50-2	B	The CAS uses chromic acid for oxidation, whereas the PAS uses periodic acid.	235-238226-228
50-3	D	Neither demonstrates the lipoid capsule of the organisms; the acid-fast techniques demonstrate the lipoid capsule of mycobacteria.	226-228, 216
50-4	C	Both the PAS and CAS depend on the formation of aldehyde groups to be reacted with Schiff reagent.	226-228
50-5	C	Both methods use Schiff reagent, which is prepared from the dye basic fuchsin.	226-228
51-1	C	Both the Gram and Giemsa techniques will stain bacteria.	222-225
51-2	B	The Giemsa and some silver methods will demonstrate *Helicobacter pylori*, but the Giemsa or Romanowsky methods are used most frequently for the demonstration of these organisms. The organisms are Gram– rods, but the Gram is not commonly used in the identification of *H pylori*.	222-225
51-3	A	Crystal violet is the primary stain for Gram+ organisms in the Gram technique.	222-223
51-4	A	The Gram stain differentiates between Gram+ and Gram– organisms; the Giemsa does not differentially stain bacteria.	222-225
51-5	D	Neither is a stain for *Legionella pneumophila*; silver techniques, such as the Dieterle or Steiner & Steiner, are preferred for these organisms.	222-225, 234-239
52-1	C	Both the Gridley and Grocott methods will demonstrate fungi.	238-241228-231
52-2	C	Both techniques depend on the formation of aldehydes.	228-231
52-3	A	The Gridley technique depends on the reaction of Schiff reagent with the aldehydes formed by oxidation.	228-229
52-4	C	Both traditional methods use chromic acid to oxidize the carbohydrates present in the cell walls to aldehydes.	228-231
52-5	D	Neither technique is a Romanowsky type stain.	228-231
53-1	A	The Fite carbol-fuchsin method will demonstrate mycobacteria.	220, 238-239
53-2	B	The Steiner & Steiner is a silver technique for *Legionella pneumophila*; these organisms will not be stained by the Fite method.	220, 238-239
53-3	A	The Fite technique used carbol-fuchsin.	220

ISBN 978-089189-6401

Question	Answer	Discussion	*Histotechnology* Page
53-4	B	The Steiner & Steiner technique is an argyrophil technique; that is, it uses an external reducing agent.	238-239
53-5	D	Neither technique depends on the formation of aldehydes.	220, 238,239
54	c	The stain is a carbol-fuchsin method; of the choices given, it would be the Kinyoun technique.	217
55	b	The primary stain is carbol-fuchsin.	217
56	a	The stain shown in image A would not be satisfactory on tissue fixed in Carnoy solution.	217
57	a	Carbol-fuchsin is more soluble in the lipids of the waxy cell wall than in acid-alcohol and therefore resists decolorization.	216
58	c	Mycobacteria are demonstrated with the carbol-fuchsin techniques as shown in image A.	217
59	a	The technique shown in image B is most likely the auramine-rhodamine stain.	222
60	d	The technique shown in image B uses fluorescence microscopy.	222
61	a	The preferred fixative for the auramine-rhodamine technique is 10% neutral buffered formalin.	221-222
62	c	The light source for fluorescence microscopes is a mercury, xenon, or halogen lamp.	56
63	a	Mycobacteria are demonstrated by the auramine-rhodamine fluorescence technique.	221-222
64	c	The Ziehl-Neelsen technique could also be used to demonstrate the organisms seen in image B.	218
65	a	The dark blue-black organisms seen in image C are Gram+.	223
66	a	The organisms seen in image C are Gram+ bacilli.	223
67	d	Crystal violet followed by an iodine mordant is responsible for the blue-black staining of the Gram+ organisms.	222-223
68	c	The Gram stain is shown in image C.	223
69	b	The technique shown in image D is the PAS stain for fungi.	227
70	d	Carbohydrates in the fungal cell walls are oxidized to aldehydes, which are then reacted with Schiff reagent.	226-227
71	a	The PAS reaction depends on periodic acid oxidation of the carbohydrates to aldehydes.	226-227
72	b	The Grocott methenamine silver is often used to stain fungi, or the structures stained rose in image D.	230-231

ISBN 978-089189-6401

Question	Answer	Discussion	*Histotechnology* Page
73	d	The control for the structures stained rose in image D must contain fungi.	226-227
74	d	Fungi are stained with the Grocott methenamine silver technique in image E.	231
75	b	Carbohydrates in the fungal cell walls are oxidized to aldehydes, which are then reacted with the methenamine silver.	230-231
76	a	Methenamine silver is the impregnating solution for the stain shown in image E.	230-231
77	d	Fungal organisms are stained black in image E.	230-231
78	a	The technique shown in image F is most likely an argyrophil method; that is, an external reducing agent must be used to reduce the silver to its visible metallic form.	234-235
79	c	The technique shown in image F is the Warthin-Starry.	234-235
80	b	The organisms demonstrated are most likely *Treponema pallidum*; the other organisms listed are not spirochetes.	234-235
81	c	The developer in the Warthin-Starry technique contains hydroquinone as the reducing agent.	234-235
82	d	The technique shown in image G is most likely the Steiner & Steiner.	239
83	c	The organisms demonstrated in image G are most likely *Helicobacter pylori*.	239
84	a	The Steiner & Steiner stain is an argyrophil technique.	24238-239
85	d	Sections are sensitized with uranyl nitrate in the Steiner & Steiner. Hydroquinone is in the developer; potassium permanganate and formaldehyde are not used in the stain.	238-239
86	b	The technique shown in image H is the Grocott; fungi may be seen in the lower right corner.	231-232
87	d	The section in image H has been left in the impregnating solution too long and the background and the organisms are markedly overstained.	231-232
88	a	The black stained structures are fungal hyphae.	231-232
89	a	Acid-fast organisms have been reported in tap water, so if tap water is used in the flotation bath, contamination of the sections may result.	217

ISBN 978-089189-6401

Question	Answer	Discussion	*Histotechnology* Page
90	c	Excess methylene blue may be removed by backing the slide up to acid-alcohol, washing well with water, and then carefully repeating the counterstaining step.	217
91	b	Periodic acid is not as strong an oxidizing agent as chromic acid, and periodic acid oxidation leads to increased background staining. Chromic acid has the advantage of decreased staining of the connective tissue; only substances that contain large quantities of carbohydrates, such as the fungal cell walls, mucin, and glycogen will remain active after chromic acid oxidation.	232
92	b	Sections should not be allowed to dry at any stage of the procedure, because drying leads to the formation of insoluble compounds that are difficult or impossible to decolorize.	224
93	c	The red stain in the Brown & Hopps Gram stain is decolorized with picric acid-acetone, so prolonging the decolorization step should remove more basic fuchsin.	223
94	d	Overdifferentiation with picric acid-acetone will decolorize Gram– organisms	223
95	b	Glycogen will stain prominently in liver sections stained with the Grocott methenamine silver technique, so digestion of the glycogen prior to staining should be used to reduce the background staining.	230, 141
96	a	The auramine-rhodamine fluorescence technique is extremely sensitive and highly specific for mycobacteria; however, care must be exercised because of the possibility of false positives.	222
97	d	The reagents used in the PAS reaction can easily be overused, leading to false negative or very faint staining; a section of kidney on all PAS control slides is the best indicator of reagent viability.	139-140
98	d	If the alcohol is not completely removed before placing the slides in the chromic acid, the chromic acid will be reduced and turn brown.	231
99	a	Prolonged impregnation with methenamine silver will cause staining of reticulin and red cells, and overstaining of fungal organisms.	230-232
100	b	False negatives, especially with *Histoplasma capsulatum*, may be obtained with periodic acid oxidation, and this oxidizer should be used with caution; chromic acid should be used, especially if this organism is suspected. *Histoplasma capsulatum* may also be difficult to demonstrate with the PAS technique.	232

ISBN 978-089189-6401

Pigments, Minerals & Cytoplasmic Granules *Questions*

1-3. Match the columns.

1. Match the tissue component on the left with the stain used to demonstrate that component on the right. Each letter may be used more than once or not at all.

Component	Stain
_____A. Argentaffin granules	a. Hall
_____B. Bile	b. Fontana-Masson
_____C. Calcium	c. Prussian blue
_____D. Hemosiderin	d. Schmorl
_____E. Melanin	e. Rhodanine
_____F. Reducing substances	f. von Kossa

2. Match the pigment, mineral, or granule on the left with the reagent used for demonstration on the right. Each letter may be used more than once or not at all.

Pigment/mineral/granule	Reagent
_____A. Argentaffin granules	a. alizarin red
_____B. Bile	b. ferric-ferricyanide
_____C. Calcium	c. Fouchet reagent
_____D. Hemosiderin	d. iodine
_____E. Melanin	e. potassium ferrocyanide

3. Match the pigment on the left with its description on the right. Use only 1 letter before each appropriate number, but each letter may be used several times or not at all.

Pigment/mineral	Description
_____A. Bile	a. endogenous/anthracotic
_____B. Carbon	b. endogenous/hematogenous
_____C. Hemosiderin	c. endogenous/nonhematogenous
_____D. Iron	d. exogenous/lipidic
_____E. Lipofuchsin	e. exogenous/anthracotic
_____F. Melanin	f. exogenous/hematogenous

ISBN 978-089189-6401

4-45. The following are multiple choice questions. Please circle the letter in front of the correct answer. There is only 1 best answer.

4. In the Prussian blue reaction for iron, the incubating solution used contains:
   a. potassium ferrocyanide and dilute hydrochloric acid
   b. potassium ferricyanide and dilute hydrochloric acid
   c. potassium ferrocyanide and dilute acetic acid
   d. ammonium sulfide

5. A method recommended for the demonstration of argentaffin granules (eg, in carcinoid tumors) is the:
   a. Fontana silver nitrate
   b. Bloch dopa reaction
   c. Bodian silver protein stain
   d. Wilder silver stain

6. A stain that may be used to demonstrate calcium is the:
   a. Gomori chromium hematoxylin
   b. Fontana-Masson
   c. von Kossa silver nitrate
   d. Schmorl method

7. Which of the following pigments will reduce silver?
   a. carbon
   b. formalin
   c. hemosiderin
   d. bile

8. Urate crystals can be demonstrated with:
   a. rhodanine
   b. potassium ferrocyanide
   c. methenamine silver
   d. alizarin red

9. A reducing or developing solution is used in which of the following techniques?
   a. Schmorl
   b. Fontana-Masson
   c. Hall
   d. Churukian-Schenk

10. Rhodanine is used to demonstrate:
    a. ferric iron
    b. copper
    c. calcium
    d. urate crystals

11. An aid to the definite identification of anthracotic pigment is its:
    a. easy removal with saturated alcoholic picric acid
    b. demonstration with the Prussian blue reaction
    c. insolubility in concentrated sulfuric acid
    d. property of birefringence

ISBN 978-089189-6401

12. When the content of tissue is to be studied by microincineration, the recommended fixative is:
    a. zinc formalin
    b. zenker solution
    c. Bouin solution
    d. formalin alcohol

13. Argentaffin granules present in cells of the gastrointestinal tract are best preserved with:
    a. absolute alcohol
    b. Carnoy solution
    c. 10% buffered formalin
    d. formalin alcohol

14. The end-product in the Prussian blue reaction is:
    a. ferric ferrocyanide
    b. ferrous ferricyanide
    c. potassium ferrocyanide
    d. potassium ferricyanide

15. The Turnbull stain is used for the detection of:
    a. reducing substances
    b. hemosiderin
    c. hemoglobin
    d. ferrous iron

16. The end product of the Turnbull blue reaction is:
    a. potassium ferric ferrocyanide
    b. potassium ferrous ferricyanide
    c. potassium ferrocyanide
    d. potassium ferricyanide

17. Red cells are very eosinophilic because of the content of:
    a. hemosiderin
    b. hemoglobin
    c. hematoidin
    d. hematein

18. Melanin can be demonstrated with the:
    a. Prussian blue reaction
    b. rhodanine method
    c. Schmorl technique
    d. von Kossa technique

19. The end product in the Schmorl reaction is:
    a. Prussian blue
    b. Turnbull blue
    c. ferric ferrocyanide
    d. colloidal iron

20. A good control for the Schmorl technique is a section of:
    a. liver
    b. pancreas
    c. kidney
    d. small intestine

ISBN 978-089189-6401

21. The preferred fixative for the Churukian-Schenk technique is:
    a. Bouin solution
    b. Carnoy solution
    c. buffered formalin
    d. absolute alcohol

22. A tissue frequently used as a control for the Fontana-Masson stain is:
    a. skin
    b. lymph node
    c. liver
    d. spleen

23. In the Hall technique, bilirubin is oxidized to biliverdin by:
    a. rhodanine
    b. potassium ferricyanide
    c. Fouchet reagent
    d. acetic acid

24. The Grimelius technique will demonstrate substances that can:
    a. bind silver but need a chemical reducer
    b. be demonstrated by metal substitution
    c. both bind and reduce silver
    d. oxidize silver to the metal

25. The preferred fixative for the Grimelius technique is:
    a. Bouin solution
    b. Carnoy solution
    c. buffered formalin
    d. Orth solution

26. The preferred fixative for the Fontana-Masson technique is:
    a. Bouin solution
    b. Carnoy solution
    c. Orth solution
    d. buffered formalin

27. Tissue that can be used as a control for the Grimelius technique is:
    a. small intestine
    b. salivary gland
    c. liver
    d. spleen

28. The Churukian-Schenk technique will demonstrate substances that can:
    a. bind silver but need a chemical reducer
    b. be demonstrated by metal substitution
    c. both bind and reduce silver
    d. oxidize silver to the metal

29. An argentaffin substance present in some tissues is:
    a. iron
    b. calcium
    c. melanin
    d. copper

30. The control for the Hall stain must contain:
    a. hemosiderin
    b. hemoglobin
    c. urate crystals
    d. bile

31. Polarized light is frequently used to demonstrate:
    a. chromaffin granules
    b. urate crystals
    c. hemoglobin
    d. tattoo pigment

32. Which of the following is usually the source of a good control for iron?
    a. gastrointestinal tract
    b. kidney
    c. spleen
    d. heart

33. Fouchet reagent is used for the demonstration of:
    a. bile
    b. calcium
    c. hemosiderin
    d. reducing substances

34. The preferred fixative for a gouty tophus is:
    a. Bouin solution
    b. B-5 solution
    c. buffered formalin
    d. absolute alcohol

35. The Fontana-Masson technique will demonstrate substances that can:
    a. bind silver but need a chemical reducer
    b. be demonstrated by metal substitution
    c. both bind and reduce silver
    d. oxidize silver to the metal

36. Pigment lying on top of the tissue is most likely:
    a. endogenous
    b. anthracotic
    c. artifact
    d. exogenous

37. Polarized light can be used to assist in the identification of which of the following pigments?
    a. anthracotic
    b. hemosiderin
    c. formalin
    d. melanin

38. Bile is stained emerald green in the method of:
    a. Hall
    b. Dahl
    c. Fontana
    d. Schmorl

ISBN 978-089189-6401

39. A good control for the Lindquist rhodanine technique is fetal:
    a. spleen
    b. kidney
    c. stomach
    d. liver

40. A substance that can both bind and reduce silver is defined as:
    a. argyrophilic
    b. argentaffin
    c. anthracotic
    d. amphoteric

41. The Schmorl technique demonstrates substances that are classified as:
    a. reducing
    b. oxidizing
    c. amphoteric
    d. leuco compounds

42. Methenamine silver is often used in the demonstration of:
    a. copper
    b. bile
    c. urates
    d. chromaffin

43. Melanin present in tissue can be bleached with the use of:
    a. alkaline alcohol
    b. iodine
    c. picric acid
    d. potassium permanganate

44. Chromaffin granules are found in cells of the:
    a. liver
    b. spleen
    c. adrenal gland
    d. lymph node

45. Which of the following is a breakdown product of hemoglobin?
    a. melanin
    b. ceroid
    c. bile
    d. lipofuscin

ISBN 978-089189-6401

46-52. Each of the following numbered words or phrases is associated with one, both, or neither of the headings listed as A or B above it. Within the parentheses on the right, place the appropriate letter for that word or phrase. Write:

A, if the numbered phrase is associated with A only
B, if the numbered phrase is associated with B only
C, if the numbered phrase is associated with both A and B
D, if the numbered phrase is associated with neither A nor B

46.

A. Argentaffin substances
B. Argyrophil substances
C. both
D. neither

1. Stained by the Fontana-Masson procedure [ ]
2. Are stained by the Grimelius procedure [ ]
3. Are stained by the Schmorl procedure [ ]
4. Cannot reduce silver [ ]
5. Require alcoholic fixatives [ ]

47.

A. Formalin pigment
B. Anthracotic pigment
C. both
D. neither

1. Is an endogenous, nonhematogenous pigment [ ]
2. Is insoluble in concentrated sulfuric acid [ ]
3. Is demonstrated with polarizing microscopy [ ]
4. Will stain with argentaffin techniques [ ]
5. Is soluble in alcoholic picric acid [ ]

48.

A. Urate crystals
B. Copper
C. both
D. neither

1. Normally present in demonstrable amounts in adult human tissue [ ]
2. Demonstrated with polarizing microscopy [ ]
3. Stained with methenamine silver [ ]
4. Stained with rhodanine [ ]
5. Must be fixed with absolute alcohol [ ]

49.

A. Calcium
B. Melanin
C. both
D. neither

1. Is demonstrated with a silver substitution method [ ]
2. Is demonstrated with an argentaffin silver method [ ]
3. Is an artifact pigment [ ]
4. Is an endogenous, nonhematogenous pigment [ ]
5. Is a mineral normally found in the body [ ]

50.

A. Prussian blue reaction
B. Turnbull blue reaction
C. both
D. neither

1. Demonstrates ferric iron [ ]
2. Demonstrates ferrous iron [ ]
3. Is an end product in the Schmorl reaction [ ]
4. Demonstrates the result of hemochromatosis [ ]
5. Requires an acid pH [ ]

51.

A. Fontana-Masson
B. Churukian-Schenk
C. both
D. neither

1. Demonstrates argyrophilic substances [ ]
2. Demonstrates argentaffin substances [ ]
3. Uses hydroquinone in the procedure [ ]
4. Uses gold chloride in the procedure [ ]
5. Is a metal substitution method [ ]

52.

A. Hemosiderin
B. Biliverdin
C. both
D. neither

1. Is a breakdown product of hemoglobin [ ]
2. Is a reaction product with Fouchet reagent [ ]
3. Is demonstrated with the Turnbull blue reaction [ ]
4. Is an endogenous, nonhematogenous pigment [ ]
5. Is the storage form of iron [ ]

ISBN 978-089189-6401

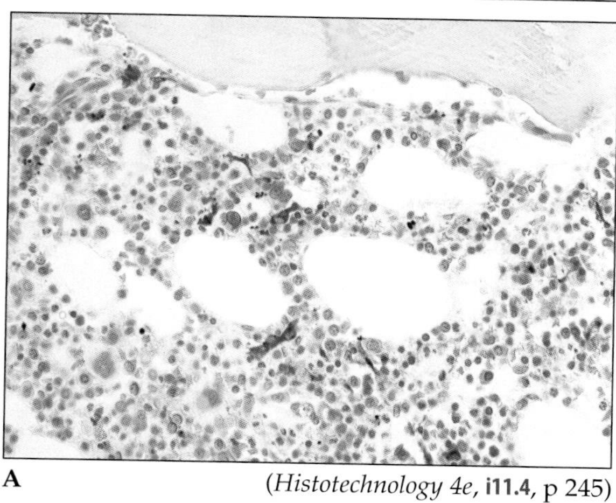

A (*Histotechnology 4e*, **i11.4**, p 245)

53-89. The following questions apply to images A-H as specified.

53. The substance stained blue in image A is most likely:
    a. a reducing substance
    b. hemosiderin
    c. ferrous iron
    d. melanin

54. The tissue shown in image A is:
    a. spleen
    b. liver
    c. lymph node
    d. bone marrow

55. The reaction demonstrated in image A is most likely the:
    a. Schmorl
    b. Prussian blue
    c. alcian blue
    d. colloidal iron

56. One of the chemicals used in the technique shown in image A is:
    a. potassium ferrocyanide
    b. colloidal iron
    c. alcian blue
    d. ferric ferrocyanide

57. A tissue commonly used as a control for the procedure shown in image A is:
    a. kidney
    b. spleen
    c. stomach
    d. lymph node

58. Which of the following is a preferred fixative for the technique shown in image A?
    a. Bouin solution
    b. Hollande
    c. Carnoy solution
    d. buffered formalin

ISBN 978-089189-6401

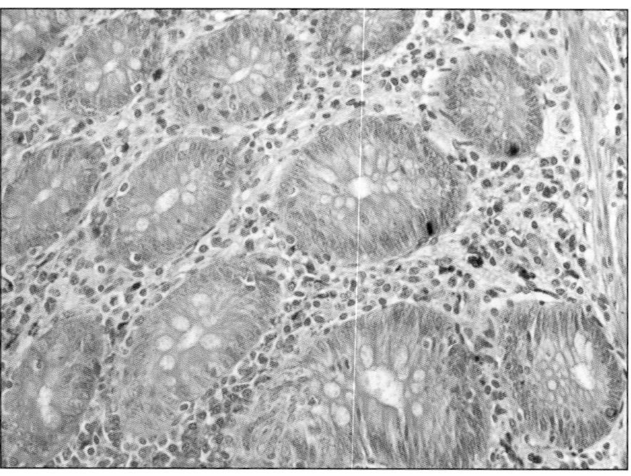

B (*Histotechnology 4e*, **i11.8**, p 248)

59. The tissue shown in image B is:
    a. cervix
    b. gastrointestinal tract
    c. lymph node
    d. salivary gland

60. The technique shown in image B is most likely the:
    a. Schmorl
    b. Prussian blue
    c. Fontana-Masson
    d. alcian blue

61. The substance stained dark blue in image B is defined as:
    a. reducing
    b. oxidizing
    c. amphoteric
    d. argyrophilic

62. The end product of the technique shown in image B is:
    a. ferric ferrocyanide
    b. Prussian blue
    c. Turnbull blue
    d. colloidal iron

63. A pigment that will give false positive results with the technique shown in image B is:
    a. anthracotic
    b. hemosiderin
    c. formalin
    d. mercury

64. The preferred fixative for the technique shown in image B is:
    a. formalin
    b. absolute alcohol
    c. Carnoy
    d. B-5

ISBN 978-089189-6401

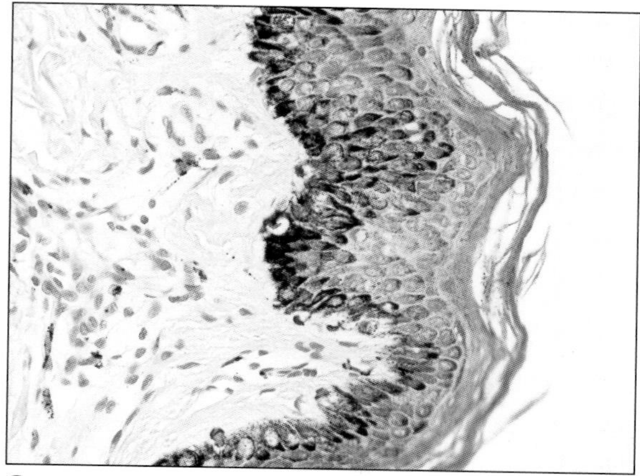

C (*Histotechnology 4e*, **i11.11**, p 249)

65. Another stain that might be used to demonstrate the substance stained dark blue in image B is the:
    a. Prussian blue
    b. Alcian blue
    c. Fontana-Masson
    d. Verhoeff-van Gieson

66. The substance stained black in image C is most likely:
    a. carbon
    b. calcium
    c. melanin
    d. silicon

67. The technique shown in image C is most likely the:
    a. Schmorl
    b. Sudan black B
    c. Wright-Giemsa
    d. Fontana-Masson

68. Poor results might be obtained with the technique shown in image C if:
    a. the sections are immersed in the silver solution at 56°C
    b. metallic forceps are used to handle the slides
    c. the silver solution stands for several hours before use
    d. the tissue was fixed in buffered formalin

69. Another tissue that might be used as a control for the procedure shown in image C is:
    a. esophagus
    b. cervix
    c. liver
    d. ileum

70. Another technique that might be used to demonstrate the substance stained black in image C is the:
    a. Schmorl
    b. alizarin red S
    c. colloidal iron
    d. Sudan black B

ISBN 978-089189-6401

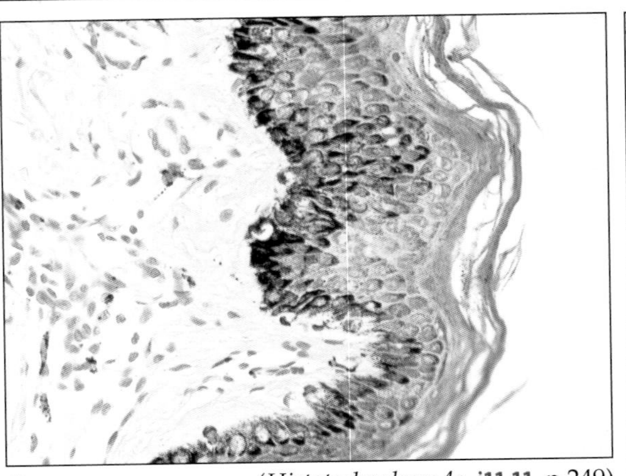

C (*Histotechnology 4e*, **i11.11**, p 249)

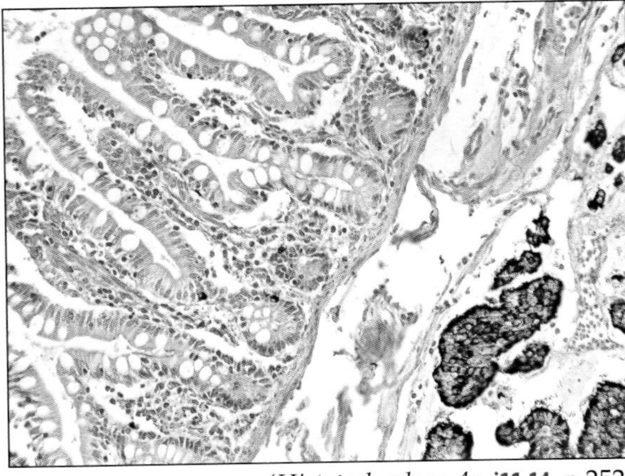

D (*Histotechnology 4e*, **i11.14**, p 252)

71. The technique shown in image C is defined as:
    a. argyrophilic
    b. argentaffinic
    c. amphoteric
    d. achromatic

72. The technique shown in image D is most likely that of:
    a. Schmorl
    b. Grimelius
    c. von Kossa
    d. Gomori

73. A chemical that is most likely used in the procedure shown in image D is:
    a. sodium thiosulfate
    b. gold chloride
    c. hydroquinone
    d. hydrochloric acid

74. Poor results might be obtained with the procedure shown in image D if:
    a. a reducing solution containing hydroquinone was used
    b. the tissue was fixed in buffered formalin
    c. the glassware was not chemically cleaned
    d. the sections were incubated at 60°C

ISBN 978-089189-6401

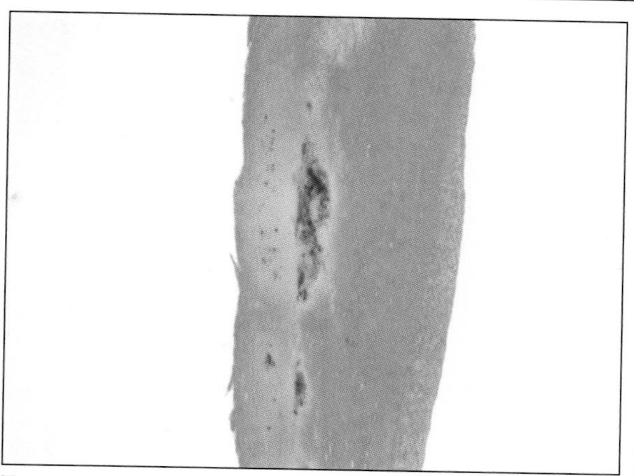

E (*Histotechnology 4e*, **i11.21**, p 258)

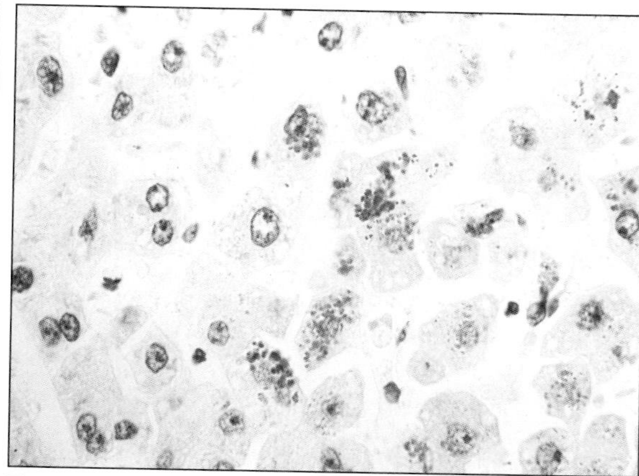

F (*Histotechnology 4e*, **i11.22**, p 259)

75. The substance stained red in image E is most likely:
    a. calcium
    b. copper
    c. amyloid
    d. hematoidin

76. The technique shown in image E is most likely the:
    a. von Kossa
    b. rhodanine
    c. alizarin red S
    d. Congo red

77. Another technique that could be used to demonstrate the substance stained red in image E is the:
    a. Congo red
    b. Fontana-Masson
    c. von Kossa
    d. Schmorl

78. Which of the following fixatives is recommended for the technique demonstrated in image E?
    a. Bouin
    b. Carnoy
    c. Hollande
    d. buffered formalin

79. The technique demonstrated in image F most likely uses:
    a. Congo red
    b. alizarin red S
    c. rhodanine
    d. acid fuchsin

80. The substance stained red in image F is most likely:
    a. calcium
    b. copper
    c. amyloid
    d. melanin

ISBN 978-089189-6401

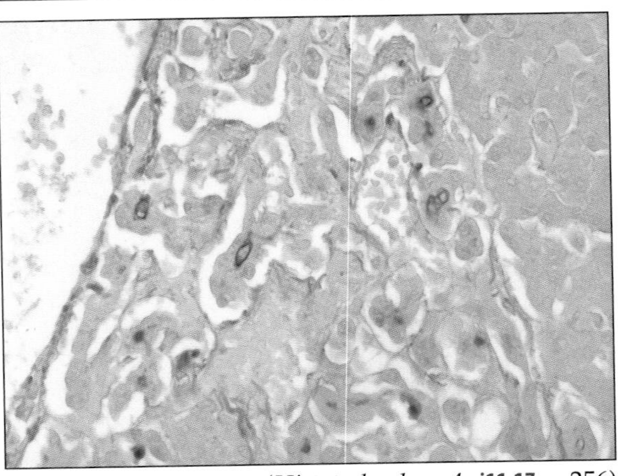

G (*Histotechnology 4e*,**i11.17**, p 256)

81. The substance stained red in image F is most frequently found in the:
    a. liver
    b. kidney
    c. bone marrow
    d. lymph nodes

82. A good control for the technique demonstrated in image F is:
    a. adult kidney
    b. fetal spleen
    c. fetal liver
    d. lymph node

83. The substance stained green in image G is most likely:
    a. calcium
    b. argentaffin granules
    c. bile
    d. hemosiderin

84. The primary reagent used in the stain shown in image G is:
    a. ferrocyanide
    b. Fouchet reagent
    c. fast green
    d. Gram iodine

85. The green stained end product in image G is :
    a. lipofuscin
    b. hemosiderin
    c. bilirubin
    d. biliverdin

ISBN 978-089189-6401

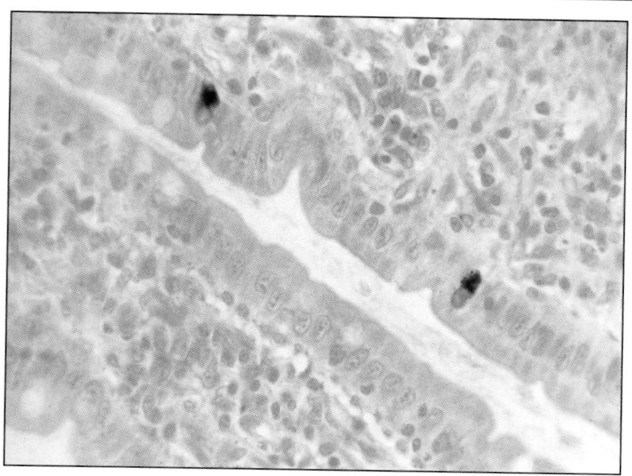

H (*Histotechnology 4e*, **i11.10**, p 249)

86. The stain shown in image H is most likely the:
    a. Fontana-Masson
    b. Churukian-Schenk
    c. Grimelius
    d. von Kossa

87. The black stained substance in image H is present in which cells?
    a. columnar epithelial
    b. argentaffin
    c. goblet
    d. Paneth

88. The stain shown in image H stains:
    a. only argyrophil granules
    b. only argentaffin granules
    c. both argyrophil and argentaffin granules
    d. neither argyrophil or argentaffin granules

89. The tissue shown in image H is:
    a. colon
    b. esophagus
    c. small intestine
    d. lung

ISBN 978-089189-6401

90-99. The following are problem solving questions.

90. Sections of bone marrow reveal no iron stores when stained with the Prussian blue technique. This is most likely an artifact due to:
    a. decalcification with a strong acid
    b. fixation with alcoholic formalin
    c. fixation with Zenker containing 3% acetic acid
    d. incubation in the staining solution for 1 hour

91. When viewed with the light microscope, a 5 µm paraffin section from tissue known to contain a gouty tophus fails to reveal any staining with the Gomori methenamine silver technique. To prevent this from happening in the future:
    a. ensure fixation with absolute alcohol
    b. cut the sections at 10 µm to 12 µm
    c. apply appropriate washing after fixation
    d. use polarizing microscopy

92. Sections of skin stained with Fontana-Masson show dark black melanosomes and dirty gray staining of both the squamous epithelium and the collagen. This is most likely the result of:
    a. poor staining with nuclear fast red
    b. prolonged incubation in the silver solution
    c. extended application of the gold chloride solution
    d. the use of contaminated glassware

93. A section of ileum stained with Fontana-Masson shows a marked black precipitate on top of the section. This could most likely be prevented in the future by:
    a. using chemically cleaned glassware
    b. increasing the incubation time
    c. omitting the use of a reducer
    d. using the silver immediately after preparation

94. A section of ileum stained with the Grimelius technique does not demonstrate any positively stained cells. This is most likely the result of:
    a. a lack of Paneth cells in the section
    b. keeping the hydroquinone in the refrigerator
    c. the use of old developer
    d. overtoning of the section

95. When viewed with the light microscope, a 5 µm paraffin section from tissue known to contain a gouty tophus fails to reveal any staining with methenamine silver. The presence of the tophus could be verified by examining the tissue with which of the following microscopes?
    a. polarizing
    b. dark field
    c. phase contrast
    d. fluorescence

ISBN 978-089189-6401

96. Control sections stained with the Prussian blue reaction show diffuse blue staining, and the solution is also blue. One possible explanation is that the:
    a. slides were incubated for 1 hour at room temperature
    b. control chosen contains a soluble form of iron
    c. staining jar was contaminated
    d. section is too thick

97. On X-ray, a breast biopsy revealed areas of microcalcification. Multiple sections of the paraffin embedded tissue stained with the H&E and von Kossa techniques fail to demonstrate these areas. This would occur if the tissue was fixed in:
    a. 10% neutral buffered formalin
    b. Bouin solution
    c. B-5 solution
    d. absolute alcohol

98. Sections of fetal liver were cut at 3 µm4 µm, stained with rhodanine for 18 hours at 37oC, and then counterstained with Mayer hematoxylin. Very little copper can be seen when the slides are examined microscopically. This is most likely because:
    a. fetal liver is not a good control
    b. the sections are too thin
    c. the staining time was prolonged
    d. the temperature was elevated

99. In her clinical studies, a student has prepared Fouchet reagent with acetic acid and ferric chloride for the demonstration of bile. Microscopic examination of the stained slides reveals a negative result. This was because Fouchet should have been prepared with:
    a. ferric sulfate and acetic acid
    b. ferric chloride and hydrochloric acid
    c. ferric ammonium sulfate and acetic acid
    d. ferric chloride and trichloroacetic acid

ISBN 978-089189-6401

100. Make 11 copies of the worksheet that follows, and complete 1 copy (try to do this without referring to the text) for each of the following techniques:

a. Prussian blue
b. Turnbull blue
c. Schmorl ferric-ferricyanide reduction
d. Fontana-Masson
e. Grimelius
f. Churukian-Schenk
g. Gomori methenamine silver
h. Hall
i. Von Kossa
j. Alizarin red S
k. Rhodanine

No answers are given for this exercise. The text must be used to check for correctness.

Staining Technique ______________________________

Preferred Fixative ______________________________

Preferred Thickness ______________________________

Microscope Used ______________________________

Control Tissue ______________________________

Major reagents	**Purpose**
Periodic acid	
Schiff reagent	
Metabisulfite rinse	
Running water	
Harris hematoxylin	

Principle of the Technique ______________________________

Purpose of Stain ______________________________

Results ______________________________

Sources of Error ______________________________

ISBN 978-089189-6401

Pigments, Minerals, & Cytoplasmic Granules *Answers*

Question	Answer	Discussion	*Histotechnology* Page
1A	b, d	Both the Fontana-Masson and Schmorl methods will stain argentaffin granules.	246-249
1B	a	Bile is stained with the Hall technique using Fouchet reagent.	255-256
1C	f	Calcium is demonstrated by the von Kossa technique.	256-257
1D	c	Hemosiderin (Fe^{+3}) is demonstrated by the Prussian blue reaction.	244
1E	b, d	Both the Fontana-Masson and the Schmorl methods will stain melanin.	246-249
1F	b, d	Both the Fontana-Masson and the Schmorl methods will stain reducing substances (eg, formalin pigment, melanin, argentaffin granules).	246-249
2A	b	Ferric-ferricyanide is used in the Schmorl technique to stain argentaffin granules.	246-247
2B	c	Bile is demonstrated with Fouchet reagent in the Hall method.	255-256
2C	a	Calcium may be demonstrated with alizarin red.	257-258
2D	e	Hemosiderin is demonstrated with potassium ferrocyanide and hydrochloric acid, forming ferric-ferrocyanide (Prussian blue).	244
2E	b	Melanin is demonstrated with ferric chloride and potassium ferrocyanide in the Schmorl technique.	246-247
3A	b	Bile is an endogenous/hematogenous pigment.	242
3B	e	Carbon is an exogenous/anthracotic pigment.	242
3C	b	Hemosiderin is an endogenous/hematogenous pigment.	242
3D	b	Iron is an endogenous/hematogenous pigment.	242
3E	c	Lipofuchsin is an endogenous/nonhematogenous pigment.	242
3F	c	Melanin is an endogenous/nonhematogenous pigment.	242
4	a	Potassium ferrocyanide and dilute hydrochloric acid are used in the Prussian blue reaction for iron with the ultimate formation of ferric-ferrocyanide.	244
5	a	The Fontana-Masson technique will demonstrate argentaffin granules (have both the ability to bind silver and to reduce it to its metallic form).	248-8249

Question	Answer	Discussion	*Histotechnology* Page
6	c	Von Kossa is used to demonstrate calcium, although it is an indirect method of detecting calcium; the silver binds with the anions (carbonate & phosphate) of the calcium salts.	256-257
7	b	Formalin pigment is a reducing substance and may give a positive reaction with both the Fontana-Masson and Schmorl techniques.	246-249
8	c	Urate crystals can be demonstrated with a methenamine silver technique.	244, 254-255
9	d	The Churukian-Schenk technique demonstrates argyrophil granules, and thus requires a reducing (developing) solution; the Schmorl and Fontana-Masson are argentaffin methods, and the Hall stain requires oxidation.	253-254
10	b	Rhodanine is used to demonstrate copper.	258-259
11	c	Carbon (anthracotic pigment) may be definitely identified by its insolubility in concentrated sulfuric acid and resistance to bleaching.	242
12	d	A nonaqueous fixative should be used if tissue is to be studied by microincineration or some inorganic substances may be lost.	244
13	c	Alcoholic fixatives should not be used if argentaffin granules are to be demonstrated because of their solubility in alcohol; neutral buffered formalin is preferred.	244, 248
14	a	Ferric ferrocyanide is the end product of the Prussian blue reaction.	245
15	d	The Turnbull reaction is for the detection of ferrous iron.	246-247
16	b	The end product of the Turnbull blue reaction for ferrous iron is potassium ferrous ferricyanide.	246
17	b	Red cells are very eosinophilic because of their content of hemoglobin which stains vividly with acid (anionic) dyes.	242
18	c	The Schmorl reaction will demonstrate melanin because it is a reducing substance.	246-247
19	b	In the Schmorl reaction, ferric iron is reduced to ferrous iron when then reacts with ferricyanide to give ferrous ferricyanide (Turnbull blue).	246-247
20	d	Because of the content of argentaffin cells, small intestine is a good control for the Schmorl reaction.	244
21	c	Neutral buffered formalin is the preferred fixative for the Churukian-Schenk technique.	252

ISBN 978-089189-6401

Question	Answer	Discussion	*Histotechnology* Page
22	a	Because of the content of melanin granules in the basal layer of the epidermis, skin is frequently used as a control for the Fontana-Masson stain.	248-249
23	c	In the Hall technique, bilirubin is oxidized to biliverdin by Fouchet reagent.	255-256
24	a	The Grimelius technique will demonstrate substances that can bind silver but need a chemical reducer (argyrophil substances).	251-252
25	c	Neutral buffered formalin is the preferred fixative for the Grimelius technique.	252
26	d	Neutral buffered formalin is the preferred fixative for the Fontana-Masson stain.	248
27	a	Small intestine is a good control for the Grimelius technique, but it must be remembered that both argentaffin and argyrophil cells will stain; therefore, the Fontana-Masson must also be run to definitively differentiate the argyrophil and argentaffin granules.	252-252
28	a	The Churukian-Schenk technique will demonstrate substances that can bind silver but need a chemical reducer (argyrophil substances).	252-253
29	c	Melanin is an argentaffin substance present in some tissues.	243
30	d	Bile pigments (bilirubin is the principle bile pigment) must be present in the control tissue used for the Hall stain.	255-256
31	b	Urate crystals are readily demonstrated by polarized light.	244
32	c	Spleen is usually a good control for iron stains, because if iron is not needed immediately, it is stored in the bone marrow and spleen as hemosiderin.	242
33	a	Fouchet reagent is used for the demonstration of bile pigments; it oxidizes bilirubin present in the bile pigments to biliverdin.	255-256
34	d	Because urate crystals present in a gouty tophus are water soluble and are dissolved by aqueous fixatives, absolute alcohol fixation is preferred.	244
35	c	Substances that can both bind and reduce silver (argentaffin substances) are demonstrated by the Fontana-Masson technique.	248-249
36	c	If the pigment seen microscopically is lying on top of the tissue, it is most likely an artifact.	242
37	c	Polarized light can be used to assist in the identification of formalin pigment; the other pigments are not birefringent.	242
38	a	Bile is stained emerald green in the Hall technique.	255-256

ISBN 978-089189-6401

Question	Answer	Discussion	*Histotechnology* Page
39	d	Fetal liver provides a good control for the rhodanine technique for copper.	258-259
40	b	Argentaffin substances can both bind and reduce silver.	248
41	a	Reducing substances are demonstrated by the Schmorl technique.	246-247
42	c	Methenamine silver is often used to demonstrate urates.	254-255
43	d	Melanin can be bleached from tissues by potassium permanganate.	252
44	c	Chromaffin granules are found in cells of the adrenal gland.	244
45	c	Bile is a breakdown product of hemoglobin.	242
46-1	A	The Fontana-Masson stains only argentaffin substances, that is, substances that have the ability bind or be impregnated with silver and to reduce silver to its metallic form.	248-249
46-2	C	The Grimelius will stain both argentaffin and argyrophil substances; it will stain those that have the ability to bind and reduce silver and those that bind but require an external reducer.	251-252
46-3	A	The Schmorl technique stains reducing substances only, or the same substances that have the ability to bind and reduce silver.	246-247
46-4	B	Argyrophil substances cannot reduce silver, but require and external reducing agent.	252
46-5	D	Alcoholic fixatives should be avoided as they dissolve argentaffin granules; neutral buffered formalin is preferred.	248
47-1	D	Neither pigment is an endogenous pigment.	242
47-2	B	Anthracotic (carbon) pigment is insoluble in concentrated sulfuric acid; this aids in differentiating it from other black pigments (formalin, malarial, melanin) that are soluble in concentrated sulfuric acid.	242
47-3	A	Formalin pigment will polarize light; this is an aid to identification.	242
47-4	A	Formalin pigment is a reducing substance and will stain with argentaffin techniques.	248-249
47-5	A	Only formalin pigment is soluble in alcoholic picric acid.	242

ISBN 978-089189-6401

Question	Answer	Discussion	*Histotechnology* Page
48-1	D	Neither urate crystals nor copper is normally present in demonstrable amounts in adult human tissue; they can be demonstrated only in diseased tissue.	244
48-2	A	Urate crystals are birefringent and thus may be demonstrated with polarizing microscopy.	244
48-3	A	Urate crystals may be demonstrated with the Gomori methenamine silver technique.	244,254-255
48-4	B	Copper may be demonstrated with the rhodanine technique.	258-259
48-5	A	Urate crystals are soluble in aqueous fixatives, and tissue must be fixed in absolute alcohol if urates are to be demonstrated.	244, 254
49-1	A	Calcium is demonstrated with a silver substitution method; silver reacts with the anions attached to calcium and then is reduced to metallic silver by exposure to bright light.	256-257
49-2	B	Melanin is demonstrated with the Fontana-Masson, an argentaffin silver method.	248-249
49-3	D	Neither is an artifact pigment.	242
49-4	B	Melanin is an endogenous, nonhematogenous pigment found in skin, hair, eyes, etc.	242
49-5	A	Calcium is a mineral normally found in the body.	244
50-1	A	The Prussian blue reaction demonstrates ferric iron.	245-246
50-2	B	The Turnbull blue reaction demonstrates ferrous iron.	246-247
50-3	B	The Turnbull blue reaction is the end product of the Schmorl reaction.	247
50-4	A	Hemochromatosis is condition in which too much ferric iron (hemosiderin) is stored due to a defect in the control of iron absorption, so the stored iron could be demonstrated with the Prussian blue reaction.	245-246
50-5	C	Both reactions require an acid pH.	245-247
51-1	B	The Churukian-Schenk will stain both argentaffin and argyrophil substances; it will stain those that have the ability to bind and reduce silver and those that bind but require an external reducer.	252-253
51-2	C	Argentaffin granules are demonstrated by both stains, as the granules have the ability to both bind and reduce silver.	248-249,252-253
51-3	B	Hydroquinone, an external reducer, is used only in the Churukian-Schenk procedure.	252-253

ISBN 978-089189-6401

Question	Answer	Discussion	*Histotechnology* Page
51-4	A	Gold chloride, a toning reagent, is used only in the Fontana-Masson stain.	248-249
51-5	D	Neither technique is a metal substitution method.	248-249, 252-253
52-1	C	Both biliverdin and hemosiderin are breakdown products of hemoglobin.	242
52-2	B	Bilirubin is oxidized to biliverdin, the reaction product, by Fouchet reagent.	255-256
52-3	D	Neither is demonstrated with the Turnbull blue reaction.	245-246, 255-256
52-4	D	Both are endogenous, hematogenous pigments.	242
52-5	A	Hemosiderin is the storage form of iron.	245-246
53	b	The blue stained substance is hemosiderin (stored ferric iron) that gives the Prussian blue reaction.	245
54	d	The tissue is bone marrow; both bone spicules and hematopoietic marrow can be seen.	245
55	b	Iron is stained by the Prussian blue reaction in this image.	245
56	a	Potassium ferrocyanide and hydrochloric acid are the reagents used to react with iron giving a final product of ferric ferrocyanide.	245
57	b	Spleen is a common control because it is one of the storage sites for excess iron, which is stored as hemosiderin.	245-246
58	d	Of the solutions listed, buffered formalin is the preferred fixative for iron.	245-246
59	b	The tissue shown in image B is colon, or gastrointestinal tract.	248
60	a	The Schmorl technique has stained argentaffin cells and pseudomelanin in this section of colon.	248
61	a	Reducing substances (melanin, argentaffin granules, formalin pigment, etc.) are stained by the Schmorl technique.	246-248
62	c	The final reaction product of the Schmorl technique is Turnbull blue.	246-248
63	c	Formalin pigment is a reducing substance and will give a positive reaction with the Schmorl technique.	246-248
64	a	The preferred fixative for the Schmorl technique is buffered formalin; alcohol will dissolve argentaffin granules.	246-248
65	c	The Fontana-Masson stain can be used to stain argentaffin granules.	248-250
66	c	Melanin present in the skin is stained black in image C.	248-250

ISBN 978-089189-6401

Question	Answer	Discussion	*Histotechnology* Page
67	d	Melanin has been stained black by the Fontana-Masson technique in image C.	248-250
68	b	The Fontana-Masson is a silver technique, and poor results might be obtained if metallic forceps are used to handle the slides.	248-250
69	d	Ileum contains argentaffin cells and would also be a good control for the Fontana-Masson.	248-250
70	a	The Schmorl technique will also demonstrate melanin.	246-248
71	b	The Fontana-Masson is an argentaffin technique.	248-250
72	b	Of the techniques listed, the tissue in image D was most likely stained by the Grimelius technique.	252
73	c	The Grimelius technique requires an external reducer, and hydroquinone is used for this purpose.	251-252
74	c	The Grimelius is a silver technique, and chemically cleaned glassware and nonmetallic forceps must be used.	251-252
75	a	Calcium is stained red in image E.	258
76	c	The alizarin red S technique was used to stain calcium red in image E.	257-258
77	c	The von Kossa is more commonly used to stain calcium.	256-257
78	d	Buffered formalin is the preferred fixative for the alizarin red technique, although alcoholic formalin may also be used.	257-258
79	c	Copper has been stained by rhodanine in image F.	259
80	b	Copper has been stained red by rhodanine in image F.	259
81	a	Copper is most frequently found in liver, either fetal liver or adult liver from a patient with Wilson disease.	258-259
82	c	Fetal liver usually contains copper and may be used as a control; normal adult liver does not contain copper.	258-259
83	c	The green stained substance is bile.	256
84	b	The primary reagent in the bile stain is Fouchet reagent.	255-256
85	d	The end product in the bile stain is biliverdin.	255-256
86	a	The stain in image H is the Fontana-Masson.	249
87	b	The black stained substance are argentaffin granules present in argentaffin cells.	249

Question	Answer	Discussion	*Histotechnology* Page
88	b	The Fontana-Masson stains only argentaffin substances, or substances that have the ability to both bind and reduce silver.	248-250
89	c	The tissue is small intestine as indicated by the columnar epithelium and scattered goblet cells.	249
90	a	Strong acids will dissolve iron, and it will not be demonstrable.	246
91	a	Urate crystals present in a gouty tophus are soluble in aqueous fixatives; therefore absolute alcohol must be used.	244
92	b	Prolonged impregnation in the incubating solution will give marked nonspecific staining or a dirty gray background and loss of contrast.	249-250
93	a	Chemically cleaned glassware and nonmetallic forceps must be used with silver stains, or marked black precipitate may result.	249-250
94	c	The developer is a reducing solution that is necessary to reduce silver to its visible metallic form; old developer will not carry out this function.	251-252
95	a	Urate crystals present in a gouty tophus are birefringent, and provided that the tissue was fixed in absolute alcohol, their presence can be confirmed with polarizing microscopy.	244
96	c	If staining jars have been used for solutions containing iron, they must be chemically cleaned before use for an iron stain.	246
97	b	Acidic fixatives such as Bouin may remove calcium, and it will not be demonstrable.	20, 256-257
98	b	Sections for copper staining by the rhodanine method should be cut at 6 μm to 8 μm.	258-259
99	d	Fouchet reagent for bile staining is a mixture of trichloracetic acid, 10% ferric chloride, and distilled water.	255

ISBN 978-089189-6401

Immunohistochemistry *Questions*

1-26. The following are multiple choice questions. Please circle the letter in front of the correct answer. There is only 1 best answer.

1. An antigen is a substance that triggers the production of:
   a. immunogens
   b. immunoglobulins
   c. hormones
   d. epitopes

2. A light chain present in some antibodies is:
   a. IgM
   b. IgG
   c. IgE
   d. κ

3. Different molecular sites on antigens are known as:
   a. antibody classes
   b. heavy chains
   c. epitopes
   d. immunoglobulins

4. When an antibody labeled with a chromogen is reacted with tissue from a patient, the immunohistochemical technique is called:
   a. direct
   b. indirect
   c. avidin-biotin complex
   d. soluble enzyme immune complex

5. Which of the following is a fluorochrome?
   a. alkaline phosphatase
   b. rhodamine
   c. fast red
   d. diaminobenzidine

6. In the indirect immunohistochemical method, the:
   a. labeled antibody is reacted with the patient's tissue
   b. soluble enzyme-antienzyme complex is made in the same animal as the primary antibody used
   c. patient's serum is added to tissue sections containing known antigens
   d. technique depends on the formation of an avidin-biotin complex

ISBN 978-089189-6401

7. In the avidin-biotin methods, the primary antibody is followed by:
   a. the avidin-biotin complex
   b. biotinylated secondary antibody
   c. avidin conjugated secondary antibody
   d. enzyme conjugated secondary antibody

8. A dye that absorbs light and then emits its own light at a longer wavelength is known as:
   a. a chromogen
   b. conjugated
   c. labeled
   d. a fluorochrome

9. In some immunohistochemical techniques, alkaline phosphatase functions as the:
   a. chromogen
   b. substrate
   c. enzyme
   d. immunogen

10. Horseradish peroxidase is used in some avidin-biotin methods as the:
    a. chromogen
    b. label
    c. substrate
    d. enzyme

11. The substrate for alkaline phosphatase labeled antibodies is commonly:
    a. fast red
    b. naphthol-AS-phosphate
    c. anti-alkaline phosphatase
    d. avidin

12. Which of the following chromogens is INSOLUBLE in alcohol?
    a. fast red TR
    b. 3,3′-diaminobenzidine tetrahydrochloride (DAB)
    c. 3-amino-9-ethylcarbazole (AEC)
    d. fast blue BBN

13. If 3-amino-9-ethylcarbazole is used as the chromogen, the hematoxylin used for counterstaining should be:
    a. alcohol free
    b. double strength
    c. used regressively
    d. an iron hematoxylin

14. Tissue for immunofluorescence must be:
    a. fixed briefly in formalin and then frozen
    b. frozen and then fixed in acetone
    c. fixed in alcohol and paraffin processed
    d. frozen and unfixed

ISBN 978-089189-6401

15. A neoplasm is defined as a/an:
    a. anaplastic tumor
    b adenocarcinoma
    c. undifferentiated tumor
    d. new growth of uncontrolled cell multiplication

16. Which of the following is NOT the proper approach to validation of a new antibody?
    a. trying with no retrieval solutions
    b. trying with multiple retrieval solutions
    c. trying with multiple dilutions
    d. using only with the manufacturer's recommendations

17. When the vimentin stain is completely negative on formalin fixed tissues, this indicates that most likely the tissue has been:
    a. optimally fixed
    b. overfixed
    c. underfixed
    d unfixed

18. Besides the heat employed, another important factor in heat induced epitope retrieval (HIER) is the:
    a. enzyme solution selected
    b. use of a metallic solution
    c. composition of the solution used
    d. use of cold solutions

19. Ficin is used in immunohistochemistry:
    a. for enzyme induced epitope enhancement
    b. as the enzyme label for some antibodies
    c. as the chromogen with alkaline phosphatase
    d. in some buffer solutions

20. 0.5 mL of a 1:50 dilution of antibody is needed. How many microliters of the primary would be needed?
    a. 0.1
    b. 1.0
    c. 10.0
    d. 100.0

21. Which of the following has been eliminated with polymeric immunohistochemical staining methods?
    a. chromogen
    b. serum and avidin-biotin blocking steps
    c. heat and enzyme retrieval methods
    d. secondary antibody

22. In the peroxidase-antiperoxidase (PAP) method of antigen detection, the PAP complex is made in the same species as the:
    a. link antibody
    b. biotin labeled antibody
    c. primary antibody
    d. secondary antibody

ISBN 978-089189-6401

23. Imidazole may be used in peroxidase techniques:
    a. as the chromogen
    b. to block endogenous activity
    c. as the substrate
    d. to intensify the DAB reaction

24. Which of the following link antibodies would most likely follow a monoclonal κ primary antibody?
    a. rabbit anti-mouse
    b. rabbit anti-human
    c. rabbit anti-sheep
    d. rabbit anti-goat

25. Which of the following antibodies would NOT help classify a lymphoma:
    a. CK20
    b. CD15
    c. CD20
    d. CD3

26. Negative control slides run with each stain for a specific antibody omit the:
    a. chromogen
    b. enzyme
    c. primary antibody
    d. secondary antibody

27-43. The following statements are either true or false. Circle T if the statement is true, circle F if the statement is false.

27. Prediluted antibodies should always be used as provided by the manufacturer. **[T\F]**

28. Negative tissue antigen controls may be run by substituting for the primary antibody the diluent in which the antibody is prepared. **[T\F]**

29. One standard staining protocol may be written to cover all specimens. **[T\F]**

30. Zinc formalin preserves immunoreactivity very well. **[T\F]**

31. Multilink antibodies can be used only with monoclonal primary antibodies. **[T\F]**

32. Blocking reactions are used to block endogenous activity of the same enzyme as that used for the enzyme immune complex. **[T\F]**

33. The enzyme label for immunoperoxidase methods contains horseradish peroxidase. **[T\F]**

34. Monoclonal antibodies are often preferred over polyclonal antibodies because there is no batch-to-batch variability. **[T\F]**

35. DAB is an alcohol soluble chromogen. **[T\F]**

ISBN 978-089189-6401

36. Harris hematoxylin should not be used with 3-amino-9-ethylcarbazole (AEC) because of the alcohol present. **[T\F]**

37. Regulations regarding predictive marker staining of tissue places responsibility for documenting time in fixative on the laboratory. **[T\F]**

38. The only method of heat induced epitope retrieval involves the use of the microwave oven. **[T\F]**

39. Optimal dilutions for each antibody must be determined in your laboratory. **[T\F]**

40. Metal salts involving nickel, copper, and osmium may be used to intensify the 3-amino-9-ethylcarbazole reaction. **[T\F]**

41. Alkaline phosphatase label can be substituted for peroxidase label in most immunohistochemical methods. **[T\F]**

42. Precut control slides may be stored at room temperature indefinitely. **[T\F]**

43. The procedure for staining cytology smears is the same as the one for staining paraffin sections. **[T\F]**

44. Match the following. Each antibody on the left should be matched with the cell/disease process that it is used for on the right.

Antibody	**Cell/disease process**
_____A. CD3	a. glioblastoma
_____B. CD20	b. breast carcinoma
_____C. HMB45	c. T cell lymphoma
_____D. Her2	d. melanoma
_____E. GFAP	e. carcinoma
_____F. AE1/AE3	f. B cell lymphoma

ISBN 978-089189-6401

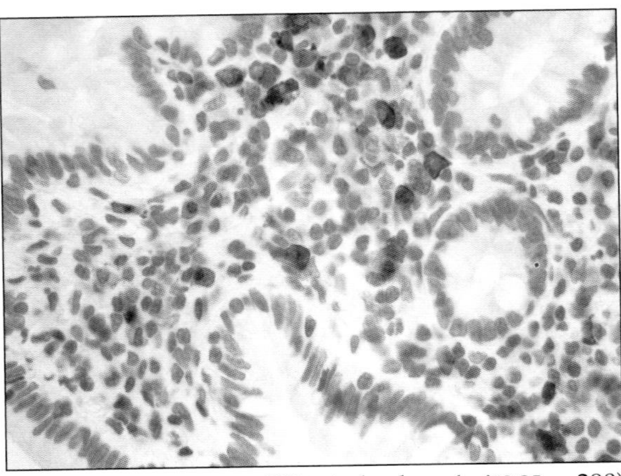

A (*Histotechnology 4e*, **i12.25**, p 290)

45-65. The following questions refer to images A-G as specified.

45. The chromogen used for the technique shown in image A is most likely:
    a. 3,3′-diaminobenzidine
    b. AEC
    c. avidin-biotin complex
    d. PAP

46. The tissue shown in image A is:
    a. cervix
    b. liver
    c. kidney
    d. gastrointestinal tract

47. The cells stained brick red in image A are:
    a. epithelial
    b. plasma
    c. fibroblasts
    d. smooth muscle

48. The substance stained brick red in image A is:
    a. collagen
    b. Golgi apparatus
    c. immunoglobulin
    d. glycogen

ISBN 978-089189-6401

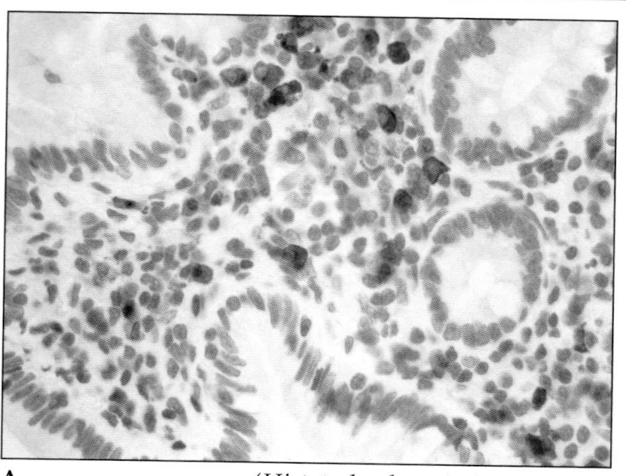

A (*Histotechnology 4e*, **i12.25**, p 290)

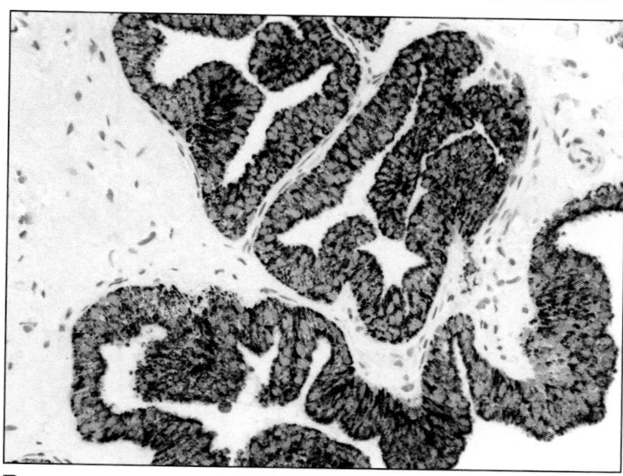

B (*Histotechnology 4e*, **i12.26**, p 291)

49. Which of the following antibodies was most likely used for the stain shown in image A?
    a. epithelial membrane antigen (EMA)
    b. leukocyte common antigen (LCA)
    c. λ
    d. S100

50. The cells with the red cytoplasmic staining in image A would show reddish pink cytoplasmic staining with which of the following?
    a. Congo red
    b. PAS
    c. MGP
    d. Best carmine

51. The tissue shown in image B is:
    a. esophagus
    b. prostate
    c. kidney
    d. skin

52. The tissue structure stained brown in image B is:
    a. epithelium
    b. dermis
    c. muscle
    d. collagen

53. The chromogen used for the technique shown in image B is most likely:
    a. DAB
    b. AEC
    c. ABC
    d. PAP

ISBN 978-089189-6401

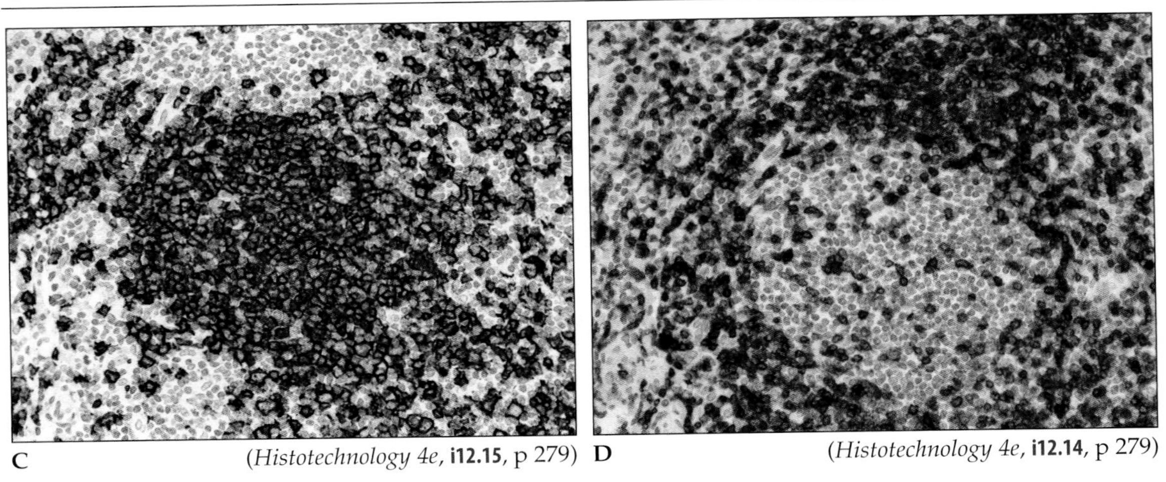

C (*Histotechnology 4e*, **i12.15**, p 279) D (*Histotechnology 4e*, **i12.14**, p 279)

54. The antibody used for the stain shown in image C is most likely:
    a. S100
    b. cytokeratin
    c. GFAP
    d. CD20

55. The cells stained brown in image C are most likely:
    a. plasma
    b. B cells
    c. T cells
    d. epithelial

56. The cells stained brown in image C are located in the lymph node:
    a. germinal center
    b. paracortex
    c. sinusoids
    d. perifollicular zone

57. The cells stained brown in image D are most likely:
    a. plasma
    b. B cells
    c T cells
    d epithelial

58. The cells stained brown in image D are most likely located in a/an:
    a. kidney
    b. lymph node
    c. esophagus
    d. melanoma

59. The antibody used for the stain shown in image D is most likely:
    a. CK20
    b. GFAP
    c. PSA
    d. CD3

ISBN 978-089189-6401

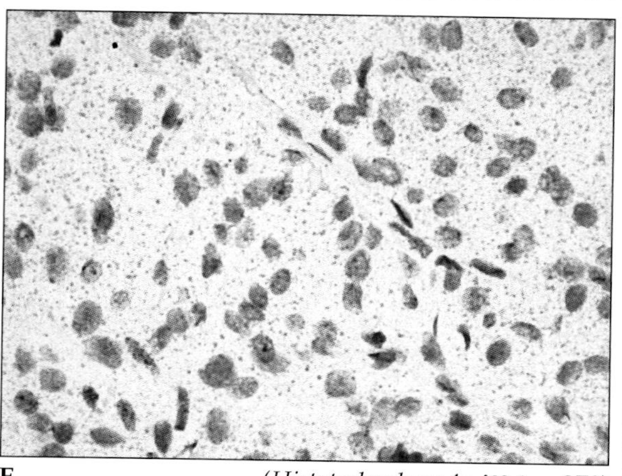

E (*Histotechnology 4e*, **i12.8**, p 270)

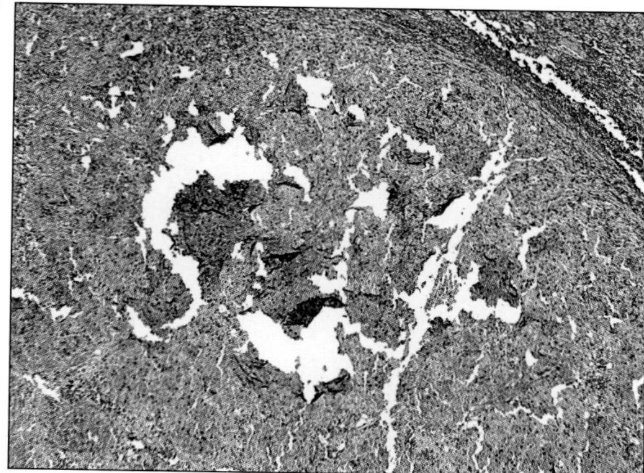

F (*Histotechnology 4e*, **i12.7**, p 268)

60. The technique used in image E is most likely:
    a. peroxidase-antiperoxidase
    b. alkaline phosphatase
    c. avidin-biotin
    d. polymeric

61. The red precipitate shown in image E is most likely due to:
    a. the wrong enzyme system
    b. prolonged incubation with the antibody
    c. improper dehydration
    d. mounting with synthetic resin

62. The problem shown in image F is most likely due to:
    a. prolonged flotation
    b. poor microtomy technique
    c. microwave slide drying
    d. antigen retrieval technique

63. One cause of the problem shown in image F might be:
    a. high pH of retrieval solution
    b. use of laboratory microwave for retrieval
    c. too much cross-linking during fixation
    d. too much adhesive in the flotation bath

ISBN 978-089189-6401

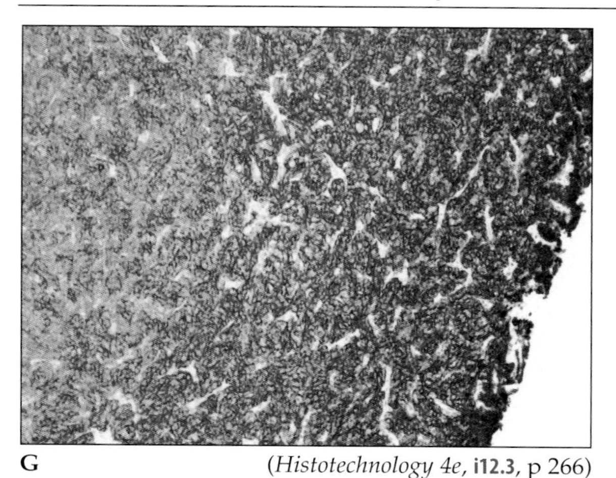

G (*Histotechnology 4e*, **i12.3**, p 266)

64. The problem demonstrated in image G is due to poor:
    a. microtomy
    b. flotation
    c. retrieval
    d. fixation

65. The problem shown in image G could most likely have been corrected by:
    a. ensuring complete fixation in formalin
    b. using cooler water in the flotation bath
    c. using a different retrieval solution
    d. ensuring that sectioning is good

66-73. The following are problem solving questions.

66. In the bloody areas of a tissue section stained with the immunoperoxidase technique, there is a marked reaction of the red blood cells. This is most likely the result of:
    a. selecting the wrong chromogen
    b. forgetting to apply nonimmune serum
    c. failure to use hydrogen peroxide
    d. prolonging incubation with the primary antibody

67. Paraffin sections stained with the immunoperoxidase technique show excess background staining. Which of the following could be the explanation for this?
    a. selecting the wrong chromogen
    b. forgetting to apply nonimmune serum
    c. overfixation with formaldehyde
    d. prolonging incubation with the secondary antibody

68. The skin control section for S100 was stained with the immunoalkaline phosphatase technique using fast red TR as the chromogen. It shows negative staining. One possible explanation might be that the:
    a. sections were dehydrated and cleared
    b. chromogen was too concentrated
    c. blocking step was omitted
    d. incubation with the link antibody was prolonged

ISBN 978-089189-6401

69. At the end of the immunoperoxidase staining procedure, it was realized that an anti-goat linking antibody was used with monoclonal HMB-45 antibody. Microscopic results should show a:
    a. negatively stained positive control and negatively stained specimen
    b. negatively stained positive control and positively stained specimen
    c. positively stained positive control and positively stained specimen
    d. positively stained positive control and negatively stained specimen

70. Both the known positive control and the specimen are negative following immunoperoxidase staining with LCA primary antibody. DAB was used as the chromogen. Which of the following could be the cause?
    a. solubility of the chromogen in dehydrating and clearing agents
    b. failure to block endogenous peroxidase
    c. wrong secondary antibody was used
    d. antigen masked during fixation

71. Excessive background is noted on both the control and specimen stained with immunoperoxidase. This might be the result of:
    a. prolonged fixation
    b. inadequate incubation with the primary
    c. protracted deparaffinization
    d. insufficient washing with buffer

72. Excessive background is noted on the specimen but not on the positive control stained with immunoperoxidase. This is most likely the result of:
    a. prolonged fixation
    b. free antigen in the tissue
    c. the wrong antibody dilution
    d. inadequate epitope retrieval

73. Both the positive control and the specimen stained with immunoalkaline phosphatase using CEA antibody show very weak staining. This is most likely the result of:
    a. failure to block endogenous alkaline phosphatase
    b. application of the wrong linking antibody
    c. incorrectly diluted primary antibody
    d. primary antibody not being added

ISBN 978-089189-6401

Immunohistochemistry *Answers*

Question	Answer	Discussion	*Histotechnology* Page
1	b	Antigens induce antibody (immunoglobulin) production by the body.	264
2	d	Light chains present in antibodies, commonly known as immunoglobulins, are either κ or λ.	264
3	c	Epitopes are the sites on antigens at which specific antibodies attach.	264
4	a	In the direct immunohistochemical method, a labeled antibody of known specificity is used to identify antigens in the patient's tissue. An example is the detection of immune complex deposition in renal biopsy specimens using direct immunohistochemical techniques.	270
5	b	Rhodamine and fluorescein isothiocyanate (FITC) are fluorochromes.	270
6	c	In the indirect immunohistochemical method, the patient's serum is added to tissue sections containing known antigens to test the patient for the presence of antibodies to those antigens.	271
7	b	In the avidin-biotin methods, the primary antibody is followed by biotinylated secondary (linking) antibody.	271
8	d	A fluorochrome is a dye that absorbs light and then emits its own light at a longer wavelength.	270
9	c	Alkaline phosphatase functions as the enzyme in alkaline phosphatase immunohistochemical procedures.	269,271
10	d	Horseradish peroxidase functions in some avidin-biotin methods as the enzyme.	289
11	b	Alkaline phosphatase is demonstrated by the use of naphthol-AS-phosphate (substrate) and a chromogen such as fast red-violet LB.	269
12	b	Of the chromogens listed, only DAB is insoluble in alcohol; AEC and alkaline phosphatase chromogens must not be exposed to alcohol or synthetic resin mountants.	269
13	a	If hematoxylin is used following AEC, it must be one that is alcohol free, such as Mayer hematoxylin.	270
14	d	Tissue for immunofluorescence must to frozen and unfixed because antigenic reactivity is least impaired and fluorescent antibody staining is strongest.	265

ISBN 978-089189-6401

Question	Answer	Discussion	*Histotechnology* Page
15	d	A neoplasm is a new growth of tissue in which cell multiplication is uncontrolled and progressive; it can be malignant or benign.	276
16	d	Prediluted antibodies must be validated for reactivity before use on patient tissue. The laboratory cannot assume that the antibody is ready to use with that laboratory's method.	272
17	b	Vimentin staining is usually excellent in paraffin sections of tissue that have been optimally fixed in formalin but is progressively lost as the length of time in the fixative increases. When the vimentin stain is completely negative, the tissue is most likely overfixed.	268
18	c	Many studies have shown that the composition of the retrieval solution is very important in HIER.	268
19	a	Ficin is one of the proteolytic enzymes used in immunohistochemistry for enzyme induced epitope enhancement (EIER).	269
20	c	10.0 µL of antibody would be needed. (0.5 mL = 500 µL; 500 µL ÷ 50 = 10 µL)	273
21	b	The serum and avidin-biotin blocking steps have been eliminated with polymeric detection methods; this has also improved turnaround times.	271
22	c	In the PAP method, the PAP complex must be made in the same species as the primary antibody in order for the secondary antibody to link them together.	271
23	d	Imidazole is an effective intensification reagent for the DAB reaction product.	276
24	a	Since monoclonal κ antibodies are usually prepared in either mice or rabbits, the linking antibody would need to be anti mouse or anti rabbit.	271
25	a	CK 20 is an antibody for colon cancer.	278
26	c	Substituting a nonimmune serum for the primary antibody is commonly done for negative controls.	272
27	F	Prediluted antibodies must be validated for reactivity before use on patient tissue; the laboratory cannot assume that the antibody is ready to use with that laboratory's method and must perform serial dilutions to validate.	272
28	T	Negative controls are those that omit the antibody during the primary incubation step and substitute for it. Commonly, the antibody diluent in which the antibody is prepared is used for this purpose.	272

ISBN 978-089189-6401

Question	Answer	Discussion	*Histotechnology* Page
29	F	A detailed procedure must be written to address each specimen requiring a nonstandard protocol because of the use of various fixatives, frozen sections, imprints, or cytocentrifuge preparations.	283
30	T	Zinc formalin preserves immunoreactivity remarkably well; because of this, some laboratories switched from 10% neutral buffered formalin to some formulation of zinc formalin for routine processing.	273
31	F	Multilink antibodies can be used with both monoclonal and polyclonal primary antibodies; they have the advantage of avoiding having to stock a variety of specific link antibodies.	276
32	T	Blocking reactions are used to block endogenous activity of the same enzyme as that used for the enzyme immune complex (endogenous peroxidase block for immunoperoxidase procedures).	274-275
33	T	The enzyme label for immunoperoxidase methods contains horseradish peroxidase.	269
34	T	An advantage of monoclonal antibodies is the lack of batch-to-batch variability.	265
35	F	DAB is not alcohol soluble, and sections may be dehydrated, cleared, and mounted with synthetic resin.	269
36	T	AEC is alcohol soluble and a nonalcoholic hematoxylin such as Mayer should be used.	270
37	T	Regulations now make the laboratory responsible for documenting the time specimens are in fixative.	266
38	F	Acceptable methods of heating other than the microwave oven are pressure cooker, vegetable steamer, and circulating water bath.	268-269
39	T	The laboratory cannot assume that an antibody is ready to use and must perform serial dilutions to validate.	272
40	F	AEC is not intensified; the metal salts listed are used to intensify the DAB reaction.	276
41	T	Alkaline phosphatase label can be substituted for peroxidase label in most immunohistochemical methods.	269-270
42	F	Storing precut control slides at room temperature for long periods is not recommended; storage at –20°C is better for most, but not all, antigens.	282
43	F	Each different type of specimen (eg, frozen sections, paraffin sections, cytology smears) must have its own protocol for immunohistochemical staining.	283

ISBN 978-089189-6401

Question	Answer	Discussion	*Histotechnology* Page
44A		CD3 is used in the identification of T cell lymphomas.	278
44B		CD20 is used in the identification of B cell lymphomas.	278
44C	d	HMB45 is used to aid in the identification of melanoma.	278
44D	b	Her2 is used in the identification of breast carcinoma.	278
44E	a	GFAP is used in the identification of glioblastomas	278
44F	e	AE1/AE3 is a cytokeratin antibody used in the identification of carcinomas.	278
45	b	The chromogen in image A is 3-amino-9-ethylcarbazole (AEC).	290
46	d	The tissue shown in image A is gastrointestinal tract.	290
47	b	The cytoplasm of plasma cells is stained red in image A.	290
48	c	The substance stained red in image A is immunoglobulin.	264-290
48	c	The antibody most likely used for image A is λ, a light chain component of some immunoglobulins.	264, 290
50	c	The plasma cells that show red cytoplasmic staining in image A would show red-pink cytoplasmic staining with the MGP.	128--129
51	b	The tissue shown in image B is prostate.	291
52	a	The tissue structure stained brown in image B is epithelium.	291
52	a	3,3′-diaminobenzidine (DAB) is the chromogen used in image B.	291
54	d	The antibody used for the stain shown in image C is most likely CD20, a marker for B cells.	279
55	b	The cells stained brown in image C are most likely B cells.	279
56	a	The cells stained brown in image C are located in the germinal center of a lymph nodule.	279
57	c	The cells stained brown in image D are most likely T cells.	279
58	b	The cells stained brown in image D are most likely located in a lymph node.	279
59	d	The antibody used in image D is most likely CD3.	279
60	b	The technique used in image E is most likely alkaline phosphatase, identified by the red color of the chromogen.	270

ISBN 978-089189-6401

Question	Answer	Discussion	*Histotechnology* Page
61	c	The red precipitate in image E is most likely due to improper dehydration. Chromogens used with this technique do not tolerate dehydration very well, and slides should be air dried or quickly dehydrated to xylene and mounted with synthetic resin.	269-270
62	d	The tissue has become detached in this section due to the antigen retrieval technique being too harsh/aggressive.	269
63	a	A high pH of the retrieval solution may cause damage to the tissue after heating in the strongly alkaline solution.	268
64	d	The tissue in image G has been incompletely fixed in formalin. The center demonstrates alcohol fixation, while the periphery shows formalin fixation.	266
65	a	Complete fixation in formalin prior to processing would have prevented the problem shown in image G.	266
66	c	If the tissue contains many red blood cells, the hydrogen peroxidase blocking step is essential to reduce nonspecific staining of RBCs.	274
67	b	If the first protein solution applied to the tissue is the primary antibody, nonspecific binding can occur. Nonimmune serum is applied just before the primary to prevent this nonspecific staining.	276
68	a	The chromogens for the alkaline phosphatase staining cannot be dehydrated and cleared as usual, and with prolonged dehydration, the alkaline phosphatase chromogen can break down.	269
69	a	Since monoclonal antibodies are most often prepared in mice or rabbits, an anti-mouse, anti-rabbit, or multilink linking secondary antibody must be used, or false negative (nonstaining) results will occur.	286
70	c	The secondary antibody must be targeted to the primary for linking to occur.	284271
71	d	Slides must be washed well between antibody applications.	288
72	b	Free antigen in the patient tissue because of necrosis, autolysis, or degeneration will cause excess background staining in the patient's tissue.	286-287
73	c	If the correct dilution of an antibody has not been determined for optimum reaction, then weak staining may result.	273

ISBN 978-089189-6401

Enzyme Histochemistry
Questions

1-32. The following are multiple choice questions. Please circle the letter in front of the correct answer. There is only 1 best answer.

1. Enzymes are:
   a. vitamins
   b. metals
   c. proteins
   d. cofactors

2. Biological oxidation occurs with the:
   a. loss of hydrogen
   b. loss of oxygen
   c. gain of hydrogen
   d. gain of electrons

3. A compound is reduced when which of the following is removed?
   a. water
   b. oxygen
   c. hydrogen
   d. electrons

4. The compound or chemical group on which a specific enzyme works is known as its:
   a. cofactor
   b. coenzyme
   c. product
   d. substrate

5. Tissue for some enzyme demonstration should be fixed if possible because:
   a. diffusion artifact is decreased
   b. enzyme activity is enhanced
   c. a wider range of temperatures can be used
   d. the concentration of the substrate is less critical

6. Tissue for enzyme studies has been fixed in cold calcium formalin. The best storage medium is:
   a. 70% alcohol
   b. cold calcium formalin solution
   c. cold physiological saline
   d. 30% sucrose with 1% gum acacia

7. Enzymes that act on substrates by adding water belong to the group known as:
   a. phosphorylases
   b. hydrolases
   c. oxidoreductases
   d. transferases

ISBN 978-089189-6401

8. The optimum procedure for freezing muscle biopsies is:
   a. isopentane at –150°C
   b. liquid nitrogen
   c. the cryostat chiller plate
   d. freon

9. The supply of isopentane is depleted, although liquid nitrogen is available, and a muscle biopsy needs to be frozen. In this case, the best method of freezing would be:
   a. the cryostat chiller plate
   b. to suspend the biopsy in liquid nitrogen alone
   c. to dust muscle with talc, then freeze in liquid nitrogen
   d. to hold the muscle in saline until isopentane can be obtained

10. The most frequently used methods of demonstrating hydrolytic enzymes involve:
    a. metallic impregnation
    b. simultaneous coupling
    c. intramolecular rearrangement
    d. the use of reduced substrate

11. When used on muscle biopsies, the α-naphthyl acetate esterase stain demonstrates:
    a. specific esterases
    b. mitochondria
    c. type II atrophy
    d. motor end plates

12. Paraffin sections may be used for which of the following stains?
    a. naphthol AS-D chloroacetate esterase
    b. α-naphthyl acetate esterase
    c. acid phosphatase
    d. reduced nicotinamide adenine dinucleotide (NADH)

13. The naphthol AS-D chloroacetate esterase demonstrates:
    a. granulocytes
    b. plasma cells
    c. mitochondria
    d. motor end plates

14. The ATPase reaction involves both:
    a. postincubation and metallic precipitation
    b. simultaneous coupling and metallic substitution
    c. self colored substrate and intramolecular rearrangement
    d. metallic precipitation and intramolecular rearrangement

15. The final colored product in the ATPase reaction is:
    a. calcium phosphate
    b. cobalt phosphate
    c. cobalt sulfide
    d. calcium sulfide

ISBN 978-089189-6401

16. With the ATPase stain, pH 9.4, on a normal muscle biopsy, the results show:
    a. dark type IIA and IIB fibers and light type I fibers
    b. light type IIA and IIB fibers and dark type I fibers
    c. dark type IIA fibers and light type IIB and type I fibers
    d. light type IIA fibers and dark type IIB and type I fibers

17. The acid phosphatase reaction demonstrates the:
    a. alcohol residue of naphthol AS-BI phosphate
    b. orthophosphate split off naphthol AS-BI phosphate
    c. use of adenosine triphosphate as the substrate
    d. postcoupling technique using a tetrazolium dye

18. The acid phosphatase reaction on muscle demonstrates:
    a. lysosomes
    b. mitochondria
    c. Z-band material
    d. regenerating fibers

19. The end product of the α-naphthyl acetate esterase, acid phosphatase, and alkaline phosphatase stains is:
    a. cobaltous sulfide
    b. an anthraquinone
    c. an azo dye
    d. a tetrazolium

20. The NADH diaphorase or reductase technique on muscle demonstrates:
    a. mitochondria, lysosomes, and endoplasmic reticulum
    b. mitochondria, Z-band material, and sarcoplasmic reticulum
    c. mitochondria, lysosomes, and endoplasmic reticulum
    d. lysosomes, Z-band material, and sarcoplasmic reticulum

21. Microscopic evaluation of the NADH diaphorase stains shows marked precipitate on the section. This is most likely the result of:
    a. mounting with an aqueous mounting medium
    b. buffering the incubating solution to pH 7.4
    c. unripened nitro blue tetrazolium solution
    d. buffering the incubating solution to pH 8.5

22. Succinic dehydrogenase procedures demonstrate:
    a. mitochondria
    b. lysosomes
    c. Z-band material
    d. sarcoplasmic reticulum

23. The absence of phosphorylase activity in muscle indicates:
    a. Pompe disease
    b. Cori disease
    c. McArdle disease
    d. normal muscle

ISBN 978-089189-6401

24. The phosphorylase stained sections were not read for several days. The best action is to:
    a. repeat the procedure
    b. restain in dilute iodine
    c. read the slides as usual
    d. recoverslip with a synthetic resin

25. Nitro blue tetrazolium functions as a:
    a. colored substrate
    b. buffer solution
    c. primer solution
    d. hydrogen acceptor

26. The endomysium is a network of connective tissue surrounding:
    a. each muscle fiber
    b. a muscle fascicle
    c. an entire muscle
    d. the tendinous insertion

27. Skeletal muscle can be identified by the presence of:
    a. intercalated disks
    b. internal nuclei
    c. branching fibers
    d. peripheral nuclei

28. Fibers that are high in oxidative enzymes are classified as:
    a. type I fibers
    b. type IIA fibers
    c. type IIB fibers
    d. type IIC fibers

29. Type II fibers would be expected to contain an abundance of:
    a. succinic dehydrogenase
    b. acid phosphatase
    c. esterase
    d. phosphorylase

30. The stain used most commonly for the diagnosis of a glycogen storage disease affecting muscle is the:
    a. Masson trichrome
    b. PTAH
    c. oil red O
    d. PAS

31. An important property of enzymes that they:
    a. slow down biological reactions
    b. are destroyed in the reaction
    c. bind to the substrate
    d. act over a large range of temperatures

ISBN 978-089189-6401

32. List 4 types of histochemical reactions for the demonstration of hydrolytic enzymes.
    a. ______________________________
    b. ______________________________
    c. ______________________________
    d. ______________________________

33. List 4 factors that influence enzyme demonstration
    a.______________________________
    b.______________________________
    c.______________________________
    d.______________________________

34. Match the following enzymes on the left with the appropriate group on the right.

Enzyme	Group
____A. Acid phosphatase	a. hydrolase
____B. Adenosine triphosphatase	b. oxidoreductase
____C. Alkaline phosphatase	c. transferase
____D. Esterase	
____E. NADH diaphorase	
____F. Phosphorylase	
____G. Succinic dehydrogenase	

35. Match the enzyme on the left with the reagent used in the demonstration of that enzyme on the right. Letters may be used more than once or not at all.

Enzyme	Reagent
____A. Acid phosphatase	a. α-naphthyl acetate
____B. ATPase	b. cobalt chloride
____C. NADH diaphorase	c. Gram iodine
____D. Nonspecific esterase	d. hexazotized pararosaniline
____E. Phosphorylase	e. naphthol AS-BI-phosphate
	f. naphthol AS-D chloroacetate
	g. nitro blue tetrazolium

ISBN 978-089189-6401

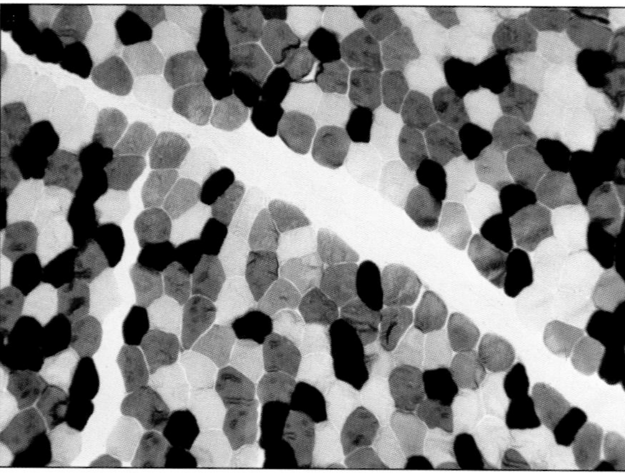

A (*Histotechnology 4e*, **i13.13**, p 305)

36-58. The following questions relate to images A-E as specified.

36. The muscle shown in image A is:
    a. cardiac muscle
    b. skeletal muscle
    c. smooth
    d. involuntary

37. The stain demonstrated in image A is the:
    a. alkaline phosphatase
    b. phosphorylase
    c. NADH diaphorase
    d. ATPase

38. If the stain was done at pH 4.6, the tissue component stained dark in image A is most likely:
    a. type I skeletal muscle fibers
    b. type IIA skeletal muscle fibers
    c. type IIB skeletal muscle fibers
    d. degenerating skeletal muscle fibers

39. The final reaction product in the technique demonstrated in image A is a/an:
    a. azo dye
    b. cobalt sulfide
    c. formazan
    d. substituted naphthol

40. If the technique in image A was done at a pH of 4.6, the muscle shows:
    a. the normal distribution of fiber types
    b. an abnormal distribution of fiber types
    c. the presence of type IIC fibers
    d. an absence of type I fibers

ISBN 978-089189-6401

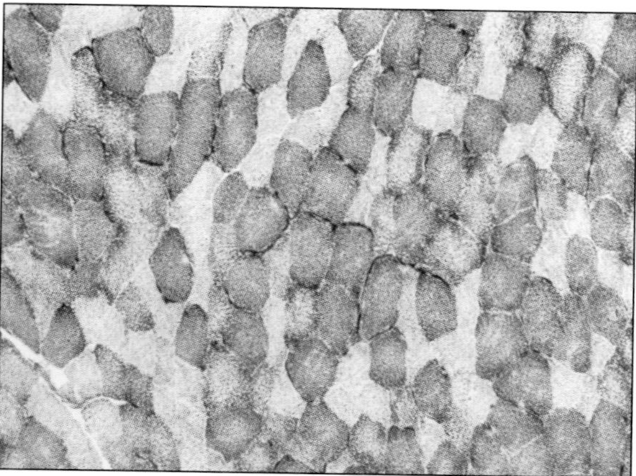

B (*Histotechnology 4e*, **i13.20**, p 309)

41. The stain demonstrated in image B is most likely the:
    a. NADH diaphorase
    b. ATPase, pH 4.2
    c. alkaline phosphatase
    d. naphthol AS-D chloroacetate esterase

42. The final reaction product in the technique demonstrated in image B is a/an:
    a. azo dye
    b. cobalt sulfide
    c. formazan
    d. substituted naphthol

43. A reagent used in the technique demonstrated in image B is:
    a. cobalt chloride
    b. a tetrazolium salt
    c. Gram iodine
    d. hexazotized pararosaniline

44. The enzyme technique demonstrated in image B belongs to which of the following groups?
    a. oxidoreductases
    b. hydrolases
    c. transfearases
    d. lipases

45. The fibers stained dark in image B are:
    a. type I
    b. type IIA
    c. type IIB
    d. type IIC

ISBN 978-089189-6401

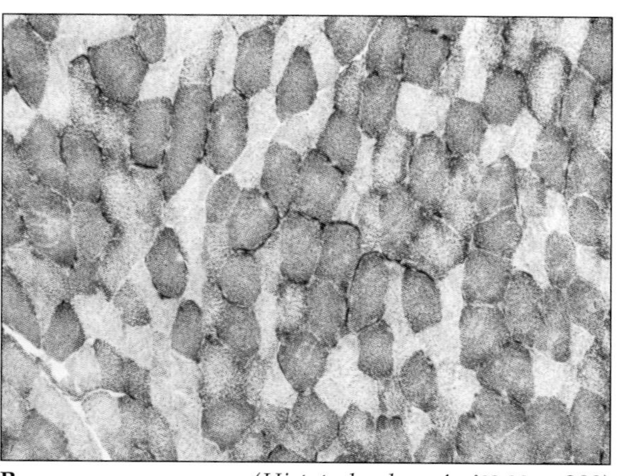

B (*Histotechnology 4e*, **i13.20**, p 309)

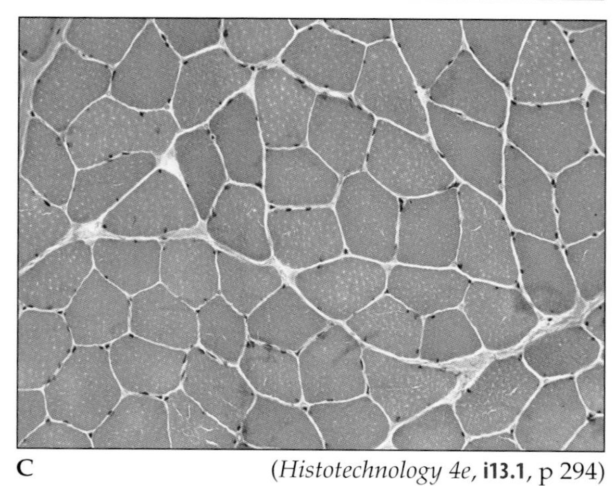

C (*Histotechnology 4e*, **i13.1**, p 294)

46. The fibers stained dark in image B would also stain dark with:
    a. ATPase 4.3
    b. phosphorylase
    c. acid phosphatase
    d. alkaline phosphatase

47. Which of the following stains gives a similar appearance on normal muscle as the stain shown in image B?
    a. phosphorylase
    b. succinic dehydrogenase
    c. ATPase
    d. alkaline phosphatase

48. Which of the following techniques should be used to examine the tissue shown in image C for McArdle disease?
    a. ATPase
    b. NADH diaphorase
    c. acid phosphatase
    d. phosphorylase

49. The muscle shown in image C is:
    a. cardiac
    b. skeletal
    c. smooth
    d. involuntary

50. Which of the following stains should be used to reliably type the fibers shown in image C?
    a. ATPase
    b. esterase
    c. acid phosphatase
    d. phosphorylase

ISBN 978-089189-6401

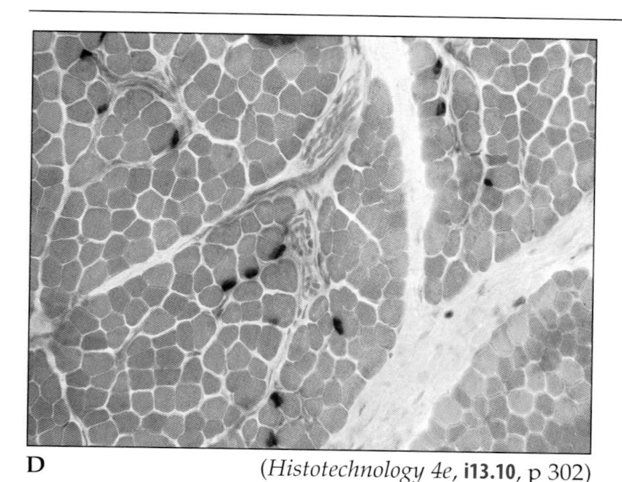

D (*Histotechnology 4e*, **i13.10**, p 302)

51. The dark stained areas seen in image D are:
    a. type I fibers
    b. target fibers
    c. motor end plates
    d. Z-band material

52. The stain shown in image D is most likely the:
    a. alkaline phosphatase
    b. phosphorylase
    c. succinic dehydrogenase
    d. α-naphthyl acetate esterase

53. The final reaction product of the technique shown in image D is a/an:
    a. metallic salt
    b. formazan
    c. azo dye
    d. polysaccharide

ISBN 978-089189-6401

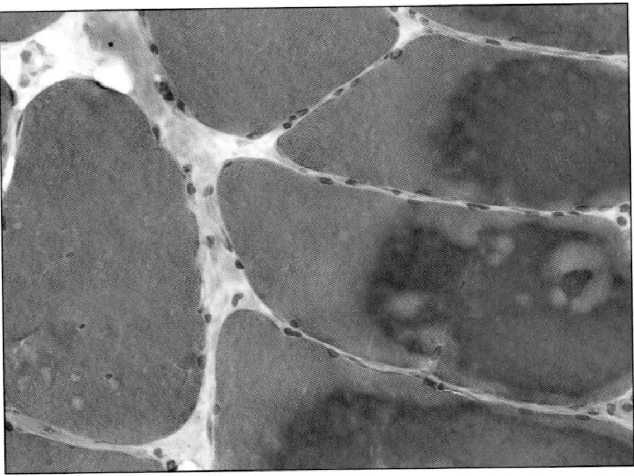

E (*Histotechnology 4e*, **i13.29**, p 314)

54. The technique shown in image E is a/an:
    a. trichrome
    b. succinic dehydrogenase
    c. alkaline phosphatase
    d. phosphorylase

55. Tissue for the stain shown in image E must be:
    a. fixed in Bouin solution
    b. fixed in neutral buffered formalin
    c. frozen and unfixed
    d. frozen and fixed in acetone

56. The artifact shown in image E is the result of:
    a. poor freezing technique
    b. overheating during processing
    c. poor staining differentiation
    d. partial fixation in formalin after freezing

57. The light green material running just to the right of the large green stained fiber in image E is:
    a. perimysium
    b. endomysium
    c. epimysium
    d. tendon sheath

ISBN 978-089189-6401

58-62. The following are problem solving questions.

58. Microscopic evaluation of an acid phosphatase stain reveals much too pale methyl green counterstain. The problem might be caused by:
    a. the addition of acetic acid
    b. solution a pH of 4.0
    c. prolonged dehydration
    d. mounting with synthetic resin

59. Macroscopic evaluation of an NADH diaphorase stain reveals aggregates and crystals of diformazan or a diformazan-protein complex. This was most likely caused by:
    a. incubating of section at room temperature
    b. mounting with synthetic resin
    c. mounting with glycerine jelly
    d. the presence of Z-band material

60. By the time the pathologists was able to examine the phosphorylase stained section, the stain had faded. The most appropriate solution is to:
    a. cut and stain new sections
    b. repeat the stain on the same sections
    c. restain in dilute Gram iodine
    d. report as stain unsatisfactory

61. Sections stained with the naphthol AS-D chloroacetate esterase stain show a brown, refractile, pigmentlike artifact scattered throughout the section. This was most likely caused by:
    a. poor hematoxylin staining
    b. prolonged washing following incubation
    c. prolonged dehydration and clearing
    d. mounting air dried slides without dipping in xylene

62. ATPase stained sections are retrieved after storage for several years. Microscopic evaluation shows marked fading of the stain. This indicates that:
    a. the stain was not properly done originally
    b. the temperature of the storage area was too cold
    c. normal fading with time has occurred
    d. the ammonium sulfide was old when used

ISBN 978-089189-6401

Enzyme Histochemistry *Answers*

Question	*Answer*	*Discussion*	*Histotechnology* **Page**
1	c	Enzymes are proteins that catalyze chemical reactions occurring in biologic systems.	295
2	a	Biological oxidation occurs with the addition of oxygen, the loss of hydrogen, or the loss of electrons.	296
3	b	A compound is reduced when there is a loss of oxygen, gain of hydrogen, or gain of electrons.	296
4	d	A substrate is the substance on which an enzyme acts.	295
5	a	Considerable diffusion artifact may be seen on unfixed frozen sections for some enzymes, particularly those that are water soluble.	296
6	d	After fixation, tissue may be stored in gum sucrose solutions (30% sucrose, 1% gum acacia) at 4°C for several weeks.	296
7	b	Hydrolases act on various substrates, usually through the addition of water; however, in some instances, water can be removed.	297
8	a	Muscle tissue is extremely subject to ice crystal artifact, and the method of freezing is critical. The optimum procedure is freezing in isopentane at –150°C.	298-300
9	c	If muscle tissue is frozen directly in liquid nitrogen, gas bubbles tend to surround the tissue and impede freezing. Dusting the muscle with talc before submersing in liquid nitrogen will prevent the formation of gas bubbles.	50
10	b	Simultaneous coupling is the most frequently used technique for demonstrating hydrolytic enzymes. The enzymes act on the substrate to release a product that is rapidly captured or coupled with a diazonium salt (to give an insoluble azo dye) or with a metallic ion.	297
11	d	Motor end plates are demonstrated on muscle by the α-naphthyl acetate esterase stain.	301-302
12	a	The naphthol AS-D chloroacetate esterase is a specific esterase stain that can be done on paraffin sections.	302-303
13	a	The naphthol AS-D chloroacetate esterase stain demonstrates granulocytes.	302-303
14	b	The ATPase reaction involves both simultaneous coupling (calcium phosphate) and metallic substitution (calcium exchanged for cobalt)	302-304

ISBN 978-089189-6401

Question	*Answer*	*Discussion*	*Histotechnology Page*
15	c	The final colored product in the ATPase reaction is cobalt sulfide. Calcium phosphate is not a colored compound, so calcium is replaced by cobalt (cobalt phosphate is not colored), and the phosphate is replaced by sulfide (from ammonium sulfide).	302-304
16	a	When performed at pH 9.4, the ATPase on a normal muscle biopsy will show dark type IIA and IIB fibers and light type I fibers.	305
17	a	The acid phosphatase reaction demonstrates the alcohol residue of naphthol AS-BI phosphate.	306
18	a	The acid phosphatase stain is considered a marker enzyme for lysosomes and will indicate inflammatory cells present in the biopsy as well as degeneration of muscle due to lysosomal activity.	306
19	c	An azo dye is the end product of the α-naphthyl acetate esterase, acid phosphatase, and alkaline phosphatase stains.	301, 306, 307
20	b	Mitochondria, Z-band material, and sarcoplasmic reticulum are all demonstrated by the NADH diaphorase reaction; lysosomes are not demonstrated.	308
20	d	At a pH of 8.0 or higher, reduced coenzymes may be able to reduce the tetrazolium salts directly and form a precipitate; the phenomenon increases progressively with an increase in pH, and it may be a major source of error if the pH is too high.	3 10
22	a	Succinic dehydrogenase procedures demonstrate only mitochondria; Z-band material and sarcoplasmic reticulum are not demonstrated.	310
23	c	The absence of phosphorylase activity in muscle is indicative of McArdle disease.	311-312
34	b	Phosphorylase stained sections are not permanent, as they are mounted with glycerine-iodine and they should be read immediately. If the slides fade before they are read, they can be re stained in dilute iodine solution.	312
25	d	Nitro blue tetrazolium is a hydrogen acceptor in the demonstration of diaphorase and NAD-dependent dehydrogenase.	308
26	a	Each muscle fiber is surrounded by a network of connective tissue known as the endomysium; bundles of muscle fibers are surrounded by the perimysium, and an entire muscle is surrounded by the epimysium.	294
27	d	Only skeletal muscle fibers have peripheral nuclei.	161

ISBN 978-089189-6401

Question	*Answer*	*Discussion*	*Histotechnology* **Page**
28	a	Type I fibers are high in oxidative enzymes found in mitochondria; they have primarily an aerobic (oxidative) metabolism.	294
29	d	Type II fibers have an anaerobic metabolism, and have abundant glycogen and glycolytic enzymes such as phosphorylase.	294
30	d	The PAS is frequently used on muscle biopsies to detect an abnormal storage of glycogen that occurs with some glycogen storage diseases.	312
31	c	Enzymes usually are very specific as to substrate; the enzyme and substrate temporarily combine to give a product, and then the enzyme is released unchanged. Enzymes speed up biological reactions and are readily inactivated by heat.	296
32	a b c d	Simultaneous capture or coupling Postincubation coupling Self colored substrate Intramolecular rearrangement	297
33	a b c d e	Treatment of tissue before and during procedure Nonoptimal substrate Nonoptimal temperature Nonoptimal pH Inhibitors	296
34A	a	Acid phosphatase is a hydrolase.	297
34B	a	Adenosine triphosphatase is a hydrolase.	297
34C	a	Alkaline phosphatase is a hydrolase.	297
34D	a	Esterases are hydrolases.	297
34E	b	NADH diaphorase is an oxidoreductase.	298
34F	c	Phosphorylase is a transferase.	298
34G	b	Succinic dehydrogenase is an oxidoreductase.	298
35A	d, e	Acid phosphatase uses hexazotized pararosaniline and naphthol AS-BI phosphate.	306
35B	b	ATPase uses cobalt chloride.	304
335C	g	NADH diaphorase uses nitro blue tetrazolium.	308-309
35D	a, d	Nonspecific esterase uses α-naphthyl acetate and hexazotized pararosaniline.	201
335E	c	Phosphorylase uses Gram iodine in the mountant.	3 11-312
36	b	The tissue shown is a cross-section of skeletal muscle, which is voluntary.	305
37	d	The stain shown in image A is an ATPase.	305
38	a	At a pH of 4.6, type I muscle fibers are very dark.	305

ISBN 978-089189-6401

Question	*Answer*	*Discussion*	***Histotechnology* Page**
39	b	The final reaction product in the ATPase reaction is cobalt sulfide.	304
40	a	The muscle in the ATPase stained section shown in image A shows the normal checkerboard distribution of fiber types.	305
41	a	The stain demonstrated in image B is the NADH diaphorase.	309
42	c	The final reaction product in the NADH diaphorase stain is a formazan.	308
43	b	A reagent used in the NADH diaphorase stain is nitro blue tetrazolium.	309
44	a	The NADH diaphorase reaction belongs to the oxidoreductases group.	298
45	a	Type I fibers stain dark with the NADH diaphorase technique.	309
46	a	Type I fibers are stained dark in image B; they would also stain dark with the ATPase 4.3.	309, 305
47	b	The succinic dehydrogenase and the NADH diaphorase stains give similar results on normal muscle.	309,311
48	d	McArdle disease can be shown by an absence of phosphorylase.	312
49	b	The tissue shown in image C is normal skeletal muscle.	294
50	a	Although other stains will show the difference between type I and type II fibers, the only reliable stain for typing is the ATPase.	303-305
51	c	The dark stained areas in image D are motor end plates.	302
52	d	The technique shown in image D is the α-naphthyl acetate esterase.	301-302
53	c	The final reaction product of the technique shown in image D is an azo dye.	301
54	a	A trichrome stain is shown in image E.	314
55	c	Tissue for the technique shown in image E must be frozen and unfixed for the proper staining.	313-314
56	d	The artifact seen in image E is due to partial fixation in formalin after freezing. Fixation will change the results, and pathologic changes will be difficult to detect.	314

ISBN 978-089189-6401

Question	*Answer*	*Discussion*	*Histotechnology* **Page**
57	a	The light green stained material is connective tissue that surrounds bundles of muscle fibers and is known as perimysium.	294
58	d	Methyl green is washed out easily during dehydration and clearing, so those steps should be done rapidly.	307
59	b	NADH diaphorase stains should not be dehydrated and cleared; they should be mounted with glycerine jelly.	309
60	c	Restain the sections in Gram iodine solution to restore the color.	312
61	d	All stains that cannot be dehydrated, but must be air dried before mounting, should be dipped in xylene before coverslipping to prevent a granular artifact (cornflaking).	303
62	c	Fading of ATPase stains normally will occur over time.	305

ISBN 978-089189-6401

Cytopreparatory Techniques *Questions*

1-23. The following are multiple choice questions. Please circle the letter in front of the correct answer. There is only 1 best answer.

1. The microscopic examination of individual cells and their morphology is known as:
   a. cytology
   b. immunology
   c. histology
   d. microbiology

2. Which of the following is categorized as a gynecologic cytology specimen?
   a. cerebral spinal fluid
   b. endocervical cells
   c. gastric washings
   d. pericardial fluids

3. Which of the following nongynecologic specimens deteriorates quickly (within 24 hours), and should be either brought to the lab immediately for cytopreparation or placed in a prefixative solution?
   a. ascites fluid
   b. gastric washings
   c. pleural fluids
   d. urine

4. Which of the following fixatives causes a different chromatin pattern for cytology fixation, making diagnosis difficult?
   a. ethanol
   b. formalin
   c. isopropyl alcohol
   d. methyl alcohol

5. For best fixation/preservation of cytology smears, fixation should occur within what time frame of being placed on a slide?
   a. 2 seconds
   b. 10 seconds
   c. 30 seconds
   d. 60 seconds

6. To prevent cells from drying after fixation, some commercial cytology spray fixatives add:
   a. acetone
   b. formaldehyde
   c. isopropyl alcohol
   d. polyethylene glycol

ISBN 978-089189-6401

7. A sputum sample was obtained, homogenized, and then centrifuged into a pellet. The best method of smear preparation from the pellet is:
   a. crosshatch
   b. crush
   c. nickel
   d. pull-apart

8. Before staining, remove the Carbowax on slides that were fixed with a commercial fixative by soaking the slide in:
   a. alcohol
   b. Saccomanno
   c. saline
   d. water

9. To collect as many cells as possible from sparsely cellular urine, the specimen should have which of the following techniques applied?
   a. crush method
   b. cytocentrifuge
   c. fine needle aspiration
   d. liquid based

10. A method for obtaining specimens from superficial or deep organs is:
   a. cytocentrification
   b. fine needle aspiration
   c. smear preparation
   d. thin layer technology

11. After smears are prepared from the first drops of cellular material from a fine needle aspirate, any residual material can be recovered by rinsing the needle with which of the following?
   a. Carbowax
   b. formalin
   c. methanol
   d. saline

12. The pathologist wants to determine if enough cells were collected during a fine needle aspirate. The air dried slide can be stained with:
   a. Diff-Quik
   b. H&E
   c. Pap
   d. trichrome

13. Which of the following cytopreparation techniques could have an immunohistochemical (IHC) stain done on it without having to change IHC protocols?
   a. cell block
   b. liquid based
   c. Saccomanno fluid
   d. cytocentrifugation

14. Cell blocks are usually fixed in:
   a. formalin
   b. methanol
   c. ethanol
   d. acetic acid

ISBN 978-089189-6401

15. Loose cellular material can be held together to make into a cell block in all of the following EXCEPT:
    a. agar
    b. albumin
    c. blood clot
    d. resin

16. All of the following are dyes found in the EA counterstain of the Pap stain EXCEPT:
    a. Bismarck brown
    b. eosin Y
    c. light green SF yellowish
    d. orange G

17. The Pap stain uses which of the following types of hematoxylin staining solutions?
    a. Harris
    b. Mayer
    c. Verhoeff
    d. Weigert

18. The mordant in the OG-6 counterstain for the Pap procedure is:
    a. aluminum sulfate
    b. ferric chloride
    c. phosphotungstic acid
    d. picric acid

19. Orange G in the Pap stain will demonstrate which component in epithelial cells?
    a. mitochondria
    b. nuclear chromatin
    c. rough endoplasmic reticulum
    d. tonofilaments

20. Which of the following cells will stain pink with the Pap stain?
    a. adenocarcinoma cells
    b. columnar cells
    c. histiocytes
    d. superficial squamous cells

21. Metabolically inactive epithelial cells will be what color with the Pap stain?
    a. blue
    b. green
    c. orange
    d. pink

22. The light green in the various EA formulations for Pap staining is very sensitive to:
    a. temperature
    b. concentration
    c. light
    d. precipitation

23. Which of the following stains will show a metachromatic staining of cytology cells?
    a. Diff-Quik
    b. Giemsa
    c. H&E
    d. toluidine blue

24-31. The following statements are either true or false. Circle T if the statement is true, circle F if the statement is false.

24. A false negative diagnosis can result from poor preparation of slides to be stained for cytology. **[T\F]**

25. Most fresh nongynecologic specimens for cytology examination can be stored in a refrigerator for 24 hours to 72 hours without fixation. **[T\F]**

26. Fixation of cytology cells while they are in a liquid state produces flat cells that are spread out. **[T\F]**

27. Cotton swabs should not be used to collect and smear cytology slides. **[T\F]**

28. Conventional Pap tests provide good quality preparations for use with automated computer image analysis. **[T\F]**

29. Hematoxylin used in Pap stains can only be used regressively. **[T\F]**

30. Orange G stains keratinized squamous cells. **[T\F]**

31. Match the specimen type on the left with the most appropriate cytology smear preparation method(s) on the right. (letters may be used more than once or not at all).

Specimen type	Smear Preparation Method
____A. Pleural fluid	a. nickel
____B. Cerebral spinal fluid	b. pull-apart
____C. Bronchial washings	c. crush
____D. Fine needle aspirate	d. cross-hatch
____E. Ascites	e. cytocentrifuge
____F. Sputum	
____G. Gastric brushings	
____H. Bloody fluids	
____I. Urine	

ISBN 978-089189-6401

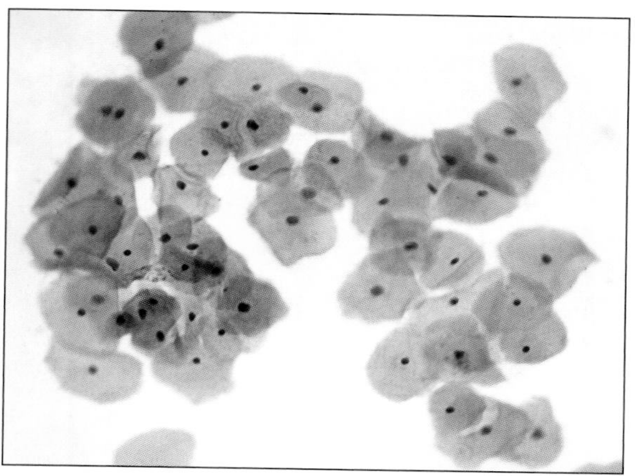

(*Histotechnology 4e*, **i14.11**, p 326)

32-35. The following questions apply to the image above.

32. The cells shown in the image are:
    a. bronchial epithelial
    b. columnar
    c. squamous
    d. cuboidal

33. The cells shown in the image are most likely from:
    a. bronchial washings
    b. cervix
    c. sputum
    d. gastric brushings

34. The stains used on the image contain all of the following dyes EXCEPT:
    a. light green
    b. phloxine
    c. orange G
    d. eosin Y

35. The preferred fixative for the cells shown in the image is:
    a. acetone
    b. formalin
    c. alcohol
    d. Carnoy

ISBN 978-089189-6401

36-42. The following are problem solving questions.

36. A cytology smear shows cells that have nuclear swelling, loss of chromatin pattern, and very pink cytoplasm. To correct this in the future:
    a. fix smear within 2 seconds of applying cells
    b. allow slides to air dry before fixing
    c. fix in 10% neutral buffered formalin
    d. lightly mist the slide with fixative

37. A smear prepared for cytology examination is obscured by red blood cells. Which of the following can be added to the fixative, to lyse the red blood cells?
    a. acetic acid
    b. formaldehyde
    c. methanol
    d. polyethylene glycol

38. The edges of a cytology smear show cells that are distorted due to being air dried. This is most common if the smear technique used was:
    a. crosshatch
    b. feather
    c. nickel
    d. pull-apart

39. A specimen of cyst fluid was centrifuged. The resultant sediment at the bottom of the tube had cells that were packed very dense. To prevent this in the future:
    a. decrease the speed
    b. increase the time
    c. use 15 mL conical tubes
    d. retain the supernatant

40. A slide of breast fluid has the cells washing off during staining. To help the cells stay on the slide:
    a. add acetic acid to the fixative
    b. fix in neutral buffered formalin
    c. make a direct smear
    d. use positively charged slides

41. On a Pap stain, no cells are seen with pink cytoplasm, instead the cytoplasm is all blue-green. This could be corrected in the future by:
    a. fixing in formalin
    b. increasing the time in the EA solution
    c. decreasing the time in the rinse water
    d. eliminating Bismarck brown

42. After staining smears with the Pap stain, the cells do not look crisp pink and blue-green, but rather have a dirty blend of colors. This can be corrected in the future by:
    a. changing the alcohols after the stains more often
    b. filtering the first dehydrant alcohol daily
    c. presoaking slides in 95% alcohol for 10 minutes
    d. decreasing staining time in EA solution

ISBN 978-089189-6401

Cytopreparatory Techniques *Answers*

Question	*Answer*	*Discussion*	*Histotechnology* Page
1	a	Diagnostic cytology is the microscopic examination of cellular material for the diagnosis of disease. Cytology relies on the examination of individual cells and their morphology.	318
2	b	Gynecologic cytology includes specimens from the female genital tract, notably from the cervix, endocervix, and vagina.	318
3	d	Because of the acidity, urine specimens are very fragile and do not tolerate long delays before cytopreparation.	319
4	b	Formalin fixation should be avoided because it creates different chromatin patterns and may hinder diagnosis.	319
5	a	Unfixed cells smeared on a slide will begin to air dry rapidly; therefore, application of the fixative must occur within 1 second to 2 seconds of the cells' contact with the slide.	319
6	d	Polyethylene glycol is added to most commercial spray fixatives to provide a protective coating and prevent cells from drying.	319
7	d	Pull-apart smears should be made from the sediment, or pellet.	321
8	a	It is necessary to soak all specimens that have been fixed with spray fixatives or Saccomanno fluid before staining to remove the Carbowax (polyethylene glycol) coating on the cells. A 10-minute soak in 95% alcohol at the beginning of staining will normally remove Carbowax.	329
9	b	Cytocentrifugation is the most common method of handling sparsely cellular specimens such as urine or spinal fluid.	323
10	b	Fine needle aspirations enable the examination of superficial organs such as breast and thyroid, and deep organs such as lung, liver, and pancreas.	324
11	d	The initial drops from the fine needle aspirate are used to make pull-apart smears. The needle can then be rinsed in physiologic saline to recover any residual specimen.	324
12	a	Diff-Quik staining can be used to determine specimen adequacy. The toluidine blue wet film method can also be used to determine cellularity during procedures.	324, 330

ISBN 978-089189-6401

Question	*Answer*	*Discussion*	*Histotechnology* Page
13	a	Because cells blocks are fixed and processed like tissue, the same protocols may be used for routine, immunohistochemical, and other special stains.	326
14	a	Cell blocks are usually fixed in formalin for processing as tissue.	326
15	d	Agar, albumin, blood clots, and a thrombin/prothrombin clot can be used to make a cell block from loose cellular material.	326
16	d	Orange G is used as a separate stain from the EA formulations in the Pap stain. EA formulations contain eosin Y, light green SF yellowish, and sometimes Bismarck brown, depending on the formulation.	328
17	a	Harris or Gill hematoxylin is used for nuclear staining in the Pap procedure.	328
18	c	Phosphotungstic acid is the mordant for OG-6 in the Pap procedure.	328
19	d	Orange G stains tonofilaments in keratin a bright orange, helping to distinguish keratinizing neoplasms.	328
20	d	Superficial squamous cells will stain pink with the eosin in the EA preparations.	329
21	d	Metabolically inactive cells show various shades of pink, while the metabolically active cells stain various shades of blue-green.	328
22	c	The light green in the various EA formulations is very sensitive to light.	329
23	d	Toluidine blue will give metachromatic staining in unfixed cells.	330
24	T	A false positive or false negative diagnosis can result from negligent cytopreparation. Cells that are poorly prepared, fixed, and stained can alter diagnoses.	318
25	T	Realistically, short delays will not cause ill effects on nongynecologic cytology specimens, and most fresh specimens can be held for 24 hours to 72 hours if refrigerated.	318
26	F	Fixation of specimens while they are in the liquid state will produce cells that are "rounded up"; they appear smaller and denser, and the fine morphologic details are more difficult to visualize.	319
27	T	The fibers of cotton swabs will absorb moisture from the specimen, causing air drying and cellular distortion.	320

ISBN 978-089189-6401

Question	*Answer*	*Discussion*	*Histotechnology* Page
28	F	Specimens for automated computer image analysis fall under liquid based cytology, and the specimens are collected into a preservative solution with either a weak methyl alcohol (ThinPrep) or ethyl alcohol (SurePath) content. Conventional smears cannot be used for liquid based cytology.	324-325
29	F	Hematoxylin staining in the Pap method can be either progressive or regressive, just as in the routine H&E.	328
30	T	Orange G stains the tonofilaments in keratin a bright orange, helping to distinguish keratinizing neoplasms.	328
31A	b, d, e	After centrifugation, smears are prepared from the sediment. This is usually done by the pull-apart method, unless the specimen contains abundant blood; in that case, the cross-hatch method is superior. If the specimen is not very cellular, cytocentrifugation may be used.	321
31B	e	Cerebral spinal fluid smears are usually prepared by cytocentrifugation.	323
31C	c	Thick mucoid specimens are usually prepared by the crush method.	322
31D	b	Fine needle aspirate smears are usually prepared by the pull-apart method.	324
31E	b, d, e	After centrifugation, smears are prepared from the sediment. This is usually done by the pull-apart method, unless the specimen contains abundant blood; in that case, the cross-hatch method is superior. If the specimen is not very cellular, cytocentrifugation may be used.	3321
31F	b, c	Thick mucoid specimens, such as sputum, are usually prepared by the crush method, unless they are treated by the Saccomanno method; in that case, pull-apart smears are made from the cellular sediment.	322
31G	a, b, d	Smears from brushings are commonly made at the time of collection by the nickel method. The brush may also be submitted in physiologic saline for processing; then either the pull-apart or cross-hatch method can be used, depending on the blood present.	318
31H	d	The cross-hatch method is the best for smears from the sediment of bloody fluids.	321
31I	e	Cytocentrifugation is the most common method of handling sparsely cellular specimens.	323

ISBN 978-089189-6401

Question	*Answer*	*Discussion*	*Histotechnology* Page
32	c	The cells shown in the image are squamous cells with abundant flattened cytoplasm and small, dark staining nuclei.	328
33	b	The cells are most likely from the cervix; this is most apparent from the uniformity of the cells.	328
34	b	Phloxine is not used in the Pap staining technique.	328-329
35	c	The preferred fixative for the cells shown in the image above is alcohol.	319
36	a	Smears should be fixed immediately after preparation while the specimen is still wet on the slide; this should occur within 1-2 seconds.	319
37	a	Acetic acid can be added to the fixative to lyse red cells; Carnoy and Clark solutions are frequently for this purpose, but slides should not be left for too long in these solutions, or chromatin detail will be affected. After 5 minutes, the slides should be transferred to 95% ethyl alcohol (or equivalent).	320
38	b	Feathered edge smears like those done for hematology should be avoided because the diagnostic cells are pushed to the edge of the smear where they immediately air dry and become useless for diagnosis.	319
39	a	Centrifugation for cytology is best performed at 2,000 rpm for ~10 minutes; higher speeds will pack the cells too tightly.	321
40	c	Direct smears should be made at the time of collection by the nickel method; the smears should be spray fixed with cytology fixative immediately before any air drying can occur.	320
41	c	Eosin rinses out of slides faster than light green, and prolonged rinsing can leave all cytoplasm stained blue-green.	329
42	a	If the counterstain colors look "dirty," it is probably because of overused alcohol rinses.	329

ISBN 978-089189-6401

Laboratory Informatics *Questions*

1-8. The following are multiple choice questions. Please circle the letter in front of the correct answer. There is only 1 best answer.

1. LIS stands for which of the following;
   a. Laboratory Instrumentation Standards
   b. Laboratory Information Standards
   c. Laboratory Information System
   d. Laboratory Instrumentation Safety

2. The initial access point in the anatomic pathology laboratory to a patient record is at:
   a. accessioning and order entry
   b. grossing of specimens
   c. pathologists test orders
   d. final diagnosis report

3. A long sequence of lines of different widths that holds alphanumeric or numeric data is known as a:
   a. 3D barcode
   b. 2D barcode
   c. 1D barcode
   d. LIS-HID connector

4. A square print pattern barcode is also known as:
   a. linear
   b. 1D
   c. 2D
   d. 3D

5. Which is NOT a benefit of electronic procedure manuals?
   a. ease of updating
   b. alert for review needed
   c. paper copy for easy staining directions
   d. electronic security

6. HIS stands for which of the following:
   a. Healthcare Information System
   b. Histopathology Information System
   c. Histopathology Instrumentation Standards
   d. Healthcare Information Standards

7. In 1996 what act mandated the privacy and security of patient information:
   a. OSHA
   b. HIPAA
   c. HIS
   d. CDC

8. Each patient artifact should have a minimum of how many unique identifiers?
   a. 1
   b. 2
   c. 3
   d. 4

9-20. The following statements are either true or false. Place a T in front of the statement if the it is true and an F in front of the statement it is false.

_____9. A patient's electronic health record may be accessed to add or review data by physicians only.

_____10. Dark color cassettes demonstrate a frequent barcode scan failure.

_____11. Advances in middleware or LIS functionality have allowed laboratories to establish an electronic chain of custody of patient artifacts.

_____12. The scanning of barcodes at each workstation decreases specimen mix-ups.

_____13. Patient demographics are maintained by HIPAA.

_____14. A patient's electronic medical record number changes with each hospital visit.

_____15. The scanning of barcodes at each workstation can assist a manager to determine the productivity of each employee.

_____16. Pathologists are not able to order add on testing , such as recuts or special stains, through the LIS.

_____17. Electronic procedure manual allow laboratories located at different geographical locations to access the same procedure readily.

_____18. All laboratory instruments require the same type of barcode.

_____19. Middleware or LIS features can assist with electronic capture of quality issues and resolutions.

_____20. Real time documentation provided by middleware allows managers to perform root cause analysis of recurring issues.

_____21. The laboratory instrumentation is normally interfaced directly with the HIS.

_____22. Standard hospital process requires a patient to be registered in the HIS in order for accessioning to take place in the LIS.

ISBN 978-089189-6401

(*Histotechnology 4e*, **i15.2**, p 332)

23-25. The following questions refer to the image above.

23. The square object to the left of the surgical number on the cassette in the image is a:
    a. linear barcode
    b. 1D barcode
    c. 2D barcode
    d. Decoration

24. The square object to the left of the surgical number on the cassette in the image most likely contains the:
    a. the name of the institution
    b. the patient's demographics
    c. the ordering physician
    d. the date accessioned

25. The square object to the left of the surgical number on the cassette in the image is normally used for all of the following EXCEPT:
    a. staining protocols
    b. real time specimen tracking
    c. technician productivity
    d. decreasing specimen mix-ups

ISBN 978-089189-6401

Laboratory Informatics *Answers*

Question	*Answer*	*Discussion*	*Histotechnology* Page
1	c	LIS is the abbreviation for Laboratory Information System.	332
2	a	Accessioning and order entry is the initial access to a patient record in anatomic pathology.	332
3	c	A 1D or linear barcode is a long sequence of lines of different widths holding alphanumeric or numeric data.	336
4	c	A 2D barcode prints in a square pattern.	336
5	c	Paper copies of staining procedures are not a benefit of electronic procedure manuals.	337
6	a	Healthcare Information Systems are abbreviated to HIS.	332
7	b	HIPAA , or the Health Information Portability Act, mandate the privacy and security of patient information.	335
8	b	Each patient artifact should contain at least 2 unique identifiers.	77, 333
9	F	A patient's electronic health record is accessed by multiple healthcare providers as data is added or reviewed.	332
10	T	Dark colored cassettes frequently cause problems with barcode scanners.	337
11	T	Advances in middleware have allowed laboratories to establish an electronic chain of custody of patient artifacts as they progress through the system	335
12	T	Scanning of barcodes at each work station will aid in decreasing specimen mix-ups and true patient identification	335-336
13	F	Patient demographics are maintained by the HIS, not HIPAA.	332
14	F	Electronic medical record numbers have allowed the use of the same number in subsequent visits.	332
15	T	The productivity of individual employees can be determined by scanning of barcodes at each workstation.	336
16	F	An advantage of the LIS is that the pathologist may order special test and they will be stamped in real time so that the laboratory can determine "first in, first out."	337

ISBN 978-089189-6401

Question	*Answer*	*Discussion*	*Histotechnology* Page
17	T	Laboratories located at different geographical locations can easily access electronic procedure manuals allowing for easy standardization of methodology.	337
18	F	Depending on the procedure or patient artifact, different barcodes may be required.	336
19	T	Middleware or LIS can assist with electronic capture of quality issues and resolutions.	338
20	T	Real time documentation provided by middleware or LIS allows managers to perform root cause analysis of issues that recur frequently.	338
21	F	Laboratory instrumentation is normally interfaced with the LIS and not the HIS.	335
22	T	Standard hospital practice is to register patients in the HIS, and this information is then available for accessioning to take place in the LIS.	232-233
23	c	The square object to the left of the surgical number is a 2D barcode.	336
24	b	The square object to the left of the surgical number on the cassette is most likely the patient's demographics and surgical number identification	335-336
25	a	Staining protocols would normally be found in electronic procedure manuals and not in a barcode.	337

ISBN 978-089189-6401